..... **Process Dynamics**

Dynamic

Behavior

of the

Production

Process . . . . **Process**

the late DONALD P. CAMPBELL, Sc.D

Consulting Engineer
Formerly Associate Professor
of Electrical Engineering
Massachusetts Institute of Technology

Dynamics

New York · John Wiley & Sons, Inc.

London · Chapman & Hall, Limited

Foreword

I am glad to have an opportunity to present to the readers of this book by my late husband, Donald P. Campbell, an expression of my gratitude to Page S. Buckley for his work in preparing the final manuscript for the publisher.

Without his assistance the publication of Don's work would have been impossible. He gave weeks of his time to editing copy, to filling in inevitable gaps and incomplete derivations. His technical assistance in carrying out this task has been invaluable and his willingness to help is certainly beyond mere thanks.

I deeply appreciate Page's expression of esteem and friendship for Don. I shall be forever grateful to him and know that those who read this book will join me in recognizing the noble action Page has taken.

Myrtis T. Campbell

Preface

The purpose of this book is to explain process physics. The material of the book comes from my work as a consulting engineer and from the research that I conducted and directed during the last ten years in feedback control theory and process control at the Massachusetts Institute of Technology.

My first encounter with instrumentation and process control was at meetings of various Engineering Societies around 1945. I was dissatisfied then with the approach used to design industrial processes and to apply automatic controls to them; I am still dissatisfied with much of the work being done in the process control field because it is not quantitative and it is not founded upon a sound theoretical basis. The fields of instrumentation and process control are little more than an empirical art. They are not a science.

I believe the history of the development of the fields tells us why. The instrumentation field grew from rather crude beginnings around 1900 along empirical lines. The needs of industry dictated designs. Research was at best what should be called expedient development or invention. Instruments for recording physical variables grew into the instrument-recorder-controller. Recent variations like the stack controllers and miniature components are not a departure from this basic pattern. With few exceptions, the instrumentation and process control field has never been approached with a view toward putting the concepts of measurement, communication, manipulation, and process dynamic response upon a sound mathematic foundation. Likewise, the approach to plant design has left much to be desired. The designs were conceived along static or steady-state lines. Designers have not taken into consideration the time lags that are inherent in the processes and plants because of the configuration of vessels—the transport distances between vessels. They do not consider that heat exchangers are parts of a hydraulic network. Nor do they consider that a flame reactor, even though it has a basic function of producing a chemical, is nevertheless an acoustic loud speaker. They do not look upon the plant as being an inherently dynamical working system.

Even today many engineers who build industrial automatic controls are so busy putting out small fires that they fail to recognize the over-all and generalized concept of a plant. Frequently this causes an engineer to add expensive control equipment to the plant in order to correct situations in poor process performance which might have never occurred had the process equipment for the plant been properly planned and designed in the first place.

Unless sound mathematical foundations are put under the practical design and development of instrument and process control systems, the field of process control will fail to reach the level of attainment found in the servomechanisms field, especially that found in modern military fire-control system design. As long as the designers of industrial process control systems concentrate upon instruments and controllers and fail to recognize the plant as the central and most fundamental issue we can not hope for much progress.

In process control, knowledge of process behavior comes first. The dynamic response of most processes can be defined quantitatively. Differential equations or other mathematical forms explain uniquely the time-varying performance of processes. Techniques which have been developed in the field of servomechanisms, and which permit the analysis and design of feedback control systems, can then be applied if process behavior is quantitatively defined. The purpose of this book is to explain process physics and to translate these basic definitions of process dynamic performance into mathematical form so that their influence upon process control system design can be shown.

First, I have tried to establish some generalizations. *What is a process?* A *process* is advance toward a particular end or objective which is achieved through an orderly pattern of manipulation despite the presence of opposed disturbance.

Processing action may be taken upon a raw material to change it into a product; upon a finished product, to move it to points of consumption; upon people, to train technicians or armies; upon paperwork—that is, upon information (loosely speaking)—to bring about office record handling, sales, inventory regulation, purchasing, and a variety of service functions.

The concept of processing must be distinguished from process equipment. Processing is a functional action, whereas process equipment constitutes the vehicle whereby processing can be accomplished.

A specific processing action can often be accomplished by more than one type or arrangement of process equipment; in fact, single processing actions rarely exist. It is more common to have several sequenced or synchronized actions. The manner in which individual processes interconnect, one with another and one acting upon another, gives an organizational pattern to the over-all process. It establishes the process *system*, which is comprised of several *unit* processes.

The manipulation of a process may be simple or intricate, manual or automatic. One person or several persons may apply purely mechanical skills to the moving of levers, setting of valves, and adjusting of machinery to accomplish production of goods. Similarly, one person or several persons equipped with books, formulae, and elemental aids may carry out very complex service operations.

Processes never operate in a condition of equilibrium. They are continuously disturbed and are continuously manipulated and corrected against these disturbances by either manual or automatic action.

The origin of the disturbances which drive processes away from their equilibrium points of operation may be external or internal to the process. Likewise, manipulations—which, incidentally, act upon the process in much the same way as do disturbances—may be externally or internally applied.

Some disturbances bring about transient variations in the process behavior which pass and never occur again. Other disturbances apply cyclic or periodic forces to a process which make the process response also cyclic or periodic. Many disturbances are random in their time variation; they do not show a repetitive time pattern, but have a predictable probability pattern of recurrence.

Disturbances may occur because raw material is supplied to a process in batches. The properties of a material may suddenly change as it flows into a process. Equipment does not always operate upon homogeneous material; so machines do not always operate smoothly. They start and stop; they exhibit various patterns of change from one equilibrium condition of operation to another according to a variety of manipulation patterns.

Plants may be built out of doors, which makes them subject to cooling action by wind, rain, or snow. The moisture, dust, and other impurities in the air can upset process operation. The manner in which man uses machine tools, printing machines, wrapping machines, and other mechanisms may impart forces to the materials that are in motion and are being processed.

Noise is also a disturbance. It is generated in processes by the very fact that processing operations take place. The flow of fluids in pipes, the movement of material through chemical reactors, and the actions taken upon heterogeneous materials during extrusion, rolling, and other forming operations generate noise.

Noise, as a secondary variable, sometimes dominates the primary variables which are being observed for the purpose of measurement and control. Noise can mask and interfere with information procurement; it can make the manipulation and regulation of a process difficult because processes respond to noise as they do to any other disturbance or manipulation.

The scope of the process field is so great that one might logically ask "Where do we begin?" The whole of physics must be encompassed; the whole of mathematics used. I believe I have been able to see a general approach to the mathematical study of processes. Processes divide into three well defined groups: (1) kinematics of materials handling; fluids in motion; extrusion, propulsion, and guidance systems; (2) thermal, mass transfer, and chemical processes; and finally; (3) the nuclear processes.

These are the chapters in this book:

1. *Kinematics of Materials Handling.* Solids, liquids, and gases flow from one place to another in processes. They build up and decline in mass or volume at storage depots. Time is required for vessels and tanks to fill or empty; time passes as objects are transported from one point to another.

Time is also needed to bring about various degrees of mixing or blending of material. The mixing process can be treated in an elemental way by assuming the extremes of perfect mixing and no mixing. A more advanced approach calls for the use of probability theory. Since the flow of material is free from force and mass effects, the handling of material is a kinematics problem.

2. *Fluids in Motion.* The basic laws of fluid mechanics must be used to express the dynamic relationships between pressure and flow when fluids flow through pipes and vessels because of the forces which are exerted upon them by gravity or by force fields generated in the fluids. Proper attention must be given to the inertia of the moving fluid, the resistance to flow due to the roughness of the pipes and the viscous-shear forces within the fluid itself, and the compressibility of the fluids and the elastance of their containers.

Two classes of problems arise: The first deals mainly with incompressible fluid flow from tanks, through pipelines, valves, and other equipment. Generally a simple treatment of hydraulic circuits by means of the Bernoulli equation and the law of continuity is adequate. The second problem arises when the fluids or their containing vessels and pipes are sufficiently compressible to vibrate or to permit waves—that is, sound waves—to travel through them. In this type of problem, a wave-equation approach is needed to predict the presence of traveling or standing waves in the process pipes and vessels.

3. *Forming, Propulsion, and Guidance.* Molten liquids flowing through orifices often encounter an environment or processing action which causes them to solidify. Sheets, webs, or filaments thus formed can be propelled and guided through mechanical, thermal, and other process operations. Again two basic classes of problems occur: First there are the processes of extrusion, casting, drawing, and rolling which are concerned with the deformation and formation of material in motion; the second problem involves the handling of a continuous elastic body in contact with mechanical-guidance equipment.

The first class of problems involves the transient or time-varying nature of plastic flow. The second involves the dynamic behavior of multiple-degree-of-freedom mechanical systems characterized by lumped or distributed parameters of mass, elastance, and damping.

Guidance systems obey the laws of simple mechanics. Webs usually have relatively little mass compared with the mass or the moment of inertia of the propelling and guiding machines. Consequently, many web-handling operations constitute mechanics problems related to the guiding machines themselves rather than the web. The tensions in webs—provided they are not being drawn—obey Hooke's law, so that the amount that the web stretches under tension is determined by the stress-strain properties of the elastic web.

4. *Thermal Process Dynamics.* Next in importance after the materials-handling processes comes the processes of heating and cooling of solids, liquids, and gases. Solids are heated to melt them. Liquids are chilled to solidify them. Liquids are boiled to produce vapors. Vapors are condensed to produce liquids.

The time of exposure of a material to a heat source may determine whether heat treating of metal, cooking of food, or sterilizing of containers takes place. Alternatively, chilling or freezing of food, or cooling of a room, requires a heat sink capable of taking away heat.

Heating or cooling can be brought about by convection, conduction, or radiation. Hot and cold materials are mixed to bring about temperature regulation. Hot bodies are brought into contact with cold ones so that heat exchange takes place. Flow reactors and combustion chambers lose heat by direct radiation to adjacent air or solid objects which have good radiation-receiving properties. Often heating is produced by direct induction in moving webs or metal objects. All materials have thermal capacitance; all have thermal conductivity. Furthermore, hot or cold solids, liquids, and gases couple thermally to the vessels, conveyors, and pipelines which contain them and which guide their flow.

The study of the dynamic behavior of thermal systems under the action of manipulating and disturbing heat sources or sinks, or by means of variation in parameters, begins with the setting-up of partial differential equations which express how heat flows in space and time. From these studies we can undertake the design of thermal process equipment so that it has proper dynamic behavior.

5. *Mass Transfer Dynamics.* Mass transfer is the movement of one or more components within or between phases of material. The operations which involve mass transfer are: absorption, crystallization, extraction, distillation, stripping, humidification, and drying. Thus, the drying of paper webs, the separation of hydrocarbons in a still, or the generation of crystals in a solution involves the mass-transfer operation superimposed upon the processes of handling of materials.

The general approach to explaining, or at least putting forth, equations which can describe mass transfer is to establish the rate equation which tells the average molal transfer per unit time of components from one phase to another. The driving force which brings about mass transfer is the concentration gradient. A fictitious "interfacial layer" is often assumed between the two phases of material, and the potential or driving force is assumed to exist across the interfacial layer. However, the basic approach is by means of the diffusion equation.

In the process of mass transfer—whether distillation, extraction, or drying is involved—the driving force between the two phases is not a simple difference between two time-varying concentrations, but rather a difference between a concentration and a function of another concentration. The driving force tends to be quite nonlinear, because the function of concentration is not a linear relationship.

6. *Chemical Process Dynamics.* Chemical processes almost always involve chemical reactions, heat transfer, and materials handling as simultaneous operations. Materials are mixed together. They are conveyed in solid, liquid, or gaseous form to a vessel in which a reaction takes place. As the reaction proceeds, heat may be absorbed or released, depending upon whether the reaction is endothermic or exothermic. Raw materials are used up and products are formed.

The reaction-rate equations of chemical kinetics govern how fast the chemical reaction takes place. The parameters in these equations are functions of the concentration of material and the temperature and pressure in the region where the reaction takes place.

To manipulate chemical reactions, the temperature and pressure in a reactor may be controlled. The concentration of an activator may be regulated. The contact time between the raw material and a catalyst bed may be increased or decreased by varying the material flow rate over the bed.

Nuclear reactions are not discussed in this book, since an adequate treatment would require too much space.

I have written this book for both the engineering student and the practicing engineer. It is not intended for beginners in process control. The reader must have some knowledge of both ordinary and partial differential equations and the Laplace transformation.* He should be familiar with the principles of automatic feedback control.†

Several problems have been prepared for each chapter. I warn the reader. Many of the problems may have no known solution. The data may be adequate, inadequate, or excessive. Part of the solving of industrial process control problems calls for us to decide whether or not the problems are worth solving.

The origin of many of the ideas which appear in this book are difficult to establish. I have had the good fortune to visit many industries and to work as a consultant for different companies whose problems about control details and regulator control helped to form my opinions that grew into the generalization I present for the reader.

One company, however, should be cited specifically, because of the great influence that my visits to their plants have had upon my training and upon my point of view. The E. I. du Pont de Nemours and Company plants have often served as my classroom and proving ground. The long friendly hours of discussion that I have enjoyed with Page S. Buckley, one of the du Pont engineers, come to light in almost every chapter.

Another important source of contribution to the material have been the graduate students who have taken my courses at Massachusetts

---

*Laplace Transformation, W. T. Thomson, Prentice-Hall, Inc., New York 1950.

Transients in Linear Systems by M. F. Gardner and J. L. Barnes, John Wiley and Sons, New York 1942.

† Principles of Servomechanisms by G. S. Brown and D. P. Campbell, John Wiley and Sons, New York 1948.

Servomechanisms and Regulating System Design, Vol. 1 by H. Chestnut and R. W. Mayer, John Wiley and Sons, New York 1951.

Automatic Feedback Control by W. R. Ahrendt and J. F. Taplin, McGraw-Hill Book Company, New York, 1951.

Institute of Technology.   In particular, L. A. Gould and H. M.
Teager carried out the research work which provided much of the
proof needed for the generalizations in the heat exchange and mass
transfer chapters.   Their assistance in reviewing this material is
greatly appreciated.

I have made no attempt to write a complete treatment on each phase
of the subject.   My objective has been to consider the process first as a
primary subject, control and regulation as secondary.   I have tried to
weave control principles into the theme of process dynamics.   The
reader who is not familiar with regulator and control theory should get
an understanding how to apply the already existing feedback control
theory to the problems of process dynamics.   The expert in feedback
control should regard this book as a primer.

Brookline, Massachusetts
July 1956

D. P. CAMPBELL

Prefatory Note

D. P. Campbell died unexpectedly on January 15, 1957. The manuscript for this book was at that time nearly complete, and, for the most part, needed only checking and editing.

The author, with his characteristic restless imagination and drive, was already considering new ideas, new research work, and revisions and extensions to this manuscript. The principal changes he had in mind were:

1. To extend the treatment of commercial heat exchangers to show their response to additional kinds of disturbances,

2. To expand the analysis of chemical reaction system dynamics, and

3. To add a chapter on nuclear reactor dynamics.

Since a substantial research program would be required to develop the necessary information for the first two items, only minor additions were made to the manuscript. In spite of the fact that the author had prepared a partial first draft, the chapter on nuclear systems was omitted because an adequate treatment would have made the book too long.

In the five years that have elapsed from the inception of this book, progress has been rapid in the fields of process dynamics and process control. New control techniques and equipment are being developed rapidly. Intensive research is underway both in industry and in universities and technical schools on the dynamics of mixing, mass transfer, chemical reactions, fluid flow, and even on materials of construction such as alloys and plastics. Dynamic testing is used not only for control studies but also to develop basic information and data for static process design. All branches of engineering are represented: electrical, mechanical, chemical, civil, and aeronautical.

What will the future bring? The methods and equations of this book have been extensively used in the chemical and petroleum industry. It has been demonstrated that many commonly encountered process control problems can be analyzed and solved by simple means. But we have really only begun. Analog and digital computers are providing a revolution in computation; new techniques for measurement of product quality are providing vastly improved means of direct process control; fundamental chemical engineering research is providing basic data for new kinds of processes. But no matter what innovations and surprises are in store for us, I believe the contents of this book will not soon be obsolete.

For assistance in checking and editing this manuscript I am greatly indebted to L. A. Gould and H. M. Teager of the Massachusetts Institute of Technology, and to H. Sandvold of the Norwegian Hydroelectric Company.

Newark, Delaware
August, 1958

PAGE S. BUCKLEY

Contents

CHAPTER 1

Kinematics of
Materials Handling

1. MATERIALS IN MOTION

Materials handling is the most extensive physical operation in modern industry. Raw materials are moved from their natural location, transported to sites of manufacture, concentrated, purified, moved through various processing operations, and changed from their original state into finished goods. The manufactured goods continue to move. They move to consumers throughout a vast product-distribution system. Even after products have been consumed, great quantities of waste and residue must be gathered, transported, stored, or dispersed in harmless concentrations in the air, the sea, and the soil.

Certain generalizations can be noted for the materials-handling processes. First, there is the concept of *flow of material*. Individual processes, as well as cascades of processes operating in unison, have a throughput—an *average flow of material* through conveyors, vessels, bins, crushers, roasting ovens, and the like.

Secondly, there is the concept of *storage* or *hold-up* as the flow of material stops between process operations. The pile of ore at the furnace, or the lumber at the building site, is storage—just as the finished goods, the inventory, in the warehouse of a factory are storage.

Storage, or hold-up, is also located within every processing operation. The pipelines, vessels, conveyor belts, furnaces, heat exchangers, and chemical reactors which constitute the processing machines, themselves contain material which is being *momentarily* held within a specific processing environment. This type of storage is generally called *hold-up*.

1

Moving materials tend to become *mixed*. They tumble and churn as they flow over one another and over the roughnesses of pipes and conduits. Stirrers and paddles also mix or "blend" them in processing vessels. The composition of solid, liquid, and gaseous mixtures becomes a problem related to materials handling. On the other hand, separation—that is, the *unmixing* of useful product from waste or residue—may be necessary.

The process operations of hold-up, throughput, mixing, blending, and composition variation may be given reasonably simple mathematical definition. The differential equations are linear, or at least *the macroscopic nature of these processes is such that linear differential equations may be used to approximate their time-varying response*. From the linear equations, transfer functions can be developed which describe the cause-and-effect dynamics of materials-handling processes.

2. FLOW OF MATERIALS

As material moves, it has the aspect of *flow*. The flow may be continuous, discontinuous, periodically fluctuating about an average flow rate, or even entirely random in its variation pattern. The material flow rate through a process is loosely called *throughput*. The quantity of material per minute passing a point in the flow path defines the *flow rate*. The units of flow become mass per unit time, volume per unit time, or objects per unit time. For batch processes, average throughput may be expressed in batches per unit time.

Flow of material must be regarded as a time-varying quantity $Q(t)$. It must also be defined with respect to a given point in a process. Thus, $Q_a(t)$ signifies that Q mass units of flow per unit time are moving past a point a in a process. As an illustration, consider the flow pattern through the process shown in Fig. 1.1. A flow $Q_a(t)$ pours into the first vessel across the reference line aa'. At the line bb' across the vessel there is a downward flow $Q_b(t)$. From the first vessel at line cc' there is the flow $Q_c(t)$. This flow drops onto a conveyor belt and becomes $Q_d(t)$ at the point indicated by the line dd'. The conveyor empties into another vessel with the flow $Q_e(t)$ at ee'. The downward flow $Q_f(t)$ at ff', about midway down the second vessel, changes into the outflow $Q_g(t)$ at the mouth of the second vessel as defined by line gg'. The "average" flow carried away from the materials-handling operation by the cars is $Q_h(t)$ past the datum line hh'.

The materials-handling system shown in Fig. 1.1 may be merely a scheme for regulating the flow of solids from an ore-crushing operation to a train loading station. None of the flows need be constant. The flow Q_g must be interrupted in order to prevent spilling the material

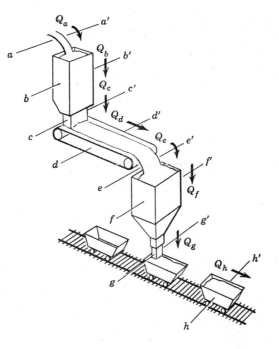

Fig. 1.1.   Flow of material.

when no car is in the loading position.   Shutting off the flow Q_g stops
the flow Q_f, but it will not necessarily stop the inflow Q_e unless there
is some coordination between the shut-off of Q_g and the flow Q_d carried by the conveyor.   The flow Q_d over the conveyor may be continuous in time and constant in magnitude, or it may vary in relation
to both since both the value of Q_c and the speed of the conveyor may
vary.   The inflow Q_a can be in batches.

From the study of the materials-handling system shown in Fig. 1.1,
it should become clear that time-varying material flow through processes, and the nature of the operations and vessels which store material
in processes, should be studied concurrently.   The flow through processes and the amount of material stored in processes are dependent.

3. STORAGE, HOLD-UP, INVENTORY

Storage is used to counteract upsets in flow.   Vessels, storage piles,
or bins are placed between progressive cascade operations.   These
provide against the rainy day: that is, having no material to feed a
production operation.   They also provide against flooding, by pre-

venting one operation in a cascade from momentarily sending more product into the next operation than can be accepted.

Storage may be part of processing itself. This type of storage is referred to as *hold-up.* It is storage which is not removable and which is inseparable from the processing operation. Hold-up is the storage of material *in* the chemical reactor, the storage of liquid and gas *in* the distillation column, the charge of ore *in* the iron furnace. It is the hold-up of material *in the environment of processing* or in the machinery that makes processing possible. However, the idea of hold-up extends beyond the process vessels themselves. There is hold-up in every pipeline and conduit that brings material to processing operations and takes it away again.

Inventory is generally considered to be the storage of finished or partially finished product, but the term may also be applied to raw materials. Looked upon broadly, inventory is no different from hold-up or any other kind of storage. However, the idea of inventory is more commonly associated with economic value than is storage or hold-up. Perhaps this is because it is easier to measure the economic value of a finished product than it is to estimate the economic value of the hold-up in the reactor of a chemical plant or the storage of raw materials or partially processed material.

Space is required for storage. Therefore, the amount of storage which can be tolerated between processing operations may be limited by the availability of free areas or volumes for use as storage facility, or by the cost associated with providing space, storage vessels, or tank farms. A high flow rate of material through a process may terminate in a manual packaging operation that requires considerable area to momentarily hold the unpackaged goods.

More important, however, is the fact that to vary the amount of storage, hold-up, or inventory in a process becomes a *time-consuming operation.* One cannot build up a storage pile in zero time, just as one cannot empty it in zero time. The level or the amount of storage cannot suddenly change in relation to changes in flow rate. Rather, the amount of storage in a pile or a bin tends to rise and fall in a transient manner, following a disturbance to the inflow and outflow. Changes in the storage value tend to *lag* behind changes in the flow. This should establish the idea of dynamic behavior even in connection with the simple processes of mass flow through bins, the holding of material in vessels, and the manner in which production and sales influence the size of inventory.

As shown in Fig. 1.2, the pile of material, the fluid in the tank, and the fluid in the coil of pipe of the heat exchanger represent storage.

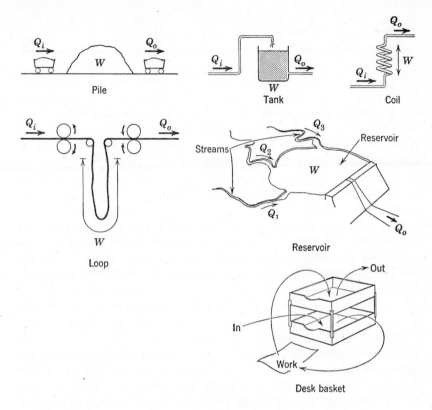

Fig. 1.2. Storage and hold-up.

The loop of steel in the soaking pit, the reservoir in a hydroelectric and flood control system are storage. Incidentally, the unfinished work in the desk basket is also storage, but the unfinished work lying on the desk is hold-up!

4. STORAGE VARIATION

Suppose that $W(t)$ tons of material are stored between process operations, as shown in Fig. 1.3. If the inflow of new material to storage is $Q_i(t)$ tons per day, and the outflow or demand upon the storage is $Q_o(t)$ tons per day, the build-up of the storage $W(t)$ will result when the mass inflow $Q_i(t)$ exceeds the mass outflow rate $Q_o(t)$; the decline, vice versa. The rate at which the tons $W(t)$ of material in storage change with respect to time is equal to the net mass flow rate $Q_i(t) - Q_o(t) =$

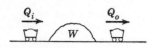

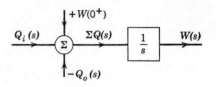

Fig. 1.3. Storage process.   Fig. 1.4. Signal-flow diagram.

$\Sigma Q(t)$, and can be expressed by the differential equation

$$\frac{dW(t)}{dt} = \sum Q = Q_i(t) - Q_o(t) \tag{1.1}$$

From eq. 1.1, the cause-and-effect transformation which relates the tons of material $W(t)$ in storage to the net mass flow rate $\Sigma Q(t)$ can be derived heuristically by merely noting that the storage level $W(t)$ can be found by integrating both sides of eq. 1.1 with respect to time. Thus

$$W(t) = \int [Q_i(t) - Q_o(t)]\, dt = \int \Sigma Q\, dt \tag{1.2}$$

Equation 1.2 shows that the variations in $W(t)$ always become the integral of the variations in $\Sigma Q(t)$. The cause-and-effect operational relationship between incremental changes in the net mass flow rate and incremental changes in the storage level is $\int dt$. The ratio $W : \Sigma Q$ takes on the aspect of a transfer function in a cause-effect transformation.

The integration operation $\int dt$ in eq. 1.2 defines the dynamic behavior of the *ideal storage process*. Furthermore, this operator—generally referred to as an "ideal or perfect integration"—can be taken as the basic relationship between storage, hold-up, or inventory, and material or mass flow rate. The signal-flow diagram* for the mass flow and storage process appears as shown in Fig. 1.4. The flow $Q_i(t)$ may be considered positive. The outflow $Q_o(t)$ may be considered negative. The net flow $\Sigma Q(t)$ is the algebraic sum of the two flows $Q_i(t)$ and $Q_o(t)$. Thus, the signal which drives or disturbs the storage process is $\Sigma Q(t) = Q_i(t) - Q_o(t)$. The process integrates the net flow and develops the storage-level variable $W(t)$ as a response.

A more fundamental way to develop the relationship between changes in flow ΣQ and changes in storage level W is to take the term-by-term Laplace transformation† for eq 1.1 and solve for the ratio of

* See Appendix 1.
† See Appendix 2.

the transformed variables $W(s):\Sigma Q(s)$. Laplace-transforming eq. 1.1 gives

$$sW(s) - W(0^+) = \Sigma Q(s) \qquad (1.3)$$

$$= Q_i(s) - Q_o(s) \qquad (1.4)$$

The term $W(s)$ in eq. 1.3 is the Laplace-transformed variable which corresponds to the storage value $W(t)$. $W(0^+)$ is the *initial value* of the storage at the time $t = 0^+$, the instant at which a disturbance in the form of $Q_i(t)$, $Q_o(t)$, or $\Sigma Q(t)$ is applied. The Laplace variable s, as it appears in eq. 1.3 as a multiplier of $W(s)$, signifies operation upon $W(s)$: The operation of multiplication in the s-domain by s is analogous to $\dfrac{dW(t)}{dt}$.

The terms on the right-hand side of the equal sign are the Laplace transformations $Q_i(s)$ and $Q_o(s)$ of the disturbing mass flow rates $Q_i(t)$ and $Q_o(t)$. Equation 1.3 can be solved for the inventory level $W(s)$. Thus

$$W(s) = \frac{1}{s}\left[\sum Q(s) + W(0^+)\right] \qquad (1.5)$$

The quantity $1/s$ in eq. 1.5 is analogous to the operator $\int dt$ in eq. 1.2. Both show that the process of storing material constitutes, in the mathematical sense, an *ideal integrating process*.

The next task will be to explore how an integral process defined by a transfer function $1/s$ responds to various types of time-varying disturbances. Provided that none of the mass flows to or from a storage pile (and in general there may be several inflows and several outflows) are functions of the level of storage W, the tons of material in storage will build up or decline in direct proportion to the integral of the net flow rate to storage. For a positive or a negative material-flow unbalance which is maintained long enough, the storage will diminish to zero or will fill the storage facility to overflowing. The time required for these limits of storage or inventory to be reached can be calculated readily by carrying out the integration of eq. 1.1 or by taking the inverse Laplace transformation on eq. 1.5 for a specifically defined time-varying net mass flow.

Table 1.1 summarizes the dynamic response of a single unregulated storage process—that is, an ideal integrating process—to a variety of mass flow-rate disturbances. The particular flow disturbances are: an impulse, a step function, a ramp function, a pulse, and a sinusoidally varying mass flow rate. In the first column of Table 1.1, the time

TABLE 1.1.   DYNAMIC RESPONSE OF UNREGULATED STORAGE PROCESSES

Disturbance $\Sigma Q(t)$	Laplace Transform $\Sigma Q(s)$	Transform of Storage Value $W(s)$	Process Response $W(t)$
Area = 1, ∞, $\Delta t = 0$	1	$\dfrac{1}{s}$	$W(t) = \mathcal{U}(t)$
1, 0	$\dfrac{1}{s}$	$\dfrac{1}{s^2}$	$W(t) = t$
ϕ, 0	$\dfrac{1}{s^2}$	$\dfrac{1}{s^3}$	$W(t) = \dfrac{t^2}{2}$
b, a, $t = 0$	$\dfrac{b(1-e^{-as})}{s}$	$\dfrac{b(1-e^{-as})}{s^2}$	ab, a, $t=0$, $W(t) = bt - b(t-a)\,\mathcal{U}(t-a)$
1, $t = 0$, $t = T$	$\dfrac{\omega}{s^2+\omega^2}$, $\omega = \dfrac{2\pi}{T}$	$\dfrac{\omega}{s(s^2+\omega^2)}$	$\dfrac{\pi}{2}$, $\dfrac{1}{\omega}$, T, $W(t) = \dfrac{1}{\omega}\,(1-\cos \omega t)$

variation of the mass flow rate $\Sigma Q(t)$ is defined. In the second column, the Laplace transformation of the flow-rate disturbance is given. The third column gives the Laplace transformation for the storage level $W(s)$ for each type of disturbance. This transformation $W(s)$ is formed by taking the product of the integration $1/s$, which defines the dynamic response of the storage process, and the transformation of the particular disturbing function $\Sigma Q(s)$. In the final column of the table, the time variation of storage $W(t)$ is shown and defined mathematically. For convenience, the initial level of storage $W(0^+)$ has been assumed to be zero, since at this point we are more concerned with discovering the manner in which $W(t)$ varies because of $\Sigma Q(t)$ than with knowing the precise amount or level of $W(t)$.

The manner in which Table 1.1 is developed proves interesting. An impulse type of disturbance of unit area has a Laplace transformation of unity. The integral with respect to time of an impulse or of unity is a step function of unit height. The step function of unit height, when integrated with respect to time, becomes a unit-slope ramp function. Thus the impulse, step, and ramp disturbances become successive integrals of one another in the time domain. In the transformation or s-domain form, the impulse is 1; the step, $1/s$; and the ramp, $1/s^2$.

According to this, if an impulse disturbance of mass flow rate could be applied to a storage vessel, the amount of material in storage would suddenly change (as does the step function) to a new level. A step function of flow disturbance, applied to a storage, hold-up, or inventory operation, must create a linearly rising or falling level of material in storage: in other words, the ramp function. A ramp function, in turn, applied as a disturbance to the inventory or storage process, has a transform which is $1/s^2$. When this is multiplied by the process operator $1/s$, which is analogous to being integrated in the time domain, the over-all operator becomes $1/s^3$. When inversely Laplace-transformed, $1/s^3$ becomes a square-law variation in time. The storage builds up according to $\frac{1}{2}t^2$.

The pulse disturbance is considered because it represents the typical manner in which flow rate to a storage or inventory may change.

The pulse can be considered as being the integral of a step disturbance of magnitude b taken over the time interval $0 < t < a$. Thus, integrating the step over a finite time interval a gives a response function which is a truncated ramp. This is the response of a storage process to a pulse.

The last item in the table, the sinusoidally varying net mass flow rate, proves to be a most interesting and important type of disturbance when applied to the ideal integrating operation of storage. A sine function integrated with respect to time, becomes a cosine function. The magnitude of the change in storage varies inversely and in proportion to the frequency ω of the sinusoidally varying flow rate. The variation in storage also lags behind the flow rate by 90 degrees in time phase. Therefore, when one notices a sinusoidally varying storage level or inventory in a vessel or bin, it must be understood that since the process is an integrating process, the origin of the disturbance must be sought in a time-varying mass flow rate which occurs 90 degrees ahead in time phase of the observed storage fluctuation.

5. STORAGE CASCADES

A procedure must be chosen for regulating the flow of material between consecutive storage vessels or inventory depots. Otherwise, neither the flow nor the inventory remains for long in equilibrium. This is especially true when the material in motion is a solid and does not exhibit the self-regulation of storage and flow inherent in some fluid* processes.

If the inflow $Q_i(t)$ to a storage vessel is positive and time-varying, and the outflow is zero, the storage vessel will fill. If the inflow is zero and the outflow $Q_o(t)$ is positive and time-varying, the vessel will empty. When two vessels are placed in cascade so that the outflow from the first is the inflow to the second, the second vessel cannot fill unless there is outflow from the first. If the outflow from the first vessel is overflow, the second vessel starts to fill only after the first has been filled. Thus a cascade of storage vessels through which flow takes place upon an "overflow basis" will fill consecutively from the first vessel to the last and will remain filled. Then steady flow will pass through the system as if no vessels were present. The opposite scheme for emptying vessels can be conceived and described.

In contrast to the overflow scheme, material can be pumped or conveyed from one storage vessel to another. The flow rate might be time-varying or constant. In order to regulate either flow or storage, some rule must be set up which establishes how the flow between vessels or storage piles varies.

6. REGULATION OF FLOW AND STORAGE

To maintain constant hold-up or storage of material at a point in the cascade of operations through which a material flows, imposes the condition that the integral of the net flow be kept zero, $\int \Sigma Q \, dt = 0$. However, the purpose of placing storage between the operations of a

* See Chapter 2 for detailed treatment of fluids in motion.

Fig. 1.5. Signal-flow diagram of a simple proportional action materials flow regulator.

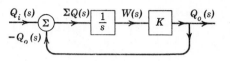

process may be to counteract throughput upsets, rather than to maintain constant inventory.

Often compromises must be accepted when storage and flow regulatory schemes are being built. If storage is to be regulated, flow must be the variable. If flow is to be regulated, storage must be the variable. One cannot regulate both simultaneously in the same process.

Flow Regulation Through Single-Storage Vessel

A simple procedure can be used to regulate the flow in a single-storage vessel. The outflow from the vessel can be made proportional to the amount of storage. Immediately, the principle of feedback regulation of flow becomes evident, as shown in Fig. 1.5. The inflow $Q_i(t)$ to the vessel has the outflow $Q_o(t)$ subtracted from it so that the difference or the error in flow $\varepsilon Q = Q_i - Q_o$ is integrated by the storage process to generate the response $W(t)$ which represents the amount of storage. If the outflow is made proportional to the amount of storage $Q_o = KW$, proportional flow regulation acts upon the storage process.

The equation which relates storage to inflow is

$$\frac{W(s)}{Q_i(s)} = \frac{\dfrac{1}{K}}{\dfrac{1}{K}s + 1} \tag{1.6}$$

The equation which relates the outflow to the inflow is

$$\frac{Q_o(s)}{Q_i(s)} = \frac{1}{\dfrac{1}{K}s + 1} \tag{1.7}$$

The impulse response of the flow-regulated process will have exponential form e^{-Kt}. The proportionality constant K of the regulator is the sole parameter which governs the nature of the dynamic response.

Proportional Flow Regulation in Storage Cascade

Consider that each of a cascade of n identical storage vessels shown in Fig. 1.6 has proportional regulation of the outflow as was described

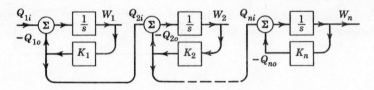

Fig. 1.6. Proportional flow regulation in a cascade of n storages.

in the previous section. For the nth storage vessel, the storage $W_n(s)$ can be related to the inflow Q_{ni} by the relation

$$\frac{W_n(s)}{Q_{ni}(s)} = \frac{\dfrac{1}{K_n}}{\dfrac{1}{K_n} s + 1} \tag{1.8}$$

If all the proportionality constants $K_1, K_2 \ldots K_n$ are equal, the storage $W_n(s)$ in any vessel can be related to the inflow $Q_{1i}(s)$ which enters the cascade.

$$\frac{W_n(s)}{Q_{1i}(s)} = \frac{\dfrac{1}{K}}{\left(\dfrac{1}{K} s + 1\right)^n} \tag{1.9}$$

Likewise, the flow from the nth vessel $Q_{no}(s)$ can be related to the inflow $Q_{1i}(s)$ by the relationship

$$\frac{Q_{no}(s)}{Q_{1i}(s)} = \frac{1}{\left(\dfrac{1}{K} s + 1\right)^n} \tag{1.10}$$

If the time scale is normalized so that $u = Kt$, the transfer functions in eqs. 1.8, 1.9, and 1.10 can be normalized in the s-domain by the change in variable $\lambda = s/K$. Thus

$$\frac{W_n(\lambda)}{Q_{1i}(\lambda)} = \frac{\dfrac{1}{K}}{(\lambda + 1)^n} \tag{1.11}$$

and

$$\frac{Q_{no}(\lambda)}{Q_{1i}(\lambda)} = \frac{1}{(\lambda + 1)^n} \tag{1.12}$$

The impulse response of the flow-regulated cascade can be determined from the impulse response solution to eqs. 1.11 and 1.12. Thus, for

$$Q_{1i}(\lambda) = K,$$

$$W_n(u) = \frac{u^{n-1}}{(n-1)!}\, e^{-u} \qquad (1.13)$$

$$Q_{no}(u) = K\, \frac{u^{n-1}}{(n-1)!}\, e^{-u} \qquad (1.14)$$

The expressions in eqs. 1.13 and 1.14 are valid for all values of n.

The curves plotted in Fig. 1.7 show the response of the storage cascade to an impulse of inflow. The first vessel receives a sudden rise in storage which diminishes according to the exponential decay law e^{-u}. The storage in the second vessel rises to a maximum value and then falls again to zero. For the third vessel, the fourth, the fifth, and so on, a rise in storage is present, but to a progressively smaller degree from vessel to vessel.

Some interesting properties occur for the cascade response. The maximum value of storage is given by

$$W_{n\,\max} = \frac{1}{(n-1)!}\, e^{(n-1)} \log e^{(n-2)} \qquad (1.15)$$

The maximum value of storage occurs at the point along the time axis

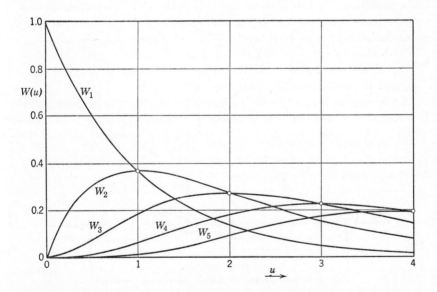

Fig. 1.7. Impulse response of a cascade of n storage vessels with proportional action material flow regulation.

where the storage-response curve for the previous vessel W_{n-1} intersects the curve W_n for the vessel under consideration. Thus Table 1.2 can be formed.

The curves of Fig. 1.7 and the data from Table 1.2 prove useful for estimating how a disturbance will be attenuated by a cascade of storage vessels. The data also indicate that disturbances tend to move through storage cascades somewhat like a wave; the maximum influence is felt in the nth vessel n units of time after the impulse occurs at the inflow to the first vessel.

TABLE 1.2.   MAXIMUM DISTURBANCE TO STORAGE CASCADE

Storage Vessel No. n	u Normalized Time at which W_n is a Maximum	Maximum Value of Storage W_n
1	0	1.000
2	1	0.368
3	2	0.269
4	3	0.236
5	4	0.198
6	5	0.175

Regulation of Storage

Since each component in the flow ΣQ to a storage has a disturbing or a manipulating influence on the storage level W, an adjustment of one or more of the flows in ΣQ to counteract changes in the other flows constitutes *regulation of storage*. When fluctuations in the inflow Q_i disturb the storage level W, the outflow Q_o must be manipulated to bring about regulation. If the outflow represents a demand upon storage, the inflow must be manipulated.

According to Fig. 1.8, which diagrams a storage regulator, a reference level of storage W_{ref} is established. The actual level W is measured. The error $\varepsilon_W = W_{ref} - W$ serves as a signal to actuate the

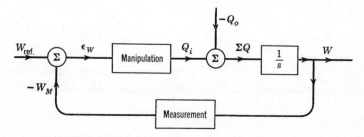

Fig. 1.8.   Signal-flow diagram showing feedback regulation of storage.

manipulation of the controlling flow. Three modes of control are possible: First, the correction of W can be continuous and some function of the error ε_W. This is called *continuous regulation*. Secondly, the level of inventory W can be measured by determining its value at regularly spaced time intervals. A comparison of the value of W at the time of the sample with the reference level W_{ref} can be made. The manipulative action can be applied in proportion to some function of the error magnitude, and maintained constant during the time interval following the action of sampling. This type of control is called "*sampling clamping*" or "*sampled pulsed*" control. Thirdly, an *off-on* type of regulation can be used. Whenever an increase in ΔQ_o, the demand upon the storage, causes W to fall below the value $W_{ref} - \Delta W$, a change ΔQ_i can be made in Q_i which is large enough to make $\Sigma Q > 0$. The level of W will then rise linearly, despite the demand Q_o. When the level of W reaches the value $W_{ref} + \Delta W$, the regulator shuts off the corrective flow: that is, ΔQ_i is made zero again. A comparison of the dynamic response for the three types of storage regulation will be developed to show how the three modes of control differ in their action and effectiveness.

Continuous and Proportional Regulation. When the manipulation of Q_i is made proportional to the error εW, the equations which describe the action of the continuous regulator become

$$\frac{dW}{dt} = Q_i - Q_o \tag{1.16}$$

$$\varepsilon_W = W_{ref} - W \tag{1.17}$$

$$Q_i = K\varepsilon_W \tag{1.18}$$

$$\frac{dW}{dt} + KW = KW_{ref} - Q_o \tag{1.19}$$

The Laplace transform of eq. 1.19 becomes

$$W(s) = \frac{1}{s + K}[KW_{ref}(s) - Q_o(s) + W(0^+)] \tag{1.20}$$

Equation 1.20 gives the level W of a continuously regulated storage system in terms of the reference level $W_{ref}(s)$, the disturbance $Q_o(s)$, and the initial value $W(0^+)$.

According to the development in Section 4, p. 7, unregulated storage has a characteristic transfer function $\dfrac{W(s)}{Q_o(s)} = \dfrac{-1}{s}$. Regulated stor-

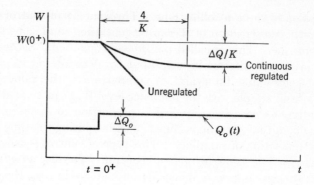

Fig. 1.9. Transient response of storage process to a sudden demand of outflow Q_o. Continuous and proportional regulation of inflow Q_i.

age for proportional and continuous manipulative action, according to eq. (20), has a characteristic transfer function $\dfrac{W(s)}{Q_o(s)} = \dfrac{-1}{s + K}$.

Figure 1.9 shows a comparison between the response $W(t)$ of the unregulated storage and the proportionally and continuously regulated storage, when both are subjected to an incremental change in outflow Q_o. Prior to the disturbance, the throughput Q may be assumed constant: that is, $Q_{i\,\mathrm{av}} = Q_{o\,\mathrm{av}}$. Thus, ΔQ_o will cause the inventory level W to decline from a reference level $W(0^+)$.

The slope at which the unregulated storage diminishes is directly proportional to ΔQ_o. The slope at which the regulated curve starts downward is determined by the regulator proportionality constant K. The unregulated system will empty the storage pile, provided the change in outflow remains constant and greater than the inflow, long enough. The regulated system will come to an equilibrium storage level $W(0^+) - \Delta Q_o/K$ following a disturbance ΔQ_o. The time required for the regulated system to reach substantially an equilibrium or steady-state condition following the step disturbance of outflow will be $4\tau = 4/K$.

Thus, for a large proportional constant K, not only will the regulation improve but the transient response will become faster. For very large values of K, a small change in outflow will not tend to make the storage level drop more than a few per cent, and the entire change will take place in a very short period of time.

Sampled and Proportional Regulation. When the regulator is a proportional-sampler-clamper with a gain K and a sampling period T, the storage level W can be written at the $(n + 1)$th sampling point in terms of the value it has at the nth point. Since the process of storage is an integration, the response equation is

$$W_{n+1} = W_n + \int_{t+nT}^{t+(n+1)T} \sum Q_n(t)\, dt \qquad (1.21)$$

from which the difference

$$W_{n+1} - W_n = (\Sigma Q_n) T \qquad (1.22)$$

results when the integration is performed. During the nth interval the net flow is

$$\Sigma Q_n = Q_{in} - Q_{on} \qquad (1.23)$$

and for proportional clamping regulator action during the nth interval, the inflow is

$$Q_{in} = K\varepsilon_{Wn} \qquad (1.24)$$

$$= K(W_{\text{ref } n} - W_n) \qquad (1.25)$$

so that the difference equation which expresses the variation in storage W_n for an outflow disturbance ΔQ_{on} is

$$W_{n+1} + (KT - 1)W_n = -\Delta Q_{on}T + KW_{\text{ref } n}T \qquad (1.26)$$

The classical solution to the difference eq. 1.26 will contain two parts: a homogeneous solution and a particular solution. To find the homogeneous solution, one chooses a trial solution of the form β^{m+n} and inserts this in eq. 1.26. The root of the characterizing equation is equal to $\beta = 1 - KT$, so that the homogeneous solution for W_n has the form $W_n = A\beta^n$.

To find the particular solution for the difference equation requires that the nature of the disturbing function ΔQ_{on} be known. For the purpose of this analysis, assume that the step function of magnitude ΔQ_o is applied to the system at the value of $t = 0^+$ which is coincident with a sample point. The clamper acts immediately and applies the correction $K\varepsilon_W$. Under these conditions, and for a reference level $W(0^+)$, the particular solution becomes

$$W_n = W(0^+) - \Delta Q_o/K \qquad (1.27)$$

The total solution is therefore the sum of the homogeneous and particular solutions.

$$W_n = A\beta^n + W(0^+) - \frac{\Delta Q_o}{K} \qquad (1.28)$$

$$W_n = A(1 - KT)^n + W(0^+) - \frac{\Delta Q_o}{K} \qquad (1.29)$$

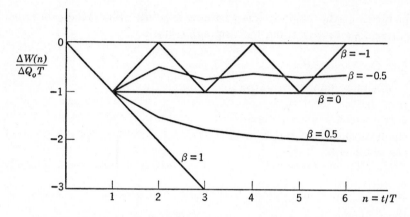

Fig. 1.10. Transient response of proportional sampler-clamper storage regulator.

The constant A in eq. 1.29 is an undetermined coefficient whose value can be found by use of the initial condition $W_o = W(0^+)$. Therefore the constant A is equal to $-\Delta Q_o/K$, and the final form of the response equation becomes

$$W_n = -\frac{\Delta Q_o}{K}[1 - \beta^n] + W(0^+) \tag{1.30}$$

$$= \Delta W_n + W(0^+) \tag{1.30a}$$

$$W_n = -\frac{\Delta Q_o T}{KT}[1 - \beta^n] + W(0^+) \tag{1.31}$$

$$W_n = -\Delta Q_o T[1 + \beta + \beta^2 + \cdots + \beta^{n-1}] + W(0^+) \tag{1.32}$$

There is no restriction placed upon whether the quantity $(1 - K)$ must be greater than, less than, or equal to unity. Therefore, even for the simple first-order system of sample-clamping regulatory action, three possible modes of response result.

For the quantity $\beta \geq 1$, β^n is a growing function for increasing n; so W_n will tend to run away. For $\beta = 0$, $\beta^n = 0$; and after one sample period, the response W_n reaches its final value. For $0 < \beta < 1$, β^n is diminishing and W_n approaches the final value $W(0^+) - \dfrac{\Delta Q_o}{K}$ from one side only. For $-1 < \beta < 0$, W_n approaches the final value $W(0^+) - \dfrac{\Delta Q_o}{K}$ in an oscillatory but damped manner. Figure 1.10 shows the typical response of the proportional sampler-clamper storage regulator subjected to a step function of flow disturbance.   Curves are shown which correspond to $\beta = 1$, 0.5, 0, -0.5, and -1.

Off–On Regulation

When the flow disturbance ΔQ_o is applied to the off–on system, and provided the value $W(t)$ is at the level $W(0^+)$, the level begins to fall at a rate which is proportional to the magnitude of ΔQ_o.   At the instant the level $W(t)$ falls to the level $W(0^+) - \Delta W$, full corrective action of the inflow will be brought to bear to increase the level of the inventory $W(t)$.   The correction flow ΔQ_i must be greater than the magnitude of the disturbance; otherwise, the level of W will continue to fall below $W(0^+) - \Delta W$.   When $\Delta Q_i > \Delta Q_o$, the level W rises in proportion to the difference $\Delta Q_i - \Delta Q_o$ until it reaches the value $W(0^+) + \Delta W$, at which time the control shuts off.   If the disturbance ΔQ_o is still in action, the cycle starts again.

As shown in Fig. 1.11, the general behavior of the off–on system is oscillatory about the desired or reference level W_{ref}.   The slopes of the rising and falling portions of $W(t)$ are determined wholly by the rela-

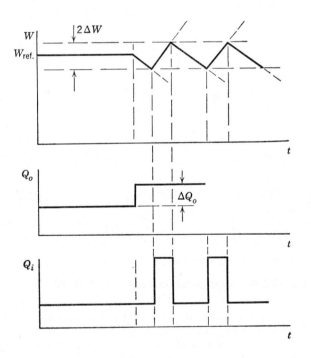

Fig. 1.11.   Off–on regulation of storage.

tive magnitudes of the disturbance and the corrective manipulation. The frequency of reversals in the time-varying pattern of $W(t)$ is also determined by these relative magnitudes of the disturbance and the manipulation.

7. CONTROL AND REGULATION OF INVENTORY

Inventory is regulated in the production and service processes so that certain economic advantages can be gained by meeting the demands of consumers with the minimum of material on hand, minimum space allotted to storage, and minimum effort devoted to the regulation. Ordinarily one might expect that the regulation of inventory would be a simple matter, but this is not quite the case.

Flow rates through production, distributing, and marketing processes cannot always be adjusted in level according to the formulae set by those who wish to regulate inventory. Production economy may depend upon making the maximum number of items per unit time, and continuing to maintain this production rate for long periods of time. Consequently, production tends to pour material into inventory at a constant flow for various time intervals. This becomes a *pulse-duration modulation* type of manipulating action as opposed to pulse-amplitude modulation described in Section 6. The important feature of the manipulating signal becomes the area under the flow pulse, for this constitutes the inventory added to the amount already in storage during each time interval. Continuous production is represented when the duration of the pulse is equal to or greater than the sampling period.

The very nature of the pulse-duration problem is nonlinear. The only obvious method for analysis is to carry out step-by-step calculations for specific problems. If the process is a single storage of a single production item, the calculations can be done readily upon a manual basis. For complicated problems of multiple storage, multiple-flow processes, multiple items, parallel production lines, and processes in which the economic factors determine the level of production and the duration of production runs, machine computation may be the only possible approach.

Pulse-Duration Modulation

An illustration of pulse-duration modulation for the regulation of a single inventory process can be given. The inventory process is represented by the integrator $1/s$. If the pulse-duration modulator has a proportional gain of K, the transfer function for the over-all process becomes K/s.

The unit step response of the inventory process is shown by the

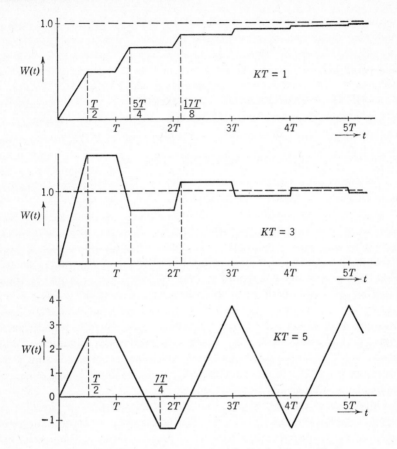

Fig. 1.12. Inventory regulation by means of pulse-duration modulation.

curves in Fig. 1.12. These curves are obtained by means of a step-by-step analysis which follows the same pattern as the amplitude-modulation problem presented in the previous section, except that the slopes of the response curve $W(t)$ are constant and the duration of the correction periods changes.

When the pulse modulator generates steps of unit positive or negative height and duration $T/2$ for a unit error input, the system remains stable for $KT < 4$. For $KT < 2$, the response $W(t)$ does not oscillate. It approaches the final value progressively from the same side. For $2 < KT < 4$, the response oscillates, but the oscillation decays progressively toward the steady-state or final value. However, for $KT > 4$, the inventory regulation system becomes unstable.

Inventory regulation is a subject in itself. Nevertheless, it is a problem in kinematics of materials handling, regardless of how complex the processes become. The understanding that storage variation is an integration process, and that flow implies transportation lag when distance is involved between producing processes and inventory provides the basic transfer operators with which to work. Computational aid is available today for handling the solution of the properly formulated equations for any degree of complexity of problem.

8. TRANSPORTATION AND TRANSPORTATION LAG

Transportation can be defined as the act of moving material from one location to another in a process. Time elapses as material is transported through the distances which separate operations or vessels. The distances, and therefore the time for transportation, are determined by the layout of plants. Sometimes the factors which govern these distances are not related solely to the problem of process control. Plants may already exist, and it may be advisable to connect them together into a cascade or some other arrangement to yield a given product. A plant may have to be built so that safety considerations take precedence over the process control. Fire lanes between process regions, and barricades, may determine separation distances. The very size of the equipment that goes into some processes is such that minimum distances of transportation between adjacent pieces of equipment are automatically determined.

During *ideal* transportation, the individual portions of the flow of material retain their identity. No mixing, blending, or interchanging of order of loads, parts, or particles takes place. Even in the event that this happens, there will still be a *transporation lag* between any two stations along the path of transport. In the material transport scheme shown in Fig. 1.13, if there is a time variation in property at station a, the instantaneous property of the flow stream at station b will differ from that of station a by virtue of its being downstream.

Consider that the material moving through the process has a property $p_a(t)$ as it passes point a at time t. The material is transported

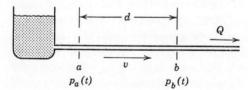

Fig. 1.13. Transportation lag in material flow.

at a constant mass flow rate Q, with an average velocity v, through a distance of transport d, to the second point b.   At point b, the material flow will have a property $p_b(t)$.   The property $p_b(t)$ lags $p_a(t)$ by the time-delay increment $\Delta t = d/v$, which is the time required for the flow to move from a to b.   Thus $p_b(t)$ can be written in terms of $p_a(t)$ with the transportation lag included.

$$p_b(t) = p_a(t - d/v) \qquad (1.33)$$

when $\Delta t = d/v$ reduces to zero, p_b and p_a become identical.

The delayed function $p_a(t - d/v)$, as expressed in eq. 1.33, has the Laplace transform

$$p_b(s) = p_a(s)e^{-(d/v)s} = p_a(s)e^{-\Delta ts} \qquad (1.34)$$

The operator $e^{-(d/v)s}$ signifies "pure" delay or "dead time."   When this operator multiplies or "operates upon" the transformation of any function, it signifies that the function is delayed in the time domain by the amount Δt.   When the sign of the exponent in the operator $e^{\Delta ts}$ is positive, the time function is advanced rather than retarded.

9. MIXING OR BLENDING—GENERAL

A probability approach should be used to study mixing.   The study of distributions of one species of particle with respect to other species of particles found in random samples taken in space and in time, the manner in which these distributions vary with the passage of time, and the determination of the mean residence time of particles in vessels constitute a fundamental approach to the study of mixing or blending.

However, some over-simplification of the problem permits a differential equation approach.   The simplified and approximate differential equations can predict the variation in composition of material in pipelines, conveyors, hold-up vessels, and process reactors "on the average."

Differential Equations Approach

Two limiting cases of mixing can be assumed—first, that *no mixing* takes place; secondly, that instantaneous and *perfect mixing* takes place.   The first situation can be illustrated in Fig. 1.14.   A mass-flow Q of material with a property p_i drops into a hold-up vessel, spreads itself evenly on the top of the material of property p_a already in the vessel, and flows downward through the vessel.   If no mixing whatsoever takes place between the upper layer and the bottom layer, and if no diffusion of material from one layer to the other takes place, the interface between the material of property p_i and the material of property p_a moves down through the hold-up vessel at a velocity determined by the average flow rate through the vessel. The hold-up vessel acts as a place in which the flow Q slows down.

The quality or composition $p_o(t)$ of the outflowing stream from a vessel in which there is no mixing at all, will lag the composition or quality $p_i(t)$ of the inflowing stream by the Δt which is required for the fluid to pass through the vessel. The transfer function which expresses this situation becomes

$$\frac{p_o(s)}{p_i(s)} = e^{-\Delta ts} \qquad (1.35)$$

The value of the dead time Δt is found by merely dividing the volume V of the material held in the vessel by the volumetric flow rate Q. The ratio V/Q has the units of time. It is approximately the average time needed for a particle to pass through the vessel along the axis of the flow.

The other situation is shown in Fig. 1.15. The new material, of property p_i, drops into the hold-up vessel and becomes *instantaneously mixed*, by means of violent agitation, with all of the material present in the entire hold-up vessel. At every instant of time, the new material of a different property is "blended" with all the material in the vessel.

The average property of the material in the perfectly mixed vessel will change because of the variations in the property of the mass inflow rate. Consider, as shown in Fig. 1.16, that two streams of different material which have mass flow rates Q_{ai} and Q_{bi} empty into a hold-up vessel in which a mass W of the mixture is held. Let the total flow $Q = Q_{ai} + Q_{bi}$ to the vessel be constant. Assume also that the

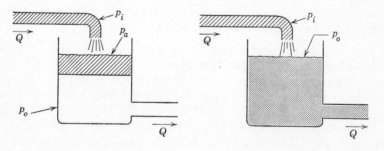

Fig. 1.14. No mixing.   Fig. 1.15. Perfect mixing.

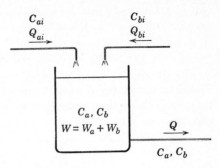

Fig. 1.16. Composition variation in a perfectly mixed vessel.

hold-up W in the vessel is essentially constant: The total inflow and outflow are equal.

One kind of mixing has been defined as *perfect;* the composition C of the mixture is everywhere the same throughout the vessel. Material added from the inflow stream mixes *instantly* with the total quantity of material held in the vessel. A change in the ratio of flows $Q_{ai} : Q_{bi}$ must bring about a change in the composition within the vessel, and consequently a change in the composition of the outflowing stream. Under these conditions, the average composition of the outflow stream Q_o will be the same as the average composition of the material everywhere in the vessel. But the composition in the vessel will be instantaneously different from the composition of the inflow.

Composition can be defined in terms of one component or the other of the mixture in the vessel or in the flow streams. Thus, the composition in the vessel will be either the ratio of the mass of the component W_a to the total mass $W = W_a + W_b$, or the mass of the component W_b to the total mass $W = W_a + W_b$. The manner in which the ratio $W_a : (W_a + W_b)$ or $W_b : (W_a + W_b)$ changes, defines variations in the composition of the vessel.

The incremental change dC_a in composition C_a in the vessel is related to the build-up or decline of the component W_a in the vessel. Thus

$$dC_a = \frac{1}{W} dW_a \qquad (1.36)$$

relates dC_a to dW_a. An incremental material balance shows that dW_a changes because of the net accumulation of component a through the addition of Q_{ai}, and the loss of component a because of the outflow of Q_{ao} during the time interval dt. Thus

$$dW_a = (Q_{ai} - Q_{ao}) \, dt \qquad (1.37)$$

Equations 1.36 and 1.37 combine to give

$$dC_a = \frac{1}{W}(Q_{ai} - Q_{ao})\,dt \qquad (1.38)$$

If both sides of eq. 1.38 are multiplied by W and divided by Q, the differential equation which relates composition C to the mass inflow disturbances is

$$\frac{W}{Q}\frac{dC_a}{dt} = \frac{Q_{ai}}{Q} - \frac{Q_{ao}}{Q} \qquad (1.39)$$

Thus a change in the ratio of $Q_{ai}:Q$ in the inflow stream constitutes a disturbance which ultimately governs how much change in composition C_a will take place. The average flow rate Q through the vessel and the hold-up W in the vessel determine how rapidly the composition in the vessel changes as a function of time.

The quantities on the right-hand side of eq. 1.39 are, by definition, compositions. Since flow Q is mass flow rate, and any component of flow Q, that is, Q_{ai} or Q_{ao}, is also mass flow rate, the ratio of a flow component to the total flow signifies composition C. On the right-hand side of eq. 1.39 the ratio $Q_{ai}:Q$ is the composition C_{ai} of the total inflow stream. The ratio $Q_{ao}:Q$ is the composition C_{ao}, but the composition C_a in the vessel is also the compoisition C_{ao} of the stream flowing out of the vessel, because the mixing is perfect. Substituting compositions C_a and C_{ai} where appropriate in eq. 1.39 gives the process-response equation

$$\frac{W}{Q}\frac{dC_a}{dt} + C_a = C_{ai} \qquad (1.40)$$

in which W and Q remain essentially constant.

The Laplace transformation of eq. 1.40 becomes

$$\frac{W}{Q}sC_a(s) + C_a(s) = \frac{W}{Q}C_a(0^+) + C_{ai}(s) \qquad (1.41)$$

If eq 1.41 is solved for $C_a(s)$, the transfer function can be found which relates the composition C_a in the vessel with respect to any disturbance to the composition C_{ai} and the initial value of composition in the vessel $C_a(0^+)$. Thus

$$C_a(s) = \frac{1}{\dfrac{W}{Q}s + 1}\left[C_{ai}(s) + \frac{W}{Q}C_a(0^+)\right] \qquad (1.42)$$

Equation 1.42 shows that the transfer function to express the cause-and-effect relationship for perfect mixing is an operator of the form $\dfrac{1}{\tau s + 1}$, in which the time constant τ equals W/Q.

Equations 1.40 and 1.42 are important results. They show that the composition C_a cannot change instantly following a transient upset in the inflow composition C_{ai}, even when perfect mixing prevails.

The fact that the differential equation which relates C_a to C_{ai} has a first-order linear form requires that the solution to the differential equation contain a term $e^{-t/(W/Q)}$ as the homogeneous portion of the total solution. The manner in which the term $e^{-t/(W/Q)}$ varies with time is established because it is an exponential, but the parameter W/Q sets the exact time scale for variation. The units of W/Q are time, so that the *ratio of the hold-up to the throughput* $W:Q$ *in a mixing or blending vessel becomes the characteristic time* τ *or the time constant* τ *of the cause-and-effect relationship.*

It is interesting to note how the signal-flow diagram shown in Fig. 1.17 develops for the mixing process. With reference to eq. 1.37, it is seen that the summation of Q_{ai} and Q_{ao} gives the net flow of component a to the mixing vessel. The net flow ΣQ_a divided by W, the hold-up, when integrated with respect to time, gives the composition C_a. However, the quantity Q_{ao} is the product of the composition C_a and the throughput Q. Therefore a negative-feedback path must be placed around the transfer function $1/Ws$. The negative feedback or degenerative feedback around the integration is inherent whenever there is an outflow of material.

Table 1.3 shows how the ideal mixing or blending process will respond to upsets caused by changes in composition in the inflow stream. The

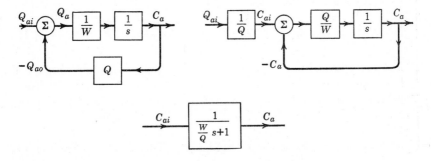

Fig. 1.17. Signal-flow diagrams for a perfectly mixed vessel or blending process.

TABLE 1.3. DYNAMIC RESPONSE OF A MIXING OR BLENDING PROCESS

Disturbance $C_i(t)$	Laplace Transform of $C_i(t)$	Laplace Transform $C_a(s)$	Outflow Composition $C_a(t)$
	1	$\dfrac{1}{\tau s + 1}$	$C_a(t) = \dfrac{1}{\tau} \times e^{-t/\tau}$
	$\dfrac{1}{s}$	$\dfrac{1}{s(\tau s + 1)}$	$C_a(t) = 1 - e^{-t/\tau}$
	$\dfrac{1}{s^2}$	$\dfrac{1}{s^2(\tau s + 1)}$	$C_a(t) = \tau(e^{-t/\tau} + \dfrac{t}{\tau} - 1)$
	$\dfrac{b(1 - e^{-as})}{s}$	$\dfrac{b(1 - e^{-as})}{s(\tau s + 1)}$	$C_a(t) = b[(1 - e^{-t/\tau}) -$ $\mathcal{U}(t - a) + e^{-\frac{(t-a)}{\tau}}]$
	$\dfrac{\omega}{s^2 + \omega^2}$ $\omega = \dfrac{2\pi}{T}$	$\dfrac{\bar{\omega}}{(\tau s + 1)(s^2 + \omega^2)}$	$C_a(t) = \dfrac{\sin(\omega t + \phi)}{\sqrt{1 + \tau^2 \omega^2}}$

first column in the table gives the nature of the time-varying disturbances to the inflow composition C_{ai}. The second column gives the transforms for these disturbances. The third column gives the combined transform of the process and the disturbing variable. The fourth column gives the time-varying composition $C_a(t)$ to be expected. The upsets which are applied to the process are an impulse, a step function, a pulse, and a sinusoidally varying inflow composition.

Probability Approach

In a vessel containing m particles, the probability that a particular particle remains after n draws is

$$P_n = \left(\frac{m}{m+1}\right)^n \tag{1.43}$$

provided for each draw a new particle is added. Equation 1.43 can be applied to the prediction of the conditions in a mixing vessel. The number of particles added in time Δt is the volume increment $\Delta V = Q\Delta t$; Q is the average flow through the vessel; and the time t can be divided into n increments, $n = \dfrac{t}{\Delta t}$. The number of particles m is replaced by volume V, the draw by ΔV, and the number of draws by $t/\Delta t$ so that

$$P = \left(\frac{V}{V+\Delta V}\right)^{\frac{t}{\Delta t}} \tag{1.44}$$

As Δt and ΔV approach zero in the limit

$$-\ln P = \frac{t}{dt}\frac{dV}{V} \tag{1.45}$$

the ratio dV/dt is equal to Q, the average flow through the vessel

$$= \frac{Q}{V}t \tag{1.46}$$

Therefore, the probability function P

$$P = y = e^{-t/\tau} \tag{1.47}$$

defines the fraction y of the liquid that is held longer than time t or the fraction

$$1 - y = 1 - e^{-t/\tau} \tag{1.48}$$

of the liquid that passes through the vessel in less than time t. *The time constant $\tau = V/Q$, the hold-up to the throughput ratio, equals the mean residence time of a particle in the vessel.*

The probability relationships in eqs. 1.47 and 1.48 also permit the equations to be written that describe how long any particle will remain in a cascade of two or more vessels. When two mixing vessels are placed in series a particle may remain part of the time in the first vessel and part of the time in the second vessel. If the total residence time t in the two vessels is divided into n parts each equal to t/n, the probability that the particle will remain in the *first* vessel longer than $t\left(\dfrac{n-1}{n}\right)$ and less than t is

$$P_{1\left(\frac{n-1}{n}\right)} = e^{-\frac{n-1}{n}x_1} - e^{-x_1} \qquad (1.49)$$

where $x_1 = t/\tau_1 = Q_1 t/V_1$. Similarly for the second fraction of time

$$P_{1\left(\frac{n-2}{n}\right)} = e^{-\frac{n-2}{n}x_1} - e^{-\frac{n-1}{n}x_1} \qquad (1.50)$$

For the jth fraction of time

$$P_{1\left(\frac{n-j}{n}\right)} = e^{-\frac{n-j}{n}x_1} - e^{-\frac{n-j-1}{n}x_1} \qquad (1.51)$$

The probability that a particle will remain in the first tank less than t/n and in the second tank at least time t is

$$P_{2(0,1)} = (1 - e^{-\frac{1}{n}x_1})e^{-x_2} \qquad (1.52)$$

For all other divisions of the time between the two tanks, the probabilities can be written

$$P_{2\left(\frac{1}{n},\frac{n-1}{n}\right)} = (e^{-\frac{1}{n}x_1} - e^{-\frac{2}{n}x_1})e^{n-1} \qquad (1.53)$$

.

.

.

.

$$P_{2\left(\frac{n-1}{n},\frac{1}{n}\right)} = (e^{-\frac{n-1}{n}x_1} - e^{-x_1})e^{-\frac{1}{n}x_2}$$

$$P_{2(1,0)} = e^{-x_2} \qquad (1.54)$$

The probability that a particle will remain in the two vessels a total time of at least t is the sum of all the individual probabilities. Thus

$$P_2 = P_{2(0,1)} + P_2 + \cdots P_2 + P_{2(1,0)} \tag{1.55}$$

When the two vessels have equal volumes V_1 and V_2, $x_1 = x_2$. Thus

$$P_2 = n(1 - e^{-\frac{1}{n}x})e^{-x} + e^{-x} \tag{1.56}$$

and for n large

$$P_2 = n\left(\frac{x}{n}\right)e^{-x} + e^{-x} \tag{1.57}$$

$$P_2 = e^{-x}(1 + x) \tag{1.58}$$

For three vessels of equal volume in a series, the expression has one term more

$$P_3 = e^{-x}\left(1 + x + \frac{x^2}{2!}\right) \tag{1.59}$$

and for four vessels

$$P_4 = e^{-x}\left(1 + x + \frac{x^2}{2!} + \frac{x^3}{3!}\right) \tag{1.60}$$

so that for a cascade of n vessels with equal hold-up volumes and the same throughput, the probability that a particle will remain in the cascade of vessels at least t units of time is

$$P_4 = e^{-x}\left(1 + x + \frac{x^2}{2!} + \frac{x^3}{3!} + \cdots\right) = 1 \tag{1.61}$$

where τ is the V/Q for a tank.

If the volumes $V_1 \neq V_2 \neq V_3$ etc. the expression for the mean residence time can be readily found from eq. 1.55, but the form of the algebra will not be as simple as for equal volume hold-up vessels.

Thus the problem of blending and mixing can be approached from a probability point of view rather than through the use of the idealized differential equations for flow and hold-up.

10. HOW TO CHOOSE THE SIZE OF A BLENDER

Mixing and blending vessels are placed in cascade with production and manufacturing operations to smooth fluctuations in the properties of material flow streams. Mistakes in operation, upsets in the environments of manufacture, or variations in the properties of raw materials may cause the fluctuations to occur.

A production operation cannot stop until these disturbances pass away, unless they are severe enough to cause the production to yield a useless product. So a hold-up or blending vessel must "blend" the flow of material whose property is a bit off from standard, with enough material which is at standard or above, so that the average property $p(t)$ of material in the flow from the blender will not change substantially even though the instantaneous property $p_i(t)$ of the inflow does.

No mixing vessel or blender can entirely eliminate the variations in the inflow-stream property $p_i(t)$. Therefore the problem of choosing the size of a blending vessel becomes a compromise: An adequate but minimum-sized hold-up W must be chosen for the blending vessel. Economy sets one extreme; performance sets the other. Also, as will be developed shortly, the lags in the mixer or blender may cause limited stability in certain types of process control operations in which feedback loops include the mixing and blending time lags.

The problem of determining W depends, to some extent, upon the nature of the variation of the inflow-stream property $p_i(t)$. The two examples which follow show how the transient response of a blender for a pulse of $p_i(t)$ of amplitude b and duration a can be related to the parameters W and Q, the hold-up and throughput, respectively; and how the amplitude of a sinusoidally varying property $p_i(t)$ can be reduced when the time constant $\tau = W/Q$ for the blending vessel is properly chosen.

Pulse Response of a Perfectly Mixed Vessel. Material flow whose property is $p_i(t)$ has a pulse type of discontinuity of magnitude b and of duration a which disturbs the average property $p(t)$ of material held in a mixing vessel. According to the development in Section 9, the response which defines the average property $p(t)$ for the mixing vessel can be predicted at any instant after the pulse starts, by taking the inverse Laplace transform of the product of the transform $\dfrac{1}{\tau s + 1}$ which defines the impulse response $p(s)$ in a perfectly mixed vessel and the transform of the pulse $p_i(s)$, which is

$$p_i(s) = \frac{b(1 - e^{-as})}{s} \tag{1.62}$$

Thus

$$p(s) = b\left(\frac{1}{\tau s + 1}\right)\left(\frac{1 - e^{-as}}{s}\right) \tag{1.63}$$

Equation 1.63 can be rearranged and divided into parts according to a partial-fraction expansion

$$p(s) = \left[\frac{k_o}{s} + \frac{k_1}{\tau s + 1} \right] (1 - e^{-as}) \tag{1.64}$$

in which the coefficients become

$$k_o = b \tag{1.65}$$

$$k_1 = -b\tau \tag{1.66}$$

The inverse Laplace transformation of eq. 1.64 becomes

$$p(t) = b\{[1 - e^{-t/\tau} - [1 - e^{-\frac{t-a}{\tau}}]\} \tag{1.67}$$

The maximum departure of the average property $p(t)$ in the mixing vessel from a zero or datum level, following the pulse disturbance, is reached at time $t = a$ units of time after the pulse of "off-quality" material has disturbed the process.

$$p_{max} = b[1 - e^{-a/\tau}] \tag{1.68}$$

Generally the duration a of a pulse will be small compared to τ, the time lag of the vessel; so eq. 1.68 can be approximated by

$$p_{max} = b \left[1 - \left(1 - \frac{a}{\tau} + \frac{a^2}{2!\tau^2} - \frac{a^3}{3!\tau^3} \cdots \right) \right] \tag{1.69}$$

$$p_{max} \simeq b \left[1 - 1 + \frac{a}{\tau} \cdots \right] \tag{1.70}$$

Since $\tau = W/Q$

$$p_{max} \simeq ba \frac{Q}{W} \tag{1.71}$$

where Q is the throughput and W is the hold-up.

Thus a figure of merit for a mixer or blending vessel can be the ratio of p_{max} to b, which becomes

$$\frac{p_{max}}{b} = \frac{\text{Ratio of peak response}}{\text{magnitude of pulse}}$$

$$= \text{duration of pulse} \times \text{mixing lag} = a \frac{Q}{W} \tag{1.72}$$

According to eq. 1.72, in a process in which Q equals 10 tons per day, it requires about 42 tons of hold-up to keep the variation in p_{max} to one per cent of b for a one-hour duration of pulse.

Pulsation Damping by a Blending Vessel. Another interesting study to make is to examine how a single blending vessel can reduce the magnitude of a periodic or sinusoidal variation in the property $p_i(t)$ of a flow of material Q through the vessel. If $p_i(t)$, which represents the property of the stream flowing into the blending vessel, is

$$p_i(t) = |p_i| \sin \omega t \qquad (1.73)$$

the property $p(t)$ of the outflow stream will be related to $p_i(t)$ by the differential equation

$$\left(\frac{W}{Q}\right) \frac{dp(t)}{dt} + p(t) = |p_i| \sin \omega t \qquad (1.74)$$

which was developed in Section 9 for perfect mixing.

The steady-state solution* to eq. 1.74 is

$$p(t) = \frac{|p_i|}{\sqrt{\tau^2 \omega^2 + 1}} \sin (\omega t + \phi) \qquad (1.75)$$

in which

$$\phi = -\tan^{-1} \omega \tau \qquad (1.76)$$

and $\tau = W : Q$ is the hold-up to throughput ratio for the blending vessel.

Thus a sinusoidally varying disturbance $p(t)$, applied to the blending process, causes the process response $p(t)$ to be a sinusoidally varying quantity; but, as shown in eqs. 1.75 and 1.76, the response of the process—that is, the average property $p(t)$—differs from $p_i(t)$ in both magnitude and phase for every value of the frequency ω.

The coefficient of the response sinusoid $\dfrac{1}{\sqrt{\tau^2 \omega^2 + 1}}$ gives the magnitude of the response $|p|$ with respect to the magnitude of the cause $|p_i|$ as a function of the frequency ω. Equation 1.76 gives the phase shift ϕ between the response p and the cause p_i as a function of frequency ω.

Figure 1.18 shows the attenuation—that is, the ratio $|p : p_i|$—and the phase shift ϕ for the blending process as a function of the dimensionless frequency $u = \tau \omega$. At zero frequency $\omega = 0$, the property p in the vessel will be exactly the same as property p_i of the inflowing stream. Thus, for slowly fluctuating property variations, that is, where the sinusoidally varying inflow property has very low frequency variations,

---

* The transient portion or homogeneous solution to the differential eq. (1.74) can be easily found, but it is not important to the study being made.

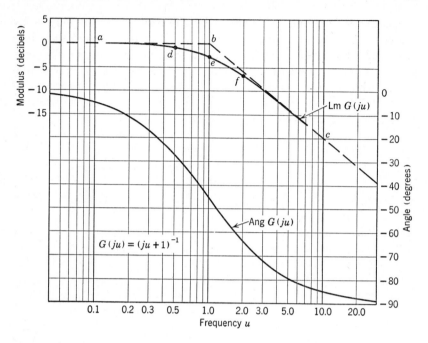

Fig. 1.18. Attenuation and phase shift characteristics for single blending vessel.

the average property p in a perfectly mixed vessel will tend to follow the variations in the inflow. There will be no phase lag between the vessel propery and the property of the inflow stream. *Hence no blending takes place!*

As the frequency ω increases the magnitude function p begins to diminish, and approaches zero as the frequency approaches large values or infinity. This indicates that the property p in the vessel will not vary at very large values of ω, in spite of the variation of inflow property p_i. Thus, *perfect blending takes place!* As higher frequencies are reached, the phase-shift curve shows that the property p in the vessel lags behind that of the disturbing function p_i. The ultimate value of the lag is $-\pi/2$ radians or -90 degrees of time phase shift as the frequency ω approaches infinity.

An interesting point to note is that when the frequency ω is equal to $1/\tau$—that is, the reciprocal of the time constant τ which characterizes the mixing or blending lag in the vessel—the magnitude function becomes 0.707 and the phase shift becomes $-\pi/4$ or -45 degrees. This frequency is a characterizing frequency for the physical system whose dynamic response is defined by the operator $1/(\tau s + 1)$ or by the vector form of operator $1/(j\omega\tau + 1)$. It indicates that for values of frequency below the critical value $\omega = 1/\tau$, the process response p has a tendency to do exactly what the input or driving function p_i does. Above the frequencies $\omega = 1/\tau$, the process attenuates all disturbances in proportion to their frequency ω, and, generally speaking, fails to respond to the disturbing variable p_i.

Figure 1.18 is an attenuation curve that can be used for sizing blending vessels, on the assumption that perfect mixing takes place in the vessel. For example, if the magnitude of the pulsation p_i is given as 0.1 unit, and the frequency at which this fluctuation is occurring is ω_1 in a throughput of Q, then the size of the blending vessel—that is, W, the amount of the hold-up—can be chosen so that $p(j\omega)$ can be kept below any specified numerical value. If it is desired that p shall not exceed 0.01 for frequencies greater than ω_1 radians per hour, the critical frequency $\omega = 1/\tau$ must be equal to 0.1 times ω_1. Therefore, $\tau = 10/\omega_1$ $= W/Q$. The value for the hold-up is $W = 10Q/\omega_1$. It is evident that, for a given pulsation in $p_i(t)$, perfect blending requires greater blender size. Therefore the cost of equipment, as well as the momentary inventory, rises. It might be better to eliminate the cause of the fluctuation.

11. QUALITY CONTROL IN A PROCESS

In some manufacturing operations, it may be desirable to place the quality of a product under automatic regulation or control. To do this requires that two conditions be met. First, the properties of the product which define its quality must be capable of being measured; secondly, a direct correlation must exist between process manipulative variables and the quality variables.

Even though these two important conditions can be met, and even though the dynamic response of the measuring apparatus and the dynamic response of the basic manufacturing process are acceptable, the precision of product-quality control that can be obtained may be limited by the time lags present in the materials-handling operations of the over-all process. The work which follows demonstrates the extent to which this can happen.

Consider that a product is made in the processing plant shown in Fig. 1.19. Assume that at the instant the product is made, it has a quality p_1, but that transport of the product occurs and blending takes place in the product recovery vessel. Thus the product made at successive instants in time in the reactor is mixed with the product held in the product recovery vessel. This causes the property p_4 of the

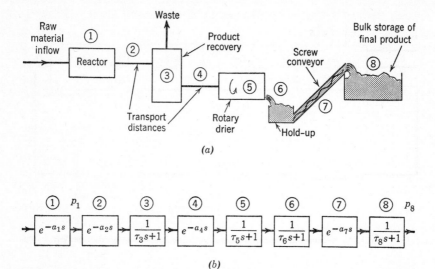

Fig. 1.19.   (a) Schematic layout of a materials-processing plant; (b) signal-flow diagram of the materials processing plant showing transport and blending lags.

product emerging from the hold-up vessel to differ from the property p_1 of the product at the instant of manufacture.

The material is next transported, dried, and transported again until it finally reaches the bulk storage or receiving bin.   The time-varying quality $p_8(t)$ of the product in the final storage bin differs from the quality $p_2(t)$ of the product which comes from the reactor because of the transportation lags and the blending which takes place in the various storage vessels before the final product is obtained.

The quality regulating system is shown in Fig. 1.20.   An instrument measures the quality p_8 and generates a signal p_m, which it sends to a quality control center.   A reference level of quality p_{ref} is compared with the measured value p_m, and the error in quality $\mathcal{E}_p = p_{\text{ref}} - p_m$ adjusts the various process control mechanisms to bring about changes in the product quality p_1 or to maintain constant quality p_1 despite various disturbances D to the process.

Many manipulations M_a, $M_b \cdots M_j$ and many disturbances D_a, $D_b \cdots D_k$ can alter the property $p_1(t)$ of the material which leaves the reactor.   Thus

$$p_1(t) = \phi(M_a, M_b \cdots M_j; D_a, D_b \cdots D_k; t)$$

However, to simplify the study consider that the quality $p_1(t)$ of the

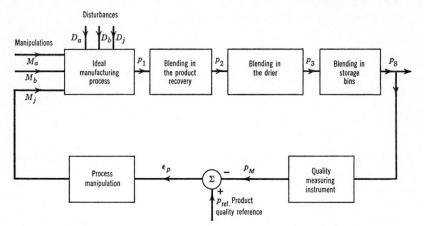

Fig. 1.20. General arrangement of feedback regulation over product quality.

product can be related to a *single* disturbance D and a *single* manipulation M, so that

$$p_1(t) = \phi(M,D,t) \tag{1.77}$$

Equation 1.77 can be linearized to express incremental changes in p_1 in terms of the incremental changes in both the disturbance D and the manipulation M. Thus

$$\Delta p_1(t) = \frac{\partial p_1}{\partial M} \Delta M(t) + \frac{\partial p_1}{\partial D} \Delta D(t) \tag{1.78}$$

$$= K_m \Delta M(t) + K_D \Delta D(t) \tag{1.79}$$

Equation 1.79 gives the static relationship between Δp_1, ΔM, and ΔD. The values for the constants k_M and k_D in eq. 1.79 can be determined from test data taken on the plant.

The dynamic behavior of the reactor will be assumed ideal. A change in D will instantly change the product property p_1; a change in M will instantly counteract the change in D, provided the change in M is applied simultaneously and in opposition to D.

The equation for cause and effect in terms of transfer functions can now be expressed for each portion of the process system.

(1) *The reactor:*

$$p_1(s) = K_m M(s) + K_D D(s) \tag{1.80}$$

(2) *The mixing in the product recovery vessel:*

$$\frac{p_3(s)}{p_2(s)} = \frac{1}{\dfrac{W_3}{Q_3}s + 1}$$

$$= \frac{1}{\tau_3 s + 1} \tag{1.81}$$

where τ_3 is the product-recovery vessel time constant. There are similar blending lags, τ_5, τ_6, and τ_8 in the rotary drier, the hold-up bin, and the bulk storage vessel for final product.

(3) *The Transportation lags:*

Between the product p_1 and p_8 there are several transport lags a_1, a_2, a_4, and a_7. Thus the over-all transport lag can be expressed as

$$\frac{p_8(s)}{p_1(s)} = e^{-as} \tag{1.82}$$

where a is the sum of all the individual transportation lags.

(5) *The measuring instrument:*

$$\frac{p_M(s)}{p_8(s)} = A(s) \tag{1.83}$$

where $A(s)$ is an undefined operator which describes the instrument dynamic behavior. For convenience, and to simplify the problem, $A(s) = 1$ will be assumed. This means that the measurement of p_8 is perfect and instantaneous.

(6) *The comparison:*

$$\mathcal{E}_p(s) = p_{\text{ref}}(s) - p_M(s) \tag{1.84}$$

(7) *The manipulation to regulate or control:*

$$\frac{M(s)}{\mathcal{E}_p(s)} = B(s) \tag{1.85}$$

where $B(s)$ is an operator which describes the dynamic behavior of the manipulator. Likewise, the manipulator will be chosen as $B(s) = K_B$ in order to simplify the problem. By combining eqs. 1.80–1.85, the manner in which the outflowing product $p_8(s)$ varies under the influence of $D(s)$ can be determined. Fig. 1.21 is the over-all signal-flow diagram.

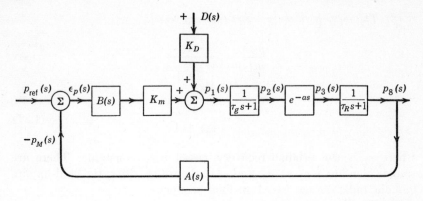

Fig. 1.21. Signal-flow diagram for feedback regulation over product quality in materials handling.

The simplified signal-flow diagram shown in Fig. 1.22 is some help in developing and studying the equation which expresses $p_8(s)$ in terms of $D(s)$. The operators X, Y, and Z, which define the three transfer functions which characterize the quality-control regulatory system, are

$$X(s) = B(s)K_m = K_B K_m \tag{1.86}$$

$$Y(s) \cong \left(\frac{1}{\tau_g s + 1}\right) (e^{-as}) \left(\frac{1}{\tau_R s + 1}\right) \tag{1.87}$$

where τ_g and τ_R are the two largest time constants between D and p_8.

$$Z(s) = A(s) = 1 \tag{1.88}$$

The variation in the product $p_8(s)$ is related to the reference signal

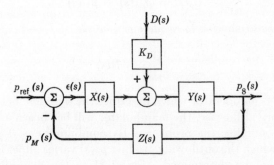

Fig. 1.22. Simplified signal-flow diagram.

p_{ref} and to the disturbance $D(s)$ according to the relation

$$p_8(s) = \frac{X(s)Y(s)}{1 + X(s)Y(s)Z(s)} \, p_{\text{ref}} \qquad (1.89)$$

$$+ \frac{K_D Y(s)}{1 + X(s)Y(s)Z(s)} \, D(s) \qquad (1.90)$$

which changes into a more useful form:

$$p_8(s) = \left[\left(\frac{XYZ}{1 + ZYZ}\right)\frac{1}{Z}\right] p_{\text{ref}} + \left[\left(\frac{XYZ}{1 + XYZ}\right)\left(\frac{K_D}{XZ}\right)\right] D \qquad (1.91)$$

by simple algebraic manipulation.

A study of the open-loop transfer function XYZ permits the dynamic response of the closed-loop regulatory system to be investigated. In fact, the open-loop transfer function XYZ fully describes the regulator dynamic response p_8/D, provided the reference value p_{ref} is kept at a constant value.

Basically, two problems are before us: first, to determine whether or not the quality regulator characterized by the several mixing lags, several transportation lags, and the idealized equipment for measurement, comparison, and control can be made stable at all; and secondly, if stable operation is possible, to determine to what extent the regulation of the quality p_8 against a disturbance D can be made precise.

The absolute stability of the system can be determined by solving the equation $1 + XYZ = 0$ for its roots in the variable s. However, the term e^{-as} gives the equation a transcendental form which makes the algebra of finding the roots somewhat tedious. The use of a graphical procedure for finding the roots proves to be more practical. To ensure absolute stability, the loop gain in the regulator $K_B K_m$ must be adjusted so that the roots of s for $1 + XYZ = 0$ are all either negative or have negative real parts. None must be pure imaginary roots, nor must any of them be positive or have positive real parts. This is the condition for absolute stability of the regulator.

However, the condition for absolute stability does not ensure that the product-quality regulator will work in a satisfactory manner. It simply guarantees that it will not become an oscillator. Therefore, to ensure a reasonable *degree of stability*, the further requirement must be added that the system shall not exhibit abnormally magnified variations in $p_8(t)$ when disturbed by a sinusoidally fluctuating quantity $D(t)$. Alternatively, if an impulse $D(t)$ disturbs the system, the envelope which bounds the decaying transient response $p_8(t)$ shall have a specified logarithmic decrement.

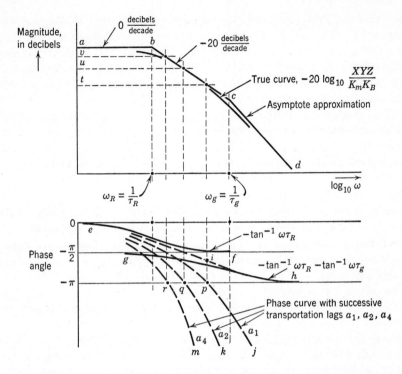

Fig. 1.23. Magnitude and angle versus frequency graphs for open-loop characteristic of the quality regulator.

Actually, the best approach to the solving of this type of problem—especially one of this order of complexity—is to use the graphical procedures developed in servomechanisms theory.* The allowable loop gain $K_m K_B$ can be determined for the closed loop for a specified resonance condition of the ratio (p_8/p_{ref}). To do this, a graph of the open-loop characteristic

$$\frac{p_8(j\omega)}{\mathcal{E}_p(j\omega)} = X(j\omega) Y(j\omega) Z(j\omega) \qquad (1.92)$$

is plotted as a function of frequency ω.

The magnitude $20 \log_{10} \dfrac{p_8(j\omega)}{\mathcal{E}_p(j\omega)}$ and angle $\dfrac{p_8(j\omega)}{\mathcal{E}_p(j\omega)}$ versus frequency ω are shown plotted in Fig. 1.23 to semilogarithmic coordinates. These

* Principles of Servomechanisms, G. S. Brown and D. P. Campbell, John Wiley & Sons, New York, 1948.

curves are called the "open-loop frequency response" of the quality regulator. The value of $K_m K_B$ is initially chosen as unity for preparing the magnitude graph. The magnitude is plotted in decibels; the phase angle, in degrees or radians. The coordinates are decibels versus frequency on a semilogarithmic scale; and angle versus frequency on the same semilogarithmic scale.

The magnitude function can be approximated by asymptotes. The true value for the function can be drawn as a curve which is displaced from the asymptotes. The frequencies $\omega = 1/\tau_R$ and $\omega = 1/\tau_g$ are spoken of as the "break" frequencies. They are numerically equal to the reciprocal of the time constants which characterize the blending aspect of the process. To construct the magnitude asymptote, the line ab is drawn through the value zero decibels. It is a line that has a slope of zero decibels per decade, and approximates the open-loop characteristic $p_8/\mathcal{E}_p$ for low frequencies. When the break frequency ω_R is reached, the time-lag factor $1/(\tau_R j\omega + 1)$ begins to influence the value $p_8/\mathcal{E}_p$ so that its value is approximated by the asymptote bc. The line bc has a slope of -20 decibels per decade.

When the frequency ω_g (that is, the second break frequency) is reached, the second time-lag factor $1/(\tau_g j\omega + 1)$ becomes effective in changing the shape of $p_8/\mathcal{E}_p$. The final asymptote cd is drawn with a slope of -40 decibels per decade. The true curve which represents $p_8/\mathcal{E}_p$ is displaced downward at the break frequencies by -3 decibels from the asymptote. At an octave above and an octave below the break frequency, the true value is one decibel *down* from the asymptote curves. Thus the true curve can be estimated after the asymptotes have been drawn.

The phase curve can be drawn by noting that the total phase $\phi(j\omega)$ is made up from three components.

$$\phi(j\omega) = \phi_R(j\omega) + \phi_g(j\omega) + \phi_T(j\omega) \tag{1.93}$$

$$\phi(j\omega) = -\tan^{-1} \omega\tau_R - \tan^{-1} - aj\omega \tag{1.94}$$

To draw the phase curve for $\phi(j\omega)$, the three components can be added. First the curve ef is drawn. At the break frequency ω_R, curve ef has the value $-\pi/4$ radians or -45 degrees. The value of ϕ_R goes from zero, as ω approaches zero, to $-\pi/2$ as ω approaches large values. At the second break frequency, another curve gh, identical in shape with curve ef, can be drawn. It goes from $-\pi/2$ to $-\pi$ as ω passes from small values to large ones. At $\omega = 1/\tau_g$, the curve gh passes through the phase value -135 degrees. Next, the composite curve eih, which represents the sum $\phi_R + \phi_g$, is formed.

To this curve *eih* as a base line, the phase shift *jωa* can be added to produce the total phase ϕ shown as curve *ejk*.

Three curves, *epj*, *eqk*, and *erm*, show the total phase ϕ for three different values of transportation lag. Curve *epj* represents the smallest value of the dead time; *eqk*, a larger value; and *erm*, the largest value. From the magnitude and phase curves as drawn in Fig. 1.23, many of the data necessary for solving this problem can now be found.

The value of gain $K_m K_B$ in the loop which will cause sustained oscillation can be found by noting the points *p*, *q*, and *r* at which the total phase curve $\phi(j\omega)$ crosses the -180 degree phase line. At these values of frequency, the system will be an oscillator if the magnitude function $20 \log_{10} XYZ$ is equal to zero decibels. Consequently, the projections of points *p*, *q*, and *r* up to the true magnitude or asymptote curve *abcd* locate the distances *at*, *au*, and *av* which define the maximum allowable value of the loop gain $K_m K_B$ for the different values of *a*, τ_g, and τ_R which characterize the quality regulator.

The magnitude and phase-versus-frequency characteristic as shown in Fig. 1.23 can be replotted as a locus on magnitude-versus-phase coordinates as shown in Fig. 1.24. The locus of constant resonance magnitude $p_8(j\omega)/p_{\text{ref}}(j\omega)$, designated by the curve M_p, can also be plotted for the same figure. A graphical solution for the condition of limited resonance results when the curve M_p is tangent with the locus of XYZ. The graphical solution yields the loop gain $K_m K_B$ and the resonant frequency ω_m of the closed-loop system for the particular value of the ratio p_8/p_{ref} at the condition of resonance. This is the maximum practical value of $K_m K_B$ for the regulatory system. Once the graphical study has yielded the maximum allowable value of gain

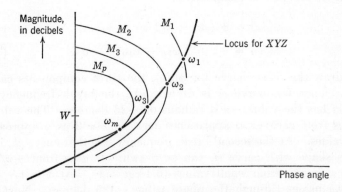

Fig. 1.24. Magnitude and phase contour chart.

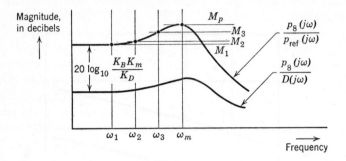

Fig. 1.25. Product quality regulator frequency response.

$K_m K_B$ for the closed loop and the resonant frequency ω_m for a specified M_p, the same graph can be used to construct the regulator performance $[p_8(j\omega)]/[D(j\omega)]$.

To determine the response of the system to disturbance requires that the response p_8/p_{ref} be first constructed as a frequency characteristic, and then modified according to the relationship

$$\frac{p_8}{D} = \left(\frac{p_8}{p_{ref}}\right)\left(\frac{K_D}{XZ}\right) \tag{1.95}$$

The procedure for constructing the regulator-performance curve from the open-loop locus XYZ on the magnitude and phase coordinates is as follows: First, the contour chart is superposed upon the magnitude and phase coordinates so that the locus XYZ crosses the M contours. The zero-decibel value of the M contour chart is located coincident with the point w on the magnitude or decibel axis. The curves other than M_p which are larger in size than the curve representing M_p will cross the XYZ contour at a number of points ω_m, ω_1, ω_2, etc. shown as dots on the XYZ locus in Fig. 1.25. At these frequency points where XYZ intersects the M contours, there will be a value of the regulator response p_8/p_{ref} which is equal to the value of M read at each intersection. These values can be plotted on magnitude-versus-frequency coordinates as shown in Fig. 1.25. Note that the maximum value of p_8 with respect to p_{ref} is equal to M_p at the frequency ω_m, which was the specified condition for a degree of stability of the system in a condition of resonance.

According to eq 1.95, if the response p_8 is known with respect to p_{ref}, then to find the response p_8 with respect to the disturbance D requires only a modification of the p_8/p_{ref} curve. In the particular problem being considered, the p_8/D curve—when the reference is held

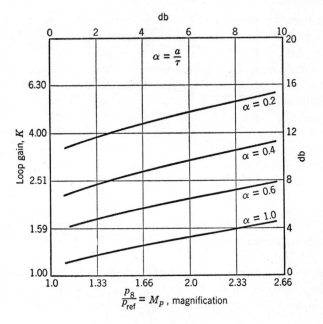

Fig. 1.26. Loop gain versus resonance magnification for closed-loop quality-control process with transportation lag a and blending lag τ in the materials-handling operation.

at zero level—will be equal to p_8/p_{ref} multiplied by the term $\dfrac{K_D}{XZ}$. Since $Z = 1$, and X is the gain of the loop $K_B K_m$, the modified curve is shown by merely subtracting the value $20 \log_{10} K_B K_m$ and adding the value $20 \log_{10} K_D$, which is a total correction of $20 \log_{10} K_B K_m/K_D$.

The magnitude of the loop gain $K_m K_B$ is limited by the stability required. It is evident that one criterion for judging the performance of the regulator is the size of $\dfrac{K_B K_m}{K_D}$. Unless $K_B K_m$ is large, precise regulation cannot be had. Yet for large values of $K_B K_m$, the degree of stability as designated by M_p may be too small.

Thus, Fig. 1.26 presents the relationship between loop gain K, the resonance magnitude M_p, and the dimensionless ratio $\alpha = \dfrac{a}{\tau}$. This chart permits the design of simple closed-loop quality regulators which have *one* blending lag τ and a total dead time in transportation of a units. The data are useful regardless of the relative location of the blending vessel to the transportation distances. However, to determine the steady-state variation in product quality for a disturbance requires that the procedure outlined in eq. 1.95 be followed.

Figure 1.26 proves useful in making rough calculations for the layout of materials-handling processes: for example, let a process be characterized by a transportation lag of five minutes ($a = 5$ minutes) and a blending lag of $\tau = 25$ minutes. The value of $\alpha = 0.2$. The maximum loop gain that can be had for a stable system with a reasonable transient response and frequency response $M_p = 2.0$ is equal to 4.8. For a sinusoidally varying unit magnitude of disturbance, the product quality will be sinusoidally fluctuating with an amplitude of approximately $2 \dfrac{K_D}{XZ}$, and the phase lag behind the disturbance of approximately 125 degrees.

Transient Response

When the transient response of the quality-control system to either a change in reference or a sudden disturbance is of interest, the presence of the transportation lag e^{-as} makes the procedure of inverse transformation difficult. However, a power series expansion of the response eq. 1.95 can be made to find the impulse or step response of the system.

The series

$$\frac{A}{1 + A} = A - A^2 + A^3 - A^4 + \cdots \tag{1.96}$$

and

$$\frac{B}{1 + AB} = \frac{1}{A} [AB - (AB)^2 + (AB)^3 - (AB)^4 + \cdots] \tag{1.97}$$

are the expansions for the general forms of the feedback equations.

For the quality control regulator, if

$$A = X(s) = K_B K_m \tag{1.98}$$

$$B = Y(s) = \frac{e^{-as}}{\tau s + 1} \tag{1.99}$$

$$Z(s) = 1 \tag{1.100}$$

the series form for the product quality $p_8(s)$ is

$$\frac{p_8(s)}{D(s)} = -\frac{1}{K_m K_B} \left[\frac{K_m K_B}{(\tau s + 1)} e^{-as} \right.$$
$$\left. - \frac{K_m{}^2 K_B{}^2}{(\tau s + 1)^2} e^{-2as} + \frac{K_m{}^3 K_B{}^3}{(\tau s + 1)^3} e^{-3as} \right] \tag{1.101}$$

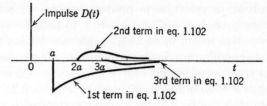

Fig. 1.27.   Impulse response $p_8(t)$ for quality-control regulator.

For an impulse disturbance $D(s) = 1$, the transient solution $p_8(t)$ becomes the summation of the inverse Laplace transform for each term in the series.   The operators e^{-as}, e^{-2as}, e^{-3as} $\cdots$ which appear in the terms of the series are "delaying" operators.   They shift each time function to the right in the time scale in proportion to the dead time.

$$p_8(t) = -\frac{1}{K_B K_m}\left[\frac{K_m K_B}{\tau}e^{-t/\tau}U(t-a) - \frac{K_m{}^2 K_B{}^2}{\tau^2}te^{-t/\tau}U(t-2a)\right.$$
$$\left. + \frac{K_m{}^3 K_B{}^3}{\tau^3}\frac{t^2}{2!}e^{-t/\tau}U(t-3a)\cdots\right] \quad (1.102)$$

Figure 1.27 shows the manner in which each term in $p_8(t)$ can be plotted and then added with all other terms in order to give the total response to the impulse.

In the event that the disturbance is not an impulse, step function, or another simple function in s, $D(s)$ can be expressed as a time function constructed by adding together as a series of pulses $\dfrac{e^{-ns} - e^{-(n-1)s}}{s}$ whose height is the value of the function and whose width equals the delay time a.   The approximate function expressed as the summation of pulses multiplied by the infinite series which represents the impulse response for the process gives a product series whose inverse Laplace transform is the transient response of the process to an arbitrary time varying disturbance.

12. CONCLUSION

In this chapter, the transfer functions for the simple materials-handling processes have been developed.   Integrations, first-order time-lag operators, and transportation-lag operators describe the general actions of moving materials from one place to another, piling them or storing them in vessels, and mixing or blending them in various proportions. The transfer functions developed for the materials-handling processes enable us to study the transient behavior of these processes when they are subjected to any describable type of disturbance or manipulation. By a slight variation which presents the transfer function in terms of the complex variable $j\omega$ instead of s, the ability of the materials-handling processes to attenuate or transmit sinusoidally varying signals over the entire spectrum from $0 < \omega < \infty$ can be studied.

The studies of storage regulation and quality control are oversimplified versions of the type of problem encountered in the industrial and business process. Nevertheless, these simple problems show how inventory and quality-control dynamics become inherently linked with the kinematics of materials-handling operations.

BIBLIOGRAPHY

"The Theory of Short-Circuiting in Continuous-Flow Mixing Vessels in Series and the Kinetics of Chemical Reactions in Such Systems," by R. B. MacMullin and M. Weber, Jr., *Trans. Am. Inst. Chem. Eng.*, **31**, 409–458 (1934–1935).

"Frequency Response Analysis of Continuous Flow Systems," by H. Kramers and G. Alberda, *Chem. Eng. Sci.*, **2**, 173–181 (1953).

"Continuous Flow Systems—Distribution of Residence Times," by P. V. Dankwerts, *Chem. Eng. Sci.*, **2**, 1–13 (1953).

CHAPTER 2

Fluids in Motion

1. INTRODUCTION

Fluids move because they are subjected to the action of forces. The gravitational force causes a pressure to develop in fluids so that tanks empty and fluid flows from one vessel to another. Pumps and compressors apply forces to fluids so that pressures develop which can move fluids from one place to another. Moreover, fluids will move if they are coupled to moving bodies.

Fluids moving under the action of forces are under a restraint which materials in free motion are not: namely, they are restrained by containing vessels or tanks, and are constrained to move in pipelines. The cause-and-effect relationship for them is determined by both the properties of the fluids and the geometry of the vessels and conduits.

Generally, force—or pressure developed from force—is a cause, and flow is an effect; but mechanisms, such as positive-displacement pumps and compressors, can be fluid flow sources. When flow is the cause, the pressures which develop throughout a fluid flow system become the effects.

More important is the fact that the pressure and flow are inherently related time-varying quantities. It may not be possible to regulate pressure and flow independently in a process. Furthermore, the fluid which fills pipelines and vessels tends to interconnect extensive arrangements of process equipment into *interacting* systems.

Some of the problems in fluid handling can be treated as if the fluid were incompressible and the pipelines and vessels were nonelastic. Pipes, valves, and other obstructions present resistance to flow. The moving fluid has mass. The forces which move the fluid are opposed by the combined friction and inertia reaction forces.

Compressible fluids or elastic containers present a more complex problem. Gases, liquids which contain gas, compressible liquids, elastic pipes and vessels, and all combinations of these exhibit a volumetric capacity effect. Thus, fluids have mass, which gives them inertance, and elastance, which establishes their volume capacity. The resistance associated with fluid motion is a result of contact between the fluid and the pipes or of shearing action between fluid and fluid.

Circuits of resistance, capacity, and inertance can be drawn to represent many of the processes of fluid handling. The lumped-parameter networks contain both linear and nonlinear circuit elements. The linear networks can be readily studied by using conventional circuit theory to determine pressure, flow, and power relationships. To predict the behavior of the nonlinear circuits, however, calls for the use of graphical methods, special mathematical techniques, analogs, or computers.

Sound waves can be set up in gases and liquids which fill the pipelines and vessels of a plant. Resonance effects can occur for various configurations of equipment and can interfere with the proper operation of processes. Acoustic energy imparted to the fluid can transfer itself to the pipes themselves, because the fluids are coupled to the pipelines and vessels. Thus, traveling waves and standing waves can also be set up in the pipelines and metal structures.

To investigate these more fundamental relationships between pressure and the velocity of particles in a gas or liquid requires a distributed-parameter approach. Partial differential equations must be used to relate pressure and flow or particle velocity. Ultimately, wave equations predict the dynamic response of distributed mass, elastance, and resistance fluid-handling processes. There is present, simultaneously with the fluid-dynamics problem, a thermodynamics issue: the material may compress isothermally or adiabatically.

The purpose of this chapter is to illustrate how intimately the dynamics of fluid-handling processes is related to the fluid characteristics, the geometric shapes and dimensions of process vessels, and the lengths of the pipelines which connect vessels and other process apparatus together. Proper consideration of these factors during process design may reduce the complexity and cost of regulator and control equipment, may eliminate the need for pulsation dampers, may reduce audio-frequency noise in a plant, and—what is most important—may reduce the cost of the plant itself by minimizing fluid hold-up and the distances of transport through pipes.

2. VARIATION OF LIQUID LEVEL

Liquid flow Q_i into a hold-up vessel, and liquid flow Q_o out of it, are related to the head h of liquid in the vessel in the same manner that inflow, outflow, and storage of material were related in Chapter 1. In fact, the differential equation

$$\frac{d}{dt}[Ah(t)] = Q_i(t) - Q_o(t) \tag{2.1}$$

has the same form and meaning as eq. 1.1, Chapter 1, the only difference being that the quantity W, which represented storage, is replaced by the product Ah, where A is the cross-sectional area of the tank.* It is a kinematics equation which describes the build-up or decline of liquid "inventory."

However, when liquid flow into a vessel or from a vessel is subjected to gravitational forces, to hydraulic pressures, or to both gravitational forces and pressures, the kinematics approach must be given up. The manner in which the head in a vessel varies is no longer adequately described by the simple procedure in Chapter 1. Hydrodynamics equations must be used instead. In particular, the laws of conservation of mass, conservation of momentum, conservation of energy and continuity must be used to express the dynamic relationship between pressure, flow, and head.

Gravitational Effects. When a stationary tank discharges under its own head, and no external pressures act upon the liquid, the Bernoulli equation

$$\frac{v^2}{2} + \frac{Pg}{\rho} + gh = \text{constant} \tag{2.2}$$

shows that the flow from an orifice or nozzle in a tank which is emptying under the action of the gravitational force becomes

$$Q_o(t) = C_d \sqrt{2gh(t)} \tag{2.3}$$

In eq. 2.3, C_d equals the coefficient of discharge, g equals the gravitational constant, and h equals the head in the vessel. By combining eq. 2.3 with eq. 2.1, the variation in head as a function of inflow Q_i can

---

* When the cross-sectional area of the tank is constant as a function of height, the derivative need not be taken of the product, but merely of the height $h(t)$. However, shaped tanks are often encountered, in which case the area A is a function of h. Therefore the derivative must be taken of the product function $A(h)h$, and both of these functions are time varying.

be expressed as

$$\frac{d}{dt}[Ah(t)] = Q_i(t) - C_d\sqrt{2gh(t)} \qquad (2.4)$$

This equation shows that if the inflow rate $Q_i(t)$ momentarily increases, the head $h(t)$ tends to increase. Because of the increase in head, the outflow $Q_o(t)$ also increases, and a self-regulating effect is present: that is, an inherent negative-feedback type of manipulation of liquid level occurs because of the action of the gravitational force. The self-regulating action described by eq. 2.4 is nonlinear because of the $\sqrt{h}$ term.

Pressure Effects. When a pressure $P(t)$ aids or retards flow from a vessel and must be considered simultaneously with the gravitational force, eq. 2.4 must be changed to the form

$$\frac{d}{dt}[Ah(t)] = Q_i(t) - C\sqrt{2gh(t) - \frac{2P(t)}{\rho}g} \qquad (2.5)$$

The term $h(t)$ under the radical on the right hand side of the equation continues to produce the self-regulating effect. The pressure term $P(t)$ under the radical is a disturbance. It has nothing to do, in itself, with the characterizing of the vessel response, and constitutes an external driving force on the system just as does the inflow $Q_i(t)$.

Equation 2.5 is also nonlinear, and before any appraisal can be made of the manner in which the head $h(t)$ will vary as a function of time, for a tank emptying against a back pressure, this equation must either be solved as it is or be linearized so that an approximate solution can be procured.

Nonlinear Response. Differential equations like eqs. (2.4) and 2.5, particularly eq. 2.4, can be solved exactly. The change in variable $\sqrt{h} = u$ reduces the equation to the form

$$2uA\frac{du}{dt} + ku = Q \qquad (2.6)$$

in which $k = C_d\sqrt{2g}$ and the disturbing flow Q_i can be considered as an average inflow $Q_{i\,ave}$ plus a fluctuating increment $\Delta Q_i(t)$. The constant k is determined by the equilibrium condition that the average inflow and the average outflow must be equal. Thus, for $Q_{i\,ave} = Q_{o\,ave}$, the equilibrium value of head h is

$$h_o = \frac{(Q_{i\,ave})^2}{k^2} \qquad (2.7)$$

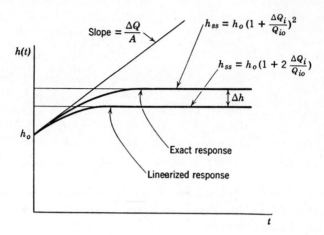

Fig. 2.1.   Response of a vessel subjected to step change of inflow ΔQ_i.

After the change of variable and a separation of the new variables have been made, the equation which describes changes in u for changes in Q is

$$-\frac{dt}{A} = \frac{2u\,du}{ku - Q} \tag{2.8}$$

whose solution can be found, by integration, to be

$$-\frac{1}{A}\int dt = 2\int_{u_o}^{u} \frac{u\,du}{ku - Q} \tag{2.9}$$

$$-\frac{t}{A} = 2\left[\frac{1}{k}(u - u_o) + \frac{Q}{k^2}\log\left(\frac{ku - Q}{ku_o - Q}\right)\right] \tag{2.10}$$

Equation 2.10 changes to the form

$$-\frac{t}{A} = \frac{2}{k}\left(\sqrt{h} - \frac{Q_{io}}{k}\right) + \frac{2(Q_{io} + \Delta Q_i)}{k^2}$$

$$\log\left(\frac{Q_{io} + \Delta Q_i - k\sqrt{h}}{\Delta Q_i}\right) \tag{2.11}$$

when the variable u is changed back to $\sqrt{h}$.

The graph of $h(t)$ versus t, as shown by Fig. 2.1, along with an analysis of eq. 2.11, reveals that, provided the level and the flow rates do not vary widely, a linear equivalent response of the form $[1 - e^{-at}]$ can be used to approximate the nonlinear response if the condition

$\dfrac{\Delta Q_i}{Q_{io}} \leq 0.2$ prevails.   This means that for most studies which involve variation in liquid level and flow, linear differential equations may be used as reasonable approximations to the dynamic behavior of this type of fluid system.

Linearized Response.   To linearize the differential equation given by eq. 2.4, let $h = h_o + z$, in which h_o is the average head in the vessel and z is a small change in head caused by flow disturbances. Thus, if $z/h_o \ll 1$, the differential equation

$$A \frac{dh}{dt} + k \sqrt{h} = Q_{i\,\mathrm{ave}} + \Delta Q_i(t) \qquad (2.12)$$

can be expressed in the form

$$A \frac{dz}{dt} + \frac{kz}{2 \sqrt{h_o}} = \Delta Q_i(t) \qquad (2.13)$$

which relates the time-varying incremental changes in head z to variations in the incremental inflow ΔQ_i.   (The back pressure P is assumed to be zero.)   According to eq. 2.13, the linearized response $z(t)$ of a vessel with an average head of liquid h_o, whose outflow Q_o is under the action of its own head, must of necessity have the exponential type of response $[1 - e^{-t/\tau}]$ for small variations of the disturbing inflow.

The transfer function which relates the variations in head z to the flow disturbance ΔQ_i has the form

$$\frac{z(s)}{\Delta Q_i(s)} = \frac{\left(\dfrac{2 \sqrt{h_o}}{k}\right)}{\left(\dfrac{2A \sqrt{h_o}}{k}\right)s + 1} \qquad (2.14)$$

$$= \frac{K}{\tau s + 1} \qquad (2.15)$$

The static sensitivity K of the process to flow disturbances is

$$K = \frac{2 \sqrt{h_o}}{k} \qquad (2.16)$$

$$K = \frac{\tau}{A} \qquad (2.16a)$$

The characteristic time τ or time constant is

$$\tau = \frac{2A \sqrt{h_o}}{k} \tag{2.17}$$

$$\tau = \frac{2A \sqrt{h_o}}{C_d \sqrt{2g}} \tag{2.17a}$$

The transfer function given by eq. 2.15 expresses the dynamic response of the process; it indicates the effectiveness of self-regulation against upsets in flow. Both the sensitivity K of the liquid-level process to flow disturbances, and the characteristic time τ indicate that the change in head z per unit change in flow Q_i will be a function of the average head h_o maintained in the vessel. The time constant τ also shows that the speed with which the vessel will adjust its head following a disturbance to the inflow is directly proportional to the cross-sectional area A of the tank, and inversely proportional to the resistance* of the exit where the flow discharges.

A conclusion to be drawn at this point is, that liquid-level variation is inherently related to the physical dimensions of a hold-up vessel and the exit restriction to flow. When the back pressure or vacuum suction pressures must be considered in closed or supercharged vessels, the differential equations change in detail, but the concept of regulating principles does not. Changes in the pressure act upon the operation as a disturbance, as do changes of the inflow.

3. CONFIGURATIONS OF VESSELS

Table 2.1 shows several arrangements of vessels whose liquid outflow, inflow, or head is under the manipulative action of pumps or of the valves located in the pipe-lines which lead to and from the vessels.

---

* In Section 7, p. 75, a thorough discussion will be given of the concept of hydraulic circuit elements. It is enough at this time to point out that whenever flow takes place through a nozzle, a length of pipe, a valve, or an entrance or exit of a tank, there will be hydraulic losses. The pressure drop across the resistance element is proportional to the square of the flow, and the form of the equation is generally

$$\Delta p = kv^2 = k'Q^2$$

However, for small flow changes about an average flow, the resistance at the exit or the resistance which is present because there is a valve in the exit pipeline is defined by the ratio $R = \dfrac{\Delta P}{\Delta Q}\bigg|_{Q=Q_o}$ or more precisely by the partial derivative $\dfrac{\partial P}{\partial Q}$ evaluated for $Q = Q_o$.

The first column shows the arrangement of the vessels and their interconnecting pipelines. The second column gives the differential equations which relate the flows Q to the heads h and other manipulating variables, and the conditions governing the use of the equations are outlined. The third column gives a signal-flow diagram of the physical system. The fourth column gives the transfer functions which relate the head to the principal manipulation variables. Linear behavior is assumed for small variations in the head in the vessels.

The first item in the table shows a vessel from which the flow Q_o is pumped in proportion to the pump speed Ω_p. The head h in the vessel varies as the integral of the net flow $\Sigma Q = Q_i - Q_o$. The process has an ideal integrating characteristic defined by the operator $1/s$. No self-regulation will be exhibited by this type of process because the outflow from the vessel is not a function of the head.

The second arrangement shows a vessel whose outflow is limited by the hydraulic resistance R^* in the outflow line. Thus the total pressure available for driving the liquid out of the tank is consumed in the pressure drop across the valve. The flow Q_o multiplied by a valve resistance R_v consumes the head h. The inflow Q_i is the disturbance to the system. This is a typical example of self-regulation in a liquid storage vessel. The dynamic response $h(s)/Q_i(s)$ is characterized by a first-order type of time-lag operator $1/(\tau s + 1)$ in which τ is defined as in eq. 2.17, section 2. The presence of the resistance R guarantees self-regulation.

The third arrangement shows two vessels in cascade, with a pipe connecting the two and presenting a resistance R_1 to the flow Q_{12}. The inflow Q_i will affect the head h_1. The flow Q_{12} from the first vessel to the second one will affect the head h_2 in the second vessel. A second resistance R_2 in the outflow from the second vessel will affect the flow Q_o. The head in the first vessel is a function of both the inflow Q_i and the outflow Q_{12} from the first vessel. The head in the second vessel h_2 is likewise a function of the inflow Q_{12} and the outflow Q_o. Since the flow Q_{12} from the first vessel to the second vessel is not dependent upon the head h_1 in the first vessel alone but upon the difference in heads $(h_1 - h_2)$ in the two vessels, we speak of this system as being an *interacting cascade* of liquid hold-up vessels. A set of simulta-

---

* For the reader who wishes to go into greater detail, it is possible to write expressions which give the exit losses from the tank, pipeline losses, and any other hydraulic losses that may occur as the liquid flows through sharp-edged orifices, sections of pipe, bends in the pipe, and the valves. The total resistance in the exit will then contain a term which is proportional to flow, and another term which is proportional to valve setting.

TABLE 2.1. DYNAMICS OF FLUID

Configuration	Differential Equations

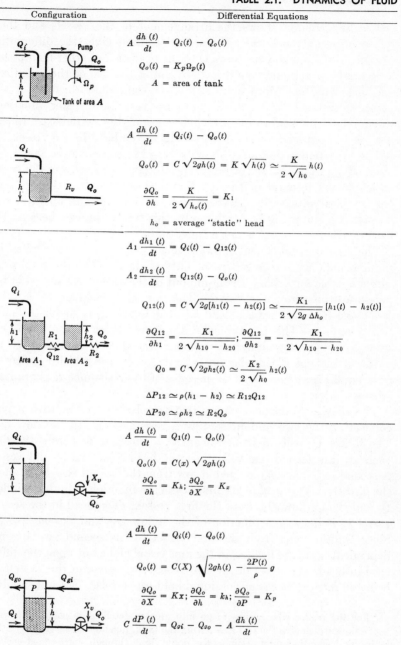

$$A \frac{dh(t)}{dt} = Q_i(t) - Q_o(t)$$

$$Q_o(t) = K_p \Omega_p(t)$$

$$A = \text{area of tank}$$

$$A \frac{dh(t)}{dt} = Q_i(t) - Q_o(t)$$

$$Q_o(t) = C\sqrt{2gh(t)} = K\sqrt{h(t)} \simeq \frac{K}{2\sqrt{h_o}} h(t)$$

$$\frac{\partial Q_o}{\partial h} = \frac{K}{2\sqrt{h_o(t)}} = K_1$$

$$h_o = \text{average "static" head}$$

$$A_1 \frac{dh_1(t)}{dt} = Q_i(t) - Q_{12}(t)$$

$$A_2 \frac{dh_2(t)}{dt} = Q_{12}(t) - Q_o(t)$$

$$Q_{12}(t) = C\sqrt{2g[h_1(t) - h_2(t)]} \simeq \frac{K_1}{2\sqrt{2g\,\Delta h_o}}[h_1(t) - h_2(t)]$$

$$\frac{\partial Q_{12}}{\partial h_1} = \frac{K_1}{2\sqrt{h_{10} - h_{20}}}; \frac{\partial Q_{12}}{\partial h_2} = -\frac{K_1}{2\sqrt{h_{10} - h_{20}}}$$

$$Q_0 = C\sqrt{2gh_2(t)} \simeq \frac{K_2}{2\sqrt{h_o}} h_2(t)$$

$$\Delta P_{12} \simeq \rho(h_1 - h_2) \simeq R_{12}Q_{12}$$

$$\Delta P_{20} \simeq \rho h_2 \simeq R_2 Q_0$$

$$A \frac{dh(t)}{dt} = Q_1(t) - Q_o(t)$$

$$Q_o(t) = C(x)\sqrt{2gh(t)}$$

$$\frac{\partial Q_o}{\partial h} = K_h; \frac{\partial Q_o}{\partial X} = K_x$$

$$A \frac{dh(t)}{dt} = Q_i(t) - Q_o(t)$$

$$Q_o(t) = C(X)\sqrt{2gh(t) - \frac{2P(t)}{\rho} g}$$

$$\frac{\partial Q_o}{\partial X} = Kx; \frac{\partial Q_o}{\partial h} = k_h; \frac{\partial Q_o}{\partial P} = K_p$$

$$C \frac{dP(t)}{dt} = Q_{vi} - Q_{vo} - A\frac{dh(t)}{dt}$$

FLOW THROUGH TANKS

Block Diagram	Transfer Functions

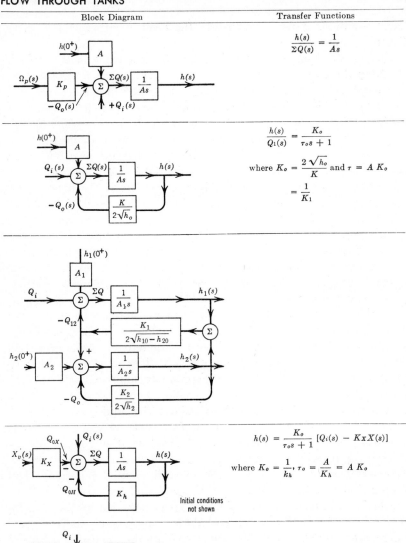

$$\frac{h(s)}{\Sigma Q(s)} = \frac{1}{As}$$

$$\frac{h(s)}{Q_i(s)} = \frac{K_o}{\tau_o s + 1}$$

where $K_o = \dfrac{2\sqrt{h_o}}{K}$ and $\tau = A\,K_o$

$$= \frac{1}{K_1}$$

$$h(s) = \frac{K_o}{\tau_o s + 1}\,[Q_i(s) - K_X X(s)]$$

where $K_o = \dfrac{1}{k_h}$, $\tau_o = \dfrac{A}{K_h} = A\,K_o$

Initial conditions not shown

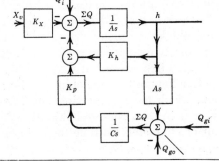

neous equations is needed to relate the head in either vessel to the disturbing flow Q_i.

The fourth arrangement in the table shows a valve in the outflow line from the vessel. The valve presents a resistance R_v to the flow. The resistance R_v is a function of the valve-stem movement X_v. If the valve stem is positioned and then kept fixed, there is no difference between this system and the system shown in item 2, in which a fixed resistance R was in the outflow line. The exception occurs when the inflow acts as a disturbance and a time-varying manipulation of the valve setting $X_v(t)$ is made. Then, two variables can modify the head h in the process: changes in the inflow Q_i disturb the liquid level; changes in the valve position X_v control the outflow head in the vessel. The flow Q_i to the process constitutes a direct and external type of disturbance. The manipulation of the valve to counteract the upset, on the other hand, constitutes a parametric type of manipulation.

Item 5 in the table shows a situation which may occur in chemical process control. A vessel with a head h, an inflow Q_i, and an outflow Q_o is under the action of a pressure $P(t)$. The pressure may be generated because gas is being released from the liquid as a result of a chemical reaction, or because the liquid is boiling. The pressure variation, the liquid head, and the resistance characteristics of the throttling valves in both the liquid and the gas flow lines must be taken into account in the equations which express dynamic response of the process.

In the pressurized vessel with gas above the liquid, an additional equation is needed to account for the fact that the volume of gas is compressible. The volume capacity*—that is, the volume of gas which is compressible—and the manner in which the gas is compressed become important in setting up the extra differential equation. The compression may be adiabatic or isothermal; and the capacity C must be calculated in terms of the volume of space occupied by the gas, the specific heats for isothermal and adiabatic compression, and the average pressure under which the compression takes place. No vessel will exhibit self-regulation when the flow is pumped from the vessel. Vessels which empty out pipes located below their surface so that gravity acts to make the flow take place, exhibit the self-regulating characteristics. Tanks which are located in cascade, but which empty into one another upon a successive free-flow basis, are noninteracting; but tanks which are in cascade and which have connecting pipelines that go below the surface of the liquids in the two vessels will always be interacting. The time constant or characteristic time for a single

* For a definition of volume capacity, see section 7, p. 77.

vessel of a self-regulating type can always be estimated in terms of the size of the vessel and the resistance-to-flow characteristic of the out-flow line.   But when two or more vessels are arranged in interacting cascade, the characteristic times for an individual vessel do not necessarily define a composite characterizing time lag for the over-all system.

4. REGULATION OF LIQUID LEVEL AND FLOW—GENERAL

Liquid level in tanks, and the flow rates through them, are *not* independent variables.   The head of liquid in a tank, and pressurization or vacuum conditions in a vessel, bring about flow variation in the fluid streams entering or leaving.   Flow changes bring about head variations in open vessels; they cause both head and pressure to vary in closed vessels.   Consequently, regulation of liquid level—whether it is self-regulation or regulation imposed by automatic means—precludes simultaneous flow regulation.   The reverse is also true.   When flow is regulated, the surges in liquid level must be accepted.

Liquid-level and fluid-flow processes are manipulated by means of pumps, compressors, and valves.   Pumps and compressors generate pressure in fluids which causes them to flow into or out of vessels despite opposing gravitational head and the resistance to flow presented by the pipes and more severe restrictions such as valves, orifices, and filters.   Valves, in contrast to pumps, manipulate or modulate liquid flows by changing the resistance in the flow path.   Thus, pumps or compressors bring about direct and external manipulation, whereas valves tend to be the parametric types of manipulators.   The pumps and compressors, or their fluid motor counterparts, can put potential energy into the fluid system or take kinetic energy away from it.   Valves can only dissipate energy; they use up the energy already in the fluid system in order to bring about manipulation.

Generally, in liquid-level problems, the fluid can be assumed to be incompressible.   However, when closed tanks contain both vapor and liquid, the compressibility and the volume of the vapor have a definite influence upon how well liquid level can be controlled.   Finally, when fluids are handled at high velocity and at high pressures, the treatment outlined in this section fails.   An approach is needed which can include the effects of fluid compressibility, the deformation of vessels and pipes, and the mass or inertia reaction effects which oppose changes in flow.

5. REGULATION OF LIQUID LEVEL

To place liquid level under control, the liquid level h must be measured, a signal h_m from the measuring device must be compared against the reference signal h_{ref}, and the difference signal $\varepsilon_h = h_{ref} - h$ must be used to energize any mechanism which can manipulate the inflow Q_i or the outflow Q_o, since this will in turn regulate the liquid level h.

Figure 2.2a and b show two liquid-level regulators. The first in Fig. 2.2a uses the error in head $\mathcal{E}_h$ to adjust the speed of a pump which in turn adjusts the outflow rate Q_o. The second in Fig. 2.2b uses a valve positioner to adjust the resistance R_v in the outflow line from the tank. The change in resistance modulates the outflow rate Q_o.

Pump Control. The regulator which uses the pump to control outflow will have dynamic response and performance characteristics identical with those that were derived for the regulation of storage or inventory, in section 6, Chapter 1. The process transfer function $\dfrac{h(s)}{Q(s)} = \dfrac{1}{As}$ is an integration. The regulation of the process by controlling the pump speed continuously and in proportion to the error $\mathcal{E}_h$, by means of a sampled-and-clamped action in proportion to the error, or by off–on action, will have transient-response curves identical with those shown in Figs. 1.10 and 1.11, Chapter 1.

Of course the pump speed in the first liquid-level regulator shown in Fig. 2.2a cannot be changed suddenly in response to changes in the error signal. The drive motor of the pump has a moment of inertia, and the motor control—whether electrical, mechanical, or hydraulic—will also have time lags. Also the valve in the second type of regulator cannot open or close instantly.

These time lags in the manipulators and control apparatus can create problems of instability in all forms of regulators. They limit the maximum gain that can be obtained in the closed-loop continuous and sampled-clamped regulators. They determine the amplitude of relaxation oscillation and the frequency of the oscillatory response of the off–on regulators.

Valve Control The level regulator which uses the valve to control the outflow from the vessel can: (1) continuously manipulate the flow; (2) adjust the flow in an off–on manner, provided the valve can be fully closed or fully opened rapidly; or (3) manipulate the valve so that it can take several positions between the limits of fully closed and fully open.

All three modes of the valve manipulation adjust the resistance to flow in the exit pipe from the tank. For discontinuous manipulation, the values of the stem position X_v determine the resistance, which in turn determines the value of the outflow. Thus, for $X_v = X_{vj}, R_v = R_{vj}$, the flow becomes

$$Q_{oj} = \frac{1}{R_v(X_{vj})} \sqrt{2gh(t)} \qquad (2.18)$$

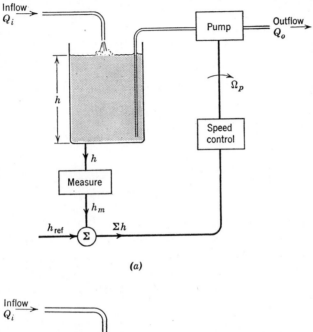

(a)

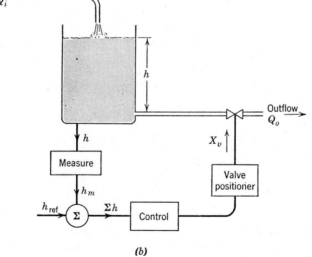

(b)

Fig. 2.2.   (a) Liquid-level control by pumping; (b) liquid-level control by throttle valve.

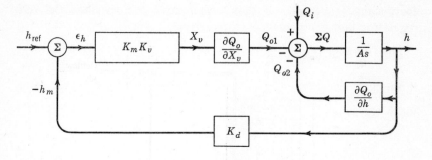

Fig. 2.3. Signal-flow diagram for the continuous regulation of liquid level by means of a valve.

The variation in head $h(t)$ is then studied by solving the nonlinear equation, eq. 2.4 or the linearized equation, eq. 2.13 given in section 2, p. 55 for the particular pattern of valve position X_v in terms of the error in head.

When the valve movement $X(t)$ is continuous, the resistance $R_v(X)$ is continuous. The nonlinear relationship

$$Q_o = \frac{1}{R_v(X)} \sqrt{2gh(t)} \tag{2.19}$$

can be linearized if eq. 2.19 is differentiated. Thus

$$dQ_o = dQ_{o1} + dQ_{o2} \tag{2.20}$$

$$= \frac{\partial Q_o}{\partial X}\bigg|_{h=\text{const.}} dX + \frac{\partial Q_o}{\partial h}\bigg|_{X=\text{const.}} dh \tag{2.21}$$

$$= K_1\, dX_v + K_2\, dh \tag{2.22}$$

in which

$$\frac{\partial Q}{\partial X}\bigg|_{h=\text{const.}} = \sqrt{2gh}\,[R_v(X)]^{-2}\frac{\partial R_v(X)}{\partial X} \tag{2.23}$$

$$\frac{\partial Q}{\partial h}\bigg|_{X=\text{const.}} = \frac{\sqrt{2g}}{2}\,[R_v(X)]^{-1}[h(t)]^{-1/2} \tag{2.24}$$

The term dQ_{o1} is the incremental change in outflow for an incremental change dX in stem movement, and the term dQ_{o2} is the incremental change in outflow for an incremental change dh in the head.

The signal-flow diagram for the continuous type of liquid-level regulator is shown in Fig. 2.3. The inflow Q_i is the disturbance. Level h is the response. The valve-stem movement X modulates the flow component Q_{o1} from the tank. The head h modulates the self-regulating flow component Q_{o2} from the tank.

The fact that the integration $\dfrac{1}{As}$ has around it a negative feedback through the constant $\dfrac{\partial Q_o}{\partial h}\bigg|_{X=\text{const.}}$ establishes for the process an operator of the form

$$h(s) = \left[\frac{\dfrac{1}{As}}{1 + \dfrac{1}{As}\left(\dfrac{\partial Q_o}{\partial h}\right)}\right]\left[\left(\frac{\partial Q_o}{\partial X}\right) X - Q_i\right] \qquad (2.25)$$

$$= \left(\frac{K}{\tau_p s + 1}\right)\left[\frac{\partial Q_o}{\partial X} X - Q_i\right] \qquad (2.26)$$

where

$$K = \frac{1}{\left(\dfrac{\partial Q_o}{\partial h}\right)\bigg|_{X=X_o}} \qquad (2.27)$$

$$\tau_p = \frac{A}{\left(\dfrac{\partial Q_o}{\partial h}\right)\bigg|_{X=X_o}} \qquad (2.28)$$

The parameter τ_p can be defined in terms of the valve resistance and vessel parameters. Thus

$$\tau_p = \frac{2}{\sqrt{2g}} A R_v(X_o) \sqrt{h_o} \qquad (2.29)$$

where h_o is the average head and X_o is the operating point for the valve stem about which small movements dX take place.

Self-regulating effects will always be present because of the resistance to flow $R_v(X)$ in the exit line, regardless of the method of valve positioning used. The loop in the signal-flow diagram which contains the variables ΣQ, h, and the outflow component Q_{o2}, constitutes a negative-feedback, self-regulatory loop.

The response of the feedback type of level regulator to inflow disturbances about an average value of liquid level is expressed by

$$\frac{h(s)}{Q_i(s)} = \frac{K_p\left(\dfrac{1}{\tau_p s + 1}\right)}{1 + K_m K_v K_p K_d \left(\dfrac{1}{\tau_p s + 1}\right)} \qquad (2.30)$$

which simplifies to

$$\frac{h(s)}{Q_i(s)} = \frac{K'}{\tau's + 1} \tag{2.31}$$

where

$$\tau' = \tau_p \left(\frac{1}{1 + K_m K_v K_p K_d}\right) \tag{2.32}$$

and

$$K' = \frac{K_p}{1 + K_m K_v K_p K_d} \tag{2.33}$$

Equation 2.26 shows that the open-loop characteristic has a single time lag τ_p. Equation 2.31 shows that the closed-loop response also has a single time lag τ'. The regulator time lag τ' will always be smaller than τ_p, because the loop gain $K = K_m K_v K_p K_d$ can always be made greater than zero. This proves to be a general situation whenever a feedback regulating arrangement is made for a system whose process member is characterized by a single-order time lag.

An interesting way to look at the level-regulator problem is to recognize that the open-loop characteristic described by eq. 2.26 can be represented by a pole in the s-plane located at the point $s = -1/\tau_p$. When a closed loop is made around the process with the time lag τ_p, the introduction of the loop gain K moves the pole at $s = -1/\tau_p$ toward or away from the origin, depending upon whether K is greater than zero or less than zero. Generally the regulator gain must be greater than zero in order to obtain good regulation. Consequently the time lag τ' will diminish. Therefore the root $s = -1/\tau'$ will become larger, and the pole will move from its original location in the negative real axis toward a new location farther from the imaginary axis of the s-plane.

In the continuous liquid-level regulator, a frequency-response characteristic can be easily prepared for the process, using the asymptote-magnitude and phase curves. The magnitude function

$$20 \log_{10} \left| \frac{h(j\omega)}{\varepsilon_h(j\omega)} \right| = 20 \log_{10} K_m K_v K_p K_d$$

$$- 20 \log_{10} \sqrt{\omega^2 {\tau_p}^2 + 1} \tag{2.34}$$

and the phase function

$$\phi(j\omega) = \tan^{-1} \omega\tau_p \tag{2.35}$$

fully describe the open-loop dynamic response. These functions are plotted in Fig. 2.4. The asymptotes which represent the open-loop

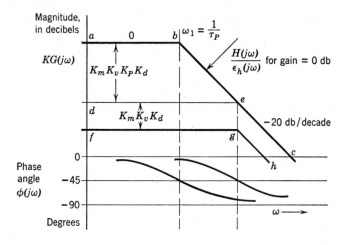

Fig. 2.4. Frequency response study for continuous liquid-level regulator.

magnitude function with unity gain are curve abc. The slope of section ab is zero decibels per decade, and the slope of section bc is -20 decibels per decade. The characteristic frequency or the break frequency is $\omega_1 = 1/\tau_p$. Thus the time constant τ_p of the self-regulated process is the parameter which determines the value of frequency at which the two asymptotes intersect.

For a proportional regulator, $X_v = K_v K_m \mathcal{E}_h$. The response of the system referred to the set point $h_m(j\omega)/h_{\text{ref}}(j\omega)$ is described by the asymptotes dec. To predict the regulating ability of the system against inflow upsets, the transfer function

$$\frac{h(j\omega)}{Q_i(j\omega)} = \left[\frac{h_m(j\omega)}{h_{\text{ref}}(j\omega)}\right] \frac{1}{K_m K_v K_d} \qquad (2.36)$$

must be studied. The asymptotes which describe $\dfrac{h(j\omega)}{Q_i(j\omega)}$, the regulator response, are curve fgh. This curve is $-K_m K_v K_d$ decibels below the curve dec.

It is interesting to interpret curve fgh. Provided the major portion of the loop gain K can be located ahead of the load-disturbance summing point where the flow Q_i acts upon the system, the changes in head for changes in inflow will tend to be small. Large values of $K_m K_v K_d$ in Fig. 2.4 are synonymous with good regulation.

The important conclusion to be reached in this study is that to accomplish tight regulation over liquid level, without resorting to unusual apparatus, requires that the major portion of the loop gain in the regulator be between the error signal ε_h and the manipulation point in the flow pattern Q_{o1}. Thus the static sensitivity of the controller mechanism, the valve positioner, and of the valve itself, expressed in terms of the change in outflow per unit change in stem movement, must be high.

If the gain cannot be made high because the time lags in the valve positioner and the controller become comparable with the lag τ_p of the tank, then as much gain as possible should be put in the loop ahead of the disturbance point, and resetting action or integral control may be needed to make the response precise.

The parameter τ_p governs the whole problem of liquid-level regulation dynamics. Self-regulation of the vessel depends upon τ_p. The maximum gain in the closed loop also depends upon τ_p or upon the ratio of τ_p to the next largest time lag in the system. The time lag τ_p is proportional to the sectional area A of the tank, the average head h_o in the tank, and the value of the resistance $R_v(X_o)$ of the valve setting at its average or mean position in the exit flow line.

6. FLOW REGULATION—INCOMPRESSIBLE FLUID

Flow takes place because a hydraulic force is exerted upon fluid. Therefore, to manipulate a process so that flow regulation or control can be accomplished requires first, that the particular hydraulic force which causes flow variation must be discovered, and next, that a counteracting force must be generated so that the disturbance can be nullified or removed.

The disturbances to flow are changes in head or changes in pressure in open or closed vessels. The variations cause flow in the connecting pipes to change. In this case, h or P is cause; flow Q is an effect. Flow can also change when various schemes for pumping fluids experience failure of equipment: for example, one pump of a combination of three pumps which operate in parallel may develop trouble. To shut the pump down substantially reduces the total liquid flow from the pumps into the process. Variation in pump speed or delivery per stroke is cause; flow change is the effect. However, generalizations are difficult. Flow problems should be given careful study; they are often deceptive.

Throttle Valve in Pipeline. Consider first a valve in a flow line. By setting the valve stem properly, the resistance of the valve can be adjusted so that the pressure drop generated across the valve will dissipate the driving pressure that tends to make flow changes. Figure 2.5 shows the throttle-valve procedure for flow control. The

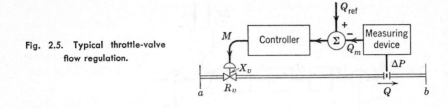

Fig. 2.5. Typical throttle-valve flow regulation.

valve setting X_v determines the resistance R_v, which in turn causes a pressure drop $P_v = Q_v R_v$ which subtracts from the total hydraulic driving force that brings about flow Q.

To regulate the flow Q, an orifice or some other flow-measuring means is located in the pipe. The flow Q in the pipe is measured. (In this instance, the differential pressure drop ΔP across an orifice generates the measured value Q_m.) The measured flow Q_m is compared with a reference value Q_{ref} and the error ε_Q is used to adjust the position of the control valve.

The equations which describe the flow regulator shown in Fig. 2.5 are:

$$Q = \frac{1}{R_v(X_v)} \sqrt{2g\,\Delta h - \frac{2\Delta P g}{\rho}} \tag{2.37}$$

$$\Delta h = h_a - h_b \tag{2.38}$$

$$\Delta P = P_a - P_b \tag{2.39}$$

$$Q_m = K_B G_B(s) Q \tag{2.40}$$

$$\varepsilon_Q = Q_{ref} - Q_m \tag{2.41}$$

$$M = K_C G_C(s) \varepsilon_Q \tag{2.42}$$

$$X_v = K_D G_D(s) M \tag{2.43}$$

The transfer functions $K_C G_C(s)$ and $K_D G_D(s)$ describe the controller and the valve positioner. The measuring instrument is described by the transfer function $K_B G_B(s)$.

The primitive block diagram of Fig. 2.6a shows the relationships between the variables. When eq. 2.37 is linearized as follows,

$$dQ = \frac{\partial Q}{\partial h}\,dh + \frac{\partial Q}{\partial P}\,dP + \frac{\partial Q}{\partial X}\,dX \tag{2.44}$$

$$dQ = K_1\,dh + K_2\,dP + K_3\,dX \tag{2.45}$$

the block diagram simplifies as shown in Fig. 2.6b.

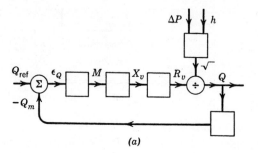

(a)

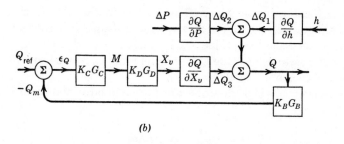

(b)

Fig. 2.6. (a) Primitive block diagram for valve type of flow regulator; (b) Linearized block
diagram for valve type of flow regulator.

The interpretation of the diagram is important. The disturbances
to the flow system are the differential head Δh and the differential
pressure ΔP, which vary across the pipe length between points a and
b. The valve resistance counteracts the disturbances by altering the
flow Q by an amount ΔQ_3, which can offset the changes ΔQ_2 and ΔQ_1
produced by Δh and ΔP, respectively.

The performance of the flow-control system, as shown, is dependent
upon the time lags in measurement and the time lags in the controller
and valve-positioning equipment. The stability of the flow regulator
is determined by the characteristic equation

$$1 + K_C G_C(s) K_D G_D(s) \left(\frac{\partial Q}{\partial X_v}\right) K_B G_B(s) = 0 \qquad (2.46)$$

Therefore the performance of the throttle-valve flow regulator appears
limited by the dynamic-response characteristics of the equipment
added to the process to provide regulation.

However, a very important relationship has been overlooked. *The*

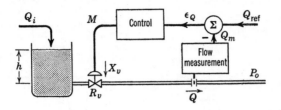

Fig. 2.7.   Hold-up vessel ahead of throttle valve in a flow regulator.

pressure ΔP and the head Δh will be functions of the flow Q!   The process dynamics is missing from the analysis!

Hold-up Vessel Ahead of Throttle Valve.   Consider next how the flow regulator dynamics changes when the flow Q is regulated on the downstream side of a hold-up vessel, as shown in Fig. 2.7.   The additional relationship which relates the process dynamics to the flow

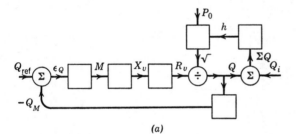

(a)

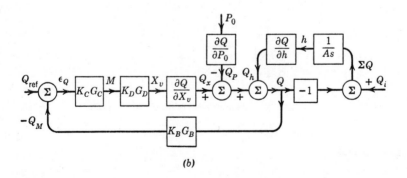

(b)

Fig. 2.8.   (a) Primitive block diagram for valve type of flow regulator with hold-up vessel ahead of the regulator; (b) Linearized block diagram for valve type of flow regulator with hold-up vessel ahead or the regulator.

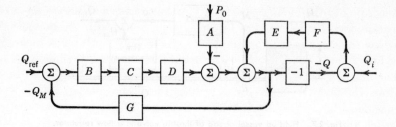

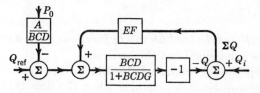

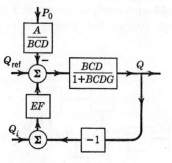

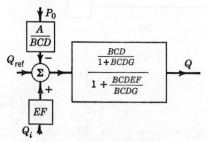

Fig. 2.9. Block diagram simplifications—flow regulator.

regulator is

$$A \frac{dh}{dt} = Q_i - Q \qquad (2.47)$$

For convenience, assume that the flow Q empties freely so that $P_0 = O$.

According to the block diagram in Fig. 2.6b, the head h across the pipe section was the disturbance to the system, along with the pressure P across the same portion of the pipe. However, in the block diagram of Fig. 2.8, the head is not the disturbance, but rather the inflow Q_i is. The net flow $Q_i - Q$ produces a change in the head, and this in turn alters the flow Q. Therefore, the disturbance has changed when one considers the process dynamics. The cause is a flow upset into the vessel, rather than a change in head. Furthermore, the very nature of a hold-up vessel prevents the head from changing instantly; consequently, the hold-up—having a first-order time-lag type of characteristic because of its self-regulating properties—tends to add this lag to the flow regulatory system.

To study the regulator behavior, the signal-flow diagram of Fig. 2.8a can be simplified, as is shown in the development of Fig. 2.8b. The successive simplifications in Fig. 2.9 show that the flow Q as a function of the reference level, the inflow to the tank, and the pressure, has the general relationship

$$Q(s) = \left[\frac{\dfrac{BCD}{1 + BCDG}}{1 + \dfrac{EF}{1 + BCDG}} \right] \left[\left(\frac{EF}{BCD} \right) Q_i(s) \right.$$

$$\left. + \left(\frac{A}{BCD} \right) P(s) + Q_{\text{ref}}(s) \right] \quad (2.48)$$

where

$$A = + \left. \frac{\partial P}{\partial P_0} \right|_{\substack{X = \text{const.} \\ h = \text{const.}}} \quad (2.49)$$

$$B = K_c G_C(s) \quad (2.50)$$

$$C = K_D G_D(s) \quad (2.51)$$

$$D = + \left. \frac{\partial Q}{\partial X_v} \right|_{\substack{P = \text{const.} \\ h = \text{const.}}} \quad (2.52)$$

$$E = \left. \frac{\partial Q}{\partial h} \right|_{\substack{X = \text{const.} \\ P_0 = \text{const.}}} \quad (2.53)$$

$$F = \frac{1}{As} \quad (2.54)$$

$$G = K_B G_B(s) \quad (2.55)$$

Pump-Speed Variation. A second procedure for regulating flow is to alter the speed or the delivery per revolution of pumps or compressors so that the flow into a pipeline or process can be varied or kept constant. Figure 2.10 shows how this can be accomplished. Pumps A, B, C, and D supply flows Q_A, Q_B, Q_C, and Q_D to a pipeline. The total flow Q is to be maintained constant. A measurement of flow Q is made. The measured value Q_m is compared with a reference Q_{ref}, and the error ε_Q causes the variable-speed drive to speed up or to slow down in order to bring about feedback regulation. Thus, the stream Q_D acts as a control flow to offset changes in the other flows.

The signal-flow diagram for the system is shown in Fig. 2.11. The net flow $Q_A + Q_B + Q_C$ disturbs the flow Q. The control flow Q_D counteracts the disturbance. The dynamics of the flow measurement is designated by the transfer function $K_B G_B$. The variable-speed drive has performance defined by $K_D G_D$. Provided the pump has no leakage and is of the positive-displacement type, the relationship between flow Q_D and the speed Ω_p is simply the constant K_p, which defines pump displacement per radian per second. In fact, if the pump is a positive-displacement type and the fluid is incompressible, the nature of the process pipes and vessels will be of no consequence in the flow-control problem.

The stability of the regulator and the precision of performance are related to the open-loop characteristic

$$\frac{Q_m}{\varepsilon_Q} = K_D G_D(s) K_B G_B(s) K_p \tag{2.56}$$

To have rapid flow regulation requires a high-performance variable-speed drive and good flow-measuring apparatus. The ultimate limita-

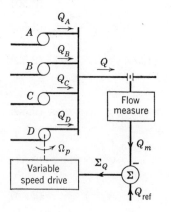

Fig. 2.10. Pump type of flow control.

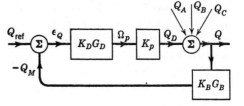

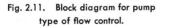

Fig. 2.11.   Block diagram for pump
         type of flow control.

tion on the regulator performance will be the cost of the equipment. The reader will learn in sections 7 and 12 of this chapter that the assumption of incompressible fluid is not often justified in liquid flow control, especially where long pipe-lines and large vessels are used. Therefore the process dynamics will ultimately rule the decisions on flow regulator design.

7. NETWORK ASPECTS OF FLUID-HANDLING SYSTEMS

Many fluid-handling processes are made up of sources of flow such as pumps or compressors and pipelines which connect these flow sources to vessels in which processing takes place.   Sources, pipelines, and vessels constitute fluid circuits.   Valves, relief valves, manifolds, surge tanks, and other components become accessory equipment.

Fluid flows into and through hydraulic or gas circuits because the sources have sufficient potential energy to create a pressure gradient throughout the fluid-handling network, or sufficient kinetic energy to drive a mass flow rate into a circuit despite opposing hydraulic pressure.   Thus pressure sources and flow sources must both be considered.

The circuit elements comprise resistance, inertance, and compressibility, or volumetric capacity.   The pipelines which connect pumps to manifolds, and manifolds to vessels, have resistance.   A pressure drop which is a function of flow rate Q occurs over the length of the flow path.   Pipes also contain a mass of fluid in motion which gives rise to the inertance.   The volumetric capacity of the pipes is proportional to the hold-up in the pipes.   The vessels which terminate pipelines generally comprise volumetric capacity.   The compressibility of fluid in these volumes must be taken into account as a circuit element. Valves represent nonlinear resistances to flow.   By virtue of their throttling operation in the flow stream, they often exhibit a much greater resistance than the resistance of a long pipeline.

Resistance.   When fluid flow takes place from vessels into pipelines, and through pipelines and valves, there are losses in the head which appear as a pressure drop.   The loss in head due to the flow out of a vessel is called an exit loss; the loss in head due to the flow of fluids through pipelines is called pipeline loss. There are also losses through the valves, bends in the pipe, and other restrictions or changes in pipeline diameters.

Generally the losses in the pipelines are large compared with the entrance and exit losses in tanks, provided the length of the pipeline is many times the diameter; and the losses through valves and bends and other restrictions are generally greater than the losses in short straight lengths of pipe—that is, any straight, moderate length of pipe.

The loss in head Δh due to the resistance in the pipelines themselves or to restrictions placed in the lines, may be regarded as a pressure drop ΔP across a resistance element R. However, the resistance to flow R is dependent upon the flow rate Q, so that the general expression which relates the pressure drop $\Delta P(t)$ and the flow $Q(t)$ is

$$\Delta P(t) = R\, Q(t) \tag{2.57}$$

Equation 2.57 can be linearized around a value Q_o so that for changes in flow dQ the pressure drop dp becomes

$$dP = \left| \frac{\partial P}{\partial Q} \right|_{Q=Q_o} dQ \tag{2.58}$$

Thus the average resistance to flow Q_o will be R_o. The incremental resistance is $\left| \dfrac{\partial P}{\partial Q} \right|_{Q=Q_o}$ which is the slope of the pressure drop versus flow curve at $Q = Q_o$.

In control-system studies dealing with fluid and liquid flow, it may be necessary to measure the pressure drop versus fluid flow through pipes and other equipment in order to determine R. Alternatively, data already exist from which R may be calculated with reasonable accuracy. When this can be done, the resistance versus flow characteristic as a nonlinear resistance is determined. Both the average and the incremental resistance values can be assigned numerical values.

Inertance. To establish the concept of inertance—that is, the mass or inertia effect associated with fluids in motion—consider that fluid of density ρ moves in a pipe of length L and cross section A. Assume that the pressure drop $P_1 - P_2$ across the length L is due solely to inertia effects. The conservation-of-momentum law can be used to determine the inertance. Thus,

$$F = M \frac{dv}{dt} \tag{2.59}$$

$$(P_1 - P_2)A = \rho \frac{V}{g} \frac{dv}{dt} \tag{2.60}$$

and since $V = LA$,

$$(P_1 - P_2)A = \rho \frac{L}{g} A \frac{dv}{dt} \qquad (2.61)$$

and since $Av = Q$, the flow, the final form of eq. 2.59 becomes

$$(P_1 - P_2) = \frac{\rho L}{gA} \frac{dQ}{dt} \qquad (2.62)$$

According to eq. 2.62, the inertance M becomes $\frac{\rho L}{gA}$, in which $\rho =$ lb/ft^3, $P =$ lb/ft^2, $L =$ ft, $g =$ ft/sec^2, and $A =$ ft^2.

For time-varying flows $Q(t)$, the inertance of the moving fluids may be appreciable, especially if the material has high density ρ or if the pipe has a small cross-sectional area A.

Compressibility and Volume Capacity. The fact that fluids compress because they are under the action of pressure creates a capacity effect for pipelines and vessels in hydraulic circuits. Total compressibility or elastance of the fluid and of the pipe or vessel must be taken into account in order to calculate the equivalent hydraulic capacitance. Sometimes only the fluids are compressible, and the vessels and pipes which contain them can be regarded as inelastic, but other situations arise in which the elasticity of the vessels must be taken into account along with fluid compression. There are some instances where the fluid may be regarded as incompressible and the pipelines and vessels as highly elastic.

When the fluid is a gas or air, in contrast to a liquid, two situations must be recognized. Slow compressions and expansions of the gas tend to take place upon an isothermal basis, whereas rapidly changing compression and expansion must be looked upon as an adiabatic process. The isothermal situation is generally the basic for calculating fluid circuit capacitance when ordinary problems of gas pieplines at low pressures are involved. The adiabatic definition of fluid circuit capacitance must be used when the pressures and fluid medium are such that they will support compressional waves whose velocity of propagation and wavelengths are in the audible-frequency range of sound. These two studies are carried out by differentiating the ideal gas law and from this determining the capacitance of the circuit as the ratio of $Q : \frac{dP}{dt}$.

When the fluid is a liquid, the compression of the liquid in an inelastic vessel or pipe section, due to pressure changes, can be calculated in terms of the bulk modulus of compression B for the fluid and the volume V under compression. From this calculation, the hydraulic capacity can be defined.   The bulk modulus of compression is defined as

$$\frac{dP}{dV/V} = B \qquad (2.63)$$

but

$$dV = Q\,dt \qquad (2.64)$$

so

$$\frac{V}{B}\frac{dP}{dt} = Q \qquad (2.65)$$

The coefficient V/B in eq. 2.65 defines the volumetric capacity C for a vessel of volume V completely filled with elastic fluid for which B is the bulk modulus of compression.   The pressure P is the pressure in the vessel.   The flow Q is the fluid-flow increment taken up in compression as P increases, or the volume V of fluid released when P decreases.   The capacity for a pipeline or section of pipe is $C = LA/B$ where L is the section length and A is the cross-sectional area.

When the vessel expands, but the liquid is incompressible, the relations between P and Q are

$$dP = K\,dV \qquad (2.66)$$

$$dV = Q\,dt \qquad (2.67)$$

$$\frac{1}{K}\frac{dP}{dt} = Q \qquad (2.68)$$

The constant $1/K$ expresses the capacity property of the expanding vessel or pipe.   The particular value of K will depend to some extent upon the geometry of the vessel in addition to the modulus of elasticity of the material from which it is made.

If there should be both expansion of the container and compression of the liquid simultaneously, the same general form of relationship given in eq. 2.65 can be used, but a composite modulus of compression B' must be calculated.   The value B' accounts for both the bulk modulus of compression B of the fluid and the elastic deformation of the containing vessel.   These equations are:

$$dP = B\frac{dV}{V} + K\,dV \qquad (2.69)$$

$$= \left(\frac{B}{V} + K\right)Q\,dt \qquad (2.70)$$

$$\frac{V}{B'}\frac{dP}{dt} = Q \qquad (2.71)$$

$$B' = B + KV \qquad (2.72)$$

The adiabatic compression of gas can be studied as follows:

$$PV^\gamma = \text{constant} \tag{2.73}$$

$$V^\gamma\, dP + V^{\gamma-1}P\, dV = 0 \tag{2.74}$$

$$dP = -V^{-1}P_0\, dV \tag{2.75}$$

$$dV = Q\, dt \tag{2.76}$$

$$\frac{V_0}{\gamma P_0}\frac{dP}{dt} = Q \tag{2.77}$$

From eq. 2.77 the capacity is

$$C = \frac{V_0}{\gamma P_0} \tag{2.78}$$

The isothermal study is made in a very similar way.

$$PV = \text{constant} \tag{2.79}$$

$$V\, dP + P\, dV = 0 \tag{2.80}$$

$$dV = Q\, dt \tag{2.81}$$

$$\left(\frac{V_0}{P_0}\right)\frac{dP}{dt} = Q \tag{2.82}$$

According to eq. 2.82, the capacity is

$$C = \frac{V_0}{P_0} \tag{2.83}$$

The isothermal and adiabatic capacity for a gas-filled pipe or vessel differs only by the constant γ, which is the ratio of the specific heats. These formulae can also be expressed in terms of the velocity of sound in the particular gaseous medium, so that the capacity of the gas under adiabatic conditions is

$$\left(\frac{V_0}{\rho_0\mu^2}\right)\frac{dP}{dt} = Q_\mu \tag{2.84}$$

where

$$\mu = \sqrt{\frac{\gamma P_0}{\rho_0}} \tag{2.85}$$

Impedance.   The three circuit elements, resistance, capacitance, and inertance, have been defined.   Rarely do fluid circuits contain elements of only one type.

A length of pipe exhibits all three effects— resistance, inertance, and

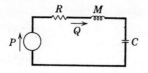

Fig. 2.12.   Pressure source driving a line terminated in a closed vessel.

capacity.   A tank and a valve constitute capacitance and resistance in parallel.   A pump may have internal resistance and capacity. Thus, in the treatment of fluid circuits, it becomes important to develop the concept of impedance.

For a pressure P applied to a short line characterized by resistance R and inertance M, and terminated in a vessel of capacity C, as shown in Fig. 2.12, the flow Q becomes

$$Q(s) = \left(\frac{1}{R + sM + \dfrac{1}{sC}} \right) P(s) \tag{2.86}$$

the impedance looking into the fluid circuit for the end where the pressure is applied.

$$Z(s) = R + sM + \frac{1}{sC} \tag{2.87}$$

When a compressor or pump drives a flow Q_p into a pipeline and vessel, as shown in Fig. 2.13a, the pressure P_0 developed in the vessel in terms of the flow Q_p can be found by circuit analysis.   Figure 13b shows the equivalent circuit.   The value for pressure P_0 is

$$\frac{P_0(s)}{Q(s)}$$

$$= \left[\frac{R_v}{R_v M C_A C_B s^3 + (C_A M + R R_v C_A C_B)s^2 + (R C_A + R_v C_A + R_v C_B)s + 1} \right] \tag{2.88}$$

where

$$C_A = C_P + \tfrac{1}{2}C \tag{2.89}$$

$$C_B = C_L + \tfrac{1}{2}C \tag{2.90}$$

The circuit diagrams of Fig. 2.13 are self-explanatory.   The schematic form of the hydraulic circuit is known, and the equivalent hydraulic network can be drawn by inspection.   Actually, fluid circuits have driving-point and transfer-impedance characteristics which can be used to relate pressures and flows anywhere in a system by means of operators in the form of $G(s)$ or $G(j\omega)$.

Sources.   Sources of fluid flow and pressure should be studied carefully.   They frequently exhibit internal resistance characteristics which are related to leakage flow.   Compressibility of fluid or deformation of metal gives the source characteristic capacity.   The pipes and passageways which connect multiple pistons to manifolds can establish inertance effects, because the fluid mass may be under severe acceleration or deceleration.

Basically there are two types of ideal sources: flow sources and pressure sources.   Practical sources differ from ideal ones because of their internal dynamic characteristics.   Thus, to represent a practical flow source, the ideal flow source generally has a shunt hydraulic admittance which defines the leakage, internal volume capacity, and inertance for the actual source.   The ideal pressure source employs an hydraulic series "impedance" to account for the difference between it and its practical counterpart.

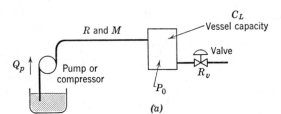

(a)

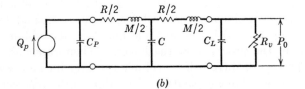

(b)

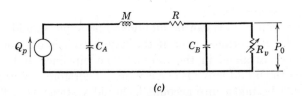

(c)

Fig. 2.13.   Flow source driving a line terminated in a vessel and a throttle valve.   (a) Schematic diagram of physical system; (b) and (c) Alternate equivalent circuits for (a).

Fluid Circuits. From the tables of circuits, it appears clear that pipelines have R, M, and C parameters; valves are mostly R, and tanks generally C. Pumps and compressors are either pressure or flow sources. They may contain source characteristics of R, M, and C.

By means of the definitions of R, M, and C given in eqs. 2.58, 2.62, and 2.65 and the concept of the hydraulic circuit, the reader should be able to express almost by inspection the fluid-flow configuration of mechanisms, pipelines, and vessels as an equivalent passive fluid circuit. From these circuits, admittance or impedance functions can be derived in terms of the Laplace-transform variable s, for studying the impulse response of a circuit; or in terms of the complex variable $j\omega$, for studying the admittance and impedance functions in a frequency-response manner. The whole range of transient and steady-state circuit theory commonly used by the electrical engineer in his studies of alternators, transmission lines, and motors can be placed at the disposal of the process engineer.

Once a person becomes familiar with the concept of hydraulic circuits, and is able to use the theorems of circuit analysis that are summarized in Appendix I, for simplifying the various diagrams, he will find it possible to write—upon an inspection basis—the hydraulic circuits for entire plants with their various configurations of pumps, compressors, pipelines, and process vessels. Thus the process designer will recognize at the outset that a tank is a volume capacity when a process is being planned. He will visualize a plant as shown in Fig. 2.13.

8. FLOW AND PRESSURE CONTROL—COMPRESSIBLE FLUID

The important distinction between liquid-level and flow regulators which operate with incompressible fluids, and pressure and flow regulators which operate with compressible fluids, is that volume capacity is present in the processes of the latter. When vapor and gas flow through processes, there will be volume capacity for all vessels. The pipes also have volume capacity. Even though the pipe capacity per unit length may be small, it may not be negligible compared with that of the process vessels.

The fact that liquids can be highly compressible should also not be overlooked. Sometimes, even if the liquid itself is not compressible, gas may be entrained in the liquid. The pipelines and the vessels containing the liquid may also be elastic. Therefore, volume-capacity effects must be taken into account in liquid systems as well as in gas systems.

The volume capacity of the pipes and vessels has significant influence upon the precision of the regulators because the capacity causes time lags in the pressure-flow dynamic relationships for the process which can cause instability.

Figure 2.14a shows how flow can be controlled. Flow measurement F is used to control the speed Ω_p of the compressor that is making gas flow into a pipeline. The pipeline terminates in a vessel such as a

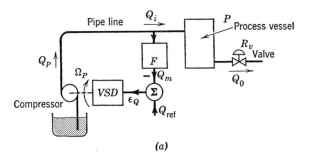

(a)

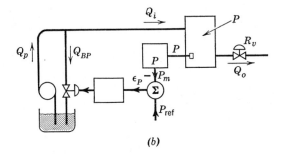

(b)

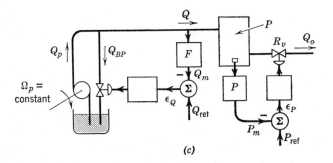

(c)

Fig. 2.14. Flow and pressure regulation in a process with compressible fluid. (a) Flow regulation; (b) Pressure regulation; (c) Flow and pressure regulation.

chemical reactor, a gas holder or a storage tank. A throttle valve maintains pressure in the vessel.

Figure 2.14b shows a pressure regulator. The pressure P in the vessel is measured. The signal P_m, after comparison with the reference P_{ref}, controls the valve. The valve is located in a by-pass or bleed line which connects the compressor output to the low-pressure intake or sump.

Finally, in the third figure, Fig. 2.14c, a combination of pressure and flow control is used on the same process. The flow is controlled by measuring the inflow Q to the vessel and causing the throttle valve in the by-pass line to fractionate the total pump flow Q_p so that the flow to the vessel is controlled. On the far side of the vessel, the let-down valve is positioned according to a pressure measurement made in the vessel. The pressure regulator keeps the pressure in the vessel constant regardless of flow changes.

Combination controls, as shown in Fig. 2.14 can interact with one another. Upsets in the flow Q can cause the pressure regulator to adjust the let-down valve. Variations in the process impedance can cause the flow to change so that the flow regulator goes into action. It is possible for this type of interaction to cause sustained *oscillation in the system*, even though each regulator is by itself stable.

9. FLOW CONTROL

The flow-control system shown in Fig. 2.14c uses a constant-speed positive-displacement pump to deliver the fluid flow Q_p. The flow Q reaches the process vessel through a pipeline. A by-pass pipeline diverts the flow Q_{BP} from the high-pressure side of the pump back into the sump.

The throttle valve in the by-pass line controls the amount of flow Q_{BP} by making the hydraulic impedance of the by-pass line small or large in comparison with the impedance of the main pipeline and process vessel. The pressure P in the process vessel varies according to the time-varying flow Q.

Control is accomplished as follows: Flow measurement is made in the pipeline to the process; the by-pass throttle-valve setting is controlled by means of a valve positioner which responds to a function of the error ε_Q between desired flow Q_{ref} and the measured flow Q_m.

In the system shown in Fig. 2.14a, the pump is driven by a variable-speed drive. The flow Q is measured at the same place in the pipeline as before. By means of appropriate motor control equipment, the error signal $\varepsilon_Q = Q_{ref} - Q_m$ manipulates the speed Ω_p of the pump. Variations in pump speed adjust the fluid flow Q to the process. In both arrangements consider that the let-down valve on the low-pressure side of the process vessel has a fixed setting.

To make a quantitative study of flow regulation requires that the physical parameters pertinent to both the static and the dynamic behavior of the process be defined. Let the average pressure maintained in the vessel be P_0. The fluid being pumped is liquid with an average density ρ_0 and viscosity μ_0. The compression of the fluid during pressure changes can be assumed isothermal. The hydraulic-circuit "lumped" parameters which define the pipeline are: inertance M for the fluid in motion, resistance to flow R, and volumetric capacitance C. The process vessel has a volume capacity C_p. The exact forms for the differential equations which describe the relationships between flow and pressure in the process pipeline and vessel have already been set up (section 7, p. 80). When fluctuations in the flows Q_{BP}, Q, and Q_o are assumed to be small, the differential equations which describe the process operation can be linearized. To the linearized differential equations which describe the process itself, transfer functions for the measuring and control equipment can be added to make the equations a complete set.

Linearized Equations for the By-Pass Regulator. The pump flow (generated) is

$$Q_p = Q_L + Q_{BP} + Q_i \tag{2.91}$$

$$Q_p = K_p \Omega_p \tag{2.92}$$

The leakage flow in the pump is

$$Q_L = K_L P_P \tag{2.93}$$

The flow in the by-pass line is

$$Q_{BP} \simeq K_3 X_{BP} + K_4 P_p \tag{2.94}$$

The pressure drop in the pipeline is

$$P_p - P \simeq (R + sM)Q_i \tag{2.95}$$

The capacity of the line can be added to that of the vessel so that

$$P = \frac{1}{(C + C_p)s} (Q_i - Q_o) \tag{2.96}$$

The outflow from the vessel is

$$Q_o \simeq K_2 P + K_1 X_1 \tag{2.97}$$

The measured flow Q_m is related to the inflow Q_i by the transfer function

$$\frac{Q_m(s)}{Q_i(s)} = K_m G_m(s) \qquad (2.98)$$

The controller dynamic response is given by the transfer function

$$\frac{M(s)}{\mathcal{E}_Q(s)} = K_c G_c(s) \qquad (2.99)$$

and the valve positioner has the transfer function

$$\frac{X_{BP}(s)}{M(s)} = K_D G_D(s) \qquad (2.100)$$

Linearized Equations for the Variable-Speed-Pump Regulator.
The pump flow is

$$Q_p = Q_L + Q_i \qquad (2.101)$$

$$Q_p = K_p \Omega_p \qquad (2.102)$$

and the pump speed Ω_p is related to the manipulation M by the transfer
function

$$\frac{\Omega_p(s)}{M(s)} = K_D' G_D'(s) \qquad (2.103)$$

The leakage flow is the same as for the by-pass type of regulator,
$Q_L = K_L P_p$. In fact, all of the other equations remain the same.
The particular transfer functions for the controller and the measuring
element will differ when different types of physical components are
used.

Hydraulic Circuits. By means of the relationships given in eqs.
2.91 through 2.103, the hydraulic circuits which describe the two systems can be developed as shown in Figs. 2.15a and b. The vessel and
the let-down valve can be regarded as an impedance

$$Z_1 = \frac{R_1}{sC_p R_v + 1} \qquad (2.104)$$

which terminates the pipeline. If the line capacity C is added to the
process capacity C_p, the impedance looking into the pipeline is:

$$Z_2 = R + sM + \frac{R_1}{s(C_p + C)R_v + 1} \qquad (2.105)$$

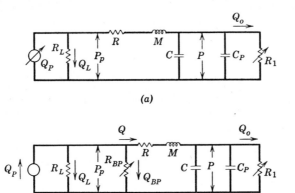

Fig. 2.15. Hydraulic circuits for two types of flow regulators. (a) Variable-speed pump flow regulator; (b) By-pass flow regulator.

The pump is a flow source. A leakage resistance $R_L = 1/K_L$ is placed in shunt across the flow source. The flow Q into the hydraulic imped-ance Z_1 establishes the pressure P_p at the entrance to the process. Fluctuations in the vessel pressure P constitute the disturbance to the flow regulator.

For the by-pass valve-type regulator, the by-pass resistance R_{BP} is variable. For the variable-speed-pump type of regulator, the flow source Q is variable. Beyond this point, one procedure would be to set the two hydraulic circuits up on an analogue computer and to study the system dynamic behavior in terms of the process parameters of resistance, inertance, and capacity.

Block Diagrams. The equations for the two regulators can also be used to set up block diagrams. The relationships between the varia-bles in the block diagrams will be the same as those for the equivalent linear circuits, provided the circuits and the diagrams are linearized in the same way.

Figure 2.16 is a block diagram which shows the self-regulation pres-ent in the process. The pump puts a flow Q_p into the system. The leakage flow Q_L in the pump is subtracted from the "ideal" pump flow. Thus the flow Q enters the process. The flow Q_o leaves the process through the let-down valve. This leaves only the compressibility component of flow to be accounted for. Thus ΣQ, when divided by the volume capacity of the process vessel and integrated, gives the pressure P in the process vessel. (For convenience in setting up the

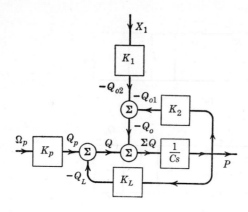

Fig. 2.16. Block diagram showing self-regulation in flow process.

block diagram, the resistance R and the inertance M of the pipeline are assumed to be zero.)   The pressure P causes an outflow component Q_{o1}.   The pressure also causes the leakage flow Q_L.   The setting X_1 of the let-down valve varies the outflow component Q_{o2}.

If the pump leakage Q_L were zero and the pump flow Q_p were not influenced by pressure P, the flow Q would remain constant regardless of the setting X_1 of the let-down valve.   However, when leakage flow Q_L occurs, as the pressure builds up in the process, the flow Q_L increases.   Therefore, for a constant pump delivery, the flow Q to the process diminishes as the pressure rises.   The *leakage flow* produces the *self-regulation* in the process when the issue is flow regulation.   The outflow component Q_{o1} is a self-regulating flow for *pressure* when the leakage is zero.   The outflow adds to the self-regulation of flow K_L $+ K_2$ when leakage is present.   These observations are borne out by eq. 2.106 in Table 2.2, which describes the behavior of the uncontrolled process.

The flow-regulator block diagrams develop by extending the diagram of the self-regulated process shown in Fig. 2.16.   The flow to the process Q is measured with a measuring device that gives a signal Q_m.   The measured value of flow is compared with the reference quantity Q_{ref} and the error ε_Q energizes a controller whose manipulation M adjusts either the pump speed Ω_o or the by-pass valve setting X_{BP}.

For the regulator with the variable-speed pump, the block diagram is shown in Fig. 2.17.   The transfer function $K_D G_D(s)$ defines the dynamic response of the variable-speed drive.   The transfer function $K_C G_C(s)$ defines the dynamic action of the controller which sets the speed of the drive.   The disturbance which upsets flow is process pressure.   If the process pressure changes, the leakage flow and the

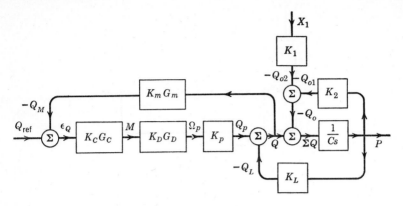

Fig. 2.17.   Block diagram of variable-speed type of flow regulator.

flow to the process will change unless there is an adjustment of the pump speed.

For the by-pass valve type of flow regulator, the block diagram shown in Fig. 2.18 is different from the diagram of Fig. 2.17 in an interesting way.   The total flow through the by-pass line is a function of both the valve setting X_{BP} and the process pressure P.   Therefore, as shown in the block diagram, a self-regulating flow component Q_{BPP} must

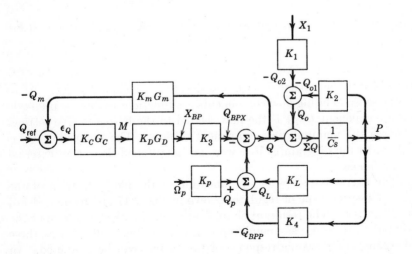

Fig. 2.18.   Block diagram for process with by-pass line and throttle valve to provide flow regulation.

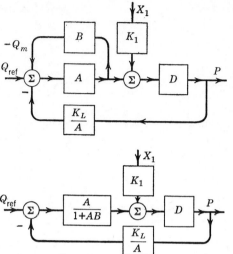

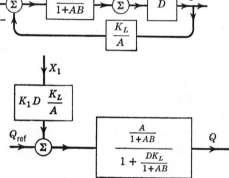

Fig. 2.19. Simplifications for block diagram of Fig. 2.17, the variable speed type of flow regulator.

be added to the leakage flow Q_L and the outflow component Q_{o1}. All of these self-regulating flow components are functions of process pressure. The component Q_{BPX} is the flow related to the by-pass valve setting. This is the manipulating component of flow. The pump flow Q_p is added to the diagram as if it were an initial condition or an external disturbance.

The successive steps in simplification of the block diagram of the variable-speed type of regulator shown in Fig. 2.17 are given in detail in Fig. 2.19. The resultant simplification of the block diagram of the throttle valve by-pass regulator is given in Fig. 2.20. From these diagrams the dynamic response of the system can be predicted. In order that the self-regulated, the variable-speed, and the by-pass-valve type of regulator can be compared, the equations for the change in flow $Q(s)$ in terms of $Q_{ref}(s)$, $X_1(s)$, and $\Omega_p(s)$ are summarized in Table 2.2.

TABLE 2.2. RESPONSE EQUATIONS FOR FLOW REGULATORS

$$A = K_cG_c(s)K_DG_D(s)K_p, \qquad B = K_mG_m(s), \qquad D = \frac{1/K_2}{\tau_p s + 1}, \qquad \tau_p = \frac{C_T}{K_2}$$

$$A' = K_cG_c(s)K_DG_D(s)K_3.$$

Self-Regulated

$$Q(s) = \frac{K_p}{1 + K_L D}\,\Omega_p(s) + \frac{DK_1K_L}{1 + K_L D}\,X_1(s) \qquad (2.106)$$

Variable-Speed Drive

$$Q(s) = \frac{\dfrac{A}{1 + AB}}{1 + \dfrac{K_L D}{1 + AB}}\,Q_{ref}(s) + \frac{\dfrac{K_L D K_1}{1 + AB}}{1 + \dfrac{K_L D}{1 + AB}}\,X_1(s) \qquad (2.107)$$

By-Pass

$$Q(s) = \frac{\dfrac{K_p}{1 + A'B}}{1 + \dfrac{(K_4 + K_L)D}{1 + A'B}}\,\Omega_p(s) + \frac{\dfrac{A'}{1 + A'B}}{1 + \dfrac{(K_4 + K_L)D}{1 + A'B}}\,Q_{ref}(s)$$

$$+ \frac{\dfrac{(K_4 + K_L)DK_1}{1 + A'B}}{1 + \dfrac{(K_4 + K_L)D}{1 + A'B}}\,X_1(s) \qquad (2.108)$$

The equations in Table 2.2 make it possible to compare the performance of the process with three different modes of regulation: [self-regulation, speed-control type of pump control, and by-pass type of valve control.

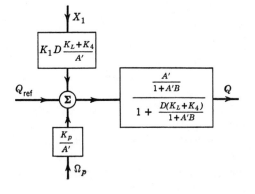

Fig. 2.20. Simplification of block diagram of Fig. 2.18, the throttle valve by-pass type of flow regulator.

In self-regulation, the flow Q will change whenever there is a change in the let-down valve setting. The time lag of the process is modified to some extent by the flow through the valve on the let-down side of the vessel and by the leakage in the pump, as given by eq. 2.106:

$$\frac{Q(s)}{X_1(s)}\bigg|_{\Omega_p=0} = \frac{K_L \dfrac{1}{K_2} K_1}{\tau_p s + 1 + K_L/K_2} = \frac{\dfrac{\left(\dfrac{K_L K_1}{K_2}\right)}{\left(1 + \dfrac{K_L}{K_2}\right)}}{\left(\dfrac{\tau_p}{1 + \dfrac{K_L}{K_2}}\right) s + 1} \tag{2.109}$$

If the pump leakage is zero, the flow into the vessel does not change as a function of the let-down valve setting. This means that the pressure in the process will build up and that it can reach dangerous levels when the system has no leakage and when the let-down valve clogs or is set for too small an outflow.

Next consider the speed-control type of system. Equation 2.107 shows that the speed-control type of flow regulator has the same general form of performance as does the self-regulating system, with the exception that there is the product term AB in the denominator of the response equation.

$$\frac{Q(s)}{X_1(s)}\bigg|_{Q_{\text{ref}}=0} = \frac{\left[\dfrac{K_L \left(\dfrac{1/K_2}{\tau_p s + 1}\right) K_1}{1 + AB}\right]}{1 + \left[\dfrac{K_L \left(\dfrac{1/K_2}{\tau_p s + 1}\right)}{1 + AB}\right]} = \frac{\dfrac{K_L K_1}{K_2}\left(\dfrac{1}{\tau_p s + 1}\right)}{1 + AB + \left(\dfrac{K_L/K_2}{\tau_p s + 1}\right)} \tag{2.110}$$

$$= \frac{\dfrac{K_L K_1}{K_2}}{(\tau_p s + 1)(1 + AB) + \dfrac{K_L}{K_2}} \tag{2.111}$$

The product AB defines the dynamic response of the equipment that measures the flow and controls the variable-speed drive, as well as the variable-speed drive itself. If there were no time lags in measurement, in the variable-speed drive, or in the control equipment, and if purely proportional regulation were used, the flow Q would vary for changes in the let-down valve setting according to the relation

$$\frac{Q(s)}{X_1(s)} = \frac{\dfrac{K_L K_1}{K_2}}{(\tau_p s + 1)(1 + K) + \dfrac{K_L}{K_2}} \tag{2.112}$$

It is clear, from eq. 2.112, that a large value of loop gain will cause the static regulation of the system to improve, since it will make the ratio $|\Delta Q/\Delta X_1|$ smaller. The presence of a large loop gain will also make the response rapid, since the influence of the process time constant τ_p will be diminished. Thus the ratio $\left|\dfrac{\Delta Q(j\omega)}{\Delta X_1(j\omega)}\right|$ will remain flat over a wide frequency range. The value of $\left|\dfrac{\Delta Q}{\Delta X_1}\right|$ will lie below zero-decibel level by an amount equal to the zero-frequency or static gain $\dfrac{K_L K_1}{K_2(1 + K) + K_L}$. When a time lag appears in the variable-speed drive, which will certainly occur, the response equation changes to the form

$$\frac{Q(s)}{X_1(s)} = \frac{\dfrac{K_L K_1}{K_2}}{(\tau_p s + 1)\left(1 + \dfrac{K}{\tau s + 1}\right) + \dfrac{K_L}{K_2}} \tag{2.113}$$

The time lag τ, which represents a single equivalent time lag for the variable-speed drive and other associated apparatus, will cause the characteristic equation of the system to become a quadratic. It will also cause the numerator to have a zero at the value $s = -1/\tau$. There will now be a maximum loop gain K which can be obtained in the proportional-type regulator with one lag in the variable-speed drive or control equipment, because if the gain K is made too large, the system response will tend to become too oscillatory.

Since there is sure to be one time lag τ, if not more than one time lag, in the control and variable-speed-drive equipment, the gain of the regulator will always be limited. The value for the gain can be determined easily, either by choosing an M_p criterion (as is used in servomechanisms analysis), by assuming that the damping ratio of a system shall be not less than approximately 0.5, or by choosing a phase-margin criterion of -45 degrees as the basis for setting the closed-loop-system gain. If the loop-gain magnitude is limited, the change in flow ΔQ for variations in process pressure or let-down valve setting may be such that the flow to the process cannot be kept from drooping or rising as the process is being adjusted for other conditions of operation.

The addition of reset or integral type of control action, in addition to the proportional control, may be required in order that the flow may be made invariant to changes in the let-down valve setting. The performance of proportional-plus-integral control action can be shown by the equation

$$\frac{Q(s)}{X_1(s)} = \frac{\dfrac{K_L K_1}{K_2}}{(\tau_p s + 1)\left(1 + K\dfrac{\tau_r s + 1}{s}\right) + \dfrac{K_L}{K_2}} \tag{2.114}$$

The term AB, in eq. 2.111, has been replaced by $K\dfrac{\tau_r s + 1}{s}$, the transfer function for proportional-plus-integral regulator action. When the fractions are cleared, the s which appears in the denominator of the control operator will transfer into the numerator of the response equation. Therefore, in the steady state, the regulator with proportional-plus-integral control action will keep the flow invariant despite changes in the let-down valve setting or process pressure variations.

The presence of time lags in the variable-speed drive or in the control apparatus will not prevent the integral action of the controller from providing the regulator with perfect static or low-frequency performance, but these lags *will* make the closed system have sufficient overall time lag so that the gain in the loop will have to be set very carefully. Otherwise, a condition of sustained oscillation could obtain for the flow regulator. This can be shown by the following equation:

$$\frac{Q(s)}{X_1(s)} = \frac{\dfrac{K_L K_1}{K_2}}{(\tau_p s + 1)\left[1 + K\dfrac{(\tau_r s + 1)}{s(\tau s + 1)}\right] + \dfrac{K_L}{K_2}} \tag{2.115}$$

The denominator is a cubic equation. The specific stability condition according to Routh's criterion for the relationship between the parameters τ_p, τ, τ_r, K, K_L, and K_2 is

$$[\tau + \tau_p(K\tau_r + 1)][\tau_p K + (K\tau_r + 1)] \geq \tau_p \tau\left(K + \frac{K_L}{K_2}\right) \tag{2.116}$$

The response equations for the by-pass control system are so similar to those for the speed-control type of system that there is no point in making a duplicate discussion. From the table, one can note that the response equation for the by-pass system, as compared with the speed-system, differs only slightly. Equation 2.108 has in its denominator the product $A'B$, which is analogous to the product AB, in that it indicates the dynamics of the measuring equipment and the valve-positioning equipment used in the by-pass type of control, as well as the control equipment. But, instead of the term K_L, which is the leakage coefficient, appearing alone (as it does in the speed-control system), there is added to the leakage coefficient K_L the term K_4, which is the self-regulating component of flow through the by-pass valve caused by pressure in the process. Otherwise, all other factors in the two systems are the same.

As far as comparing the two systems is concerned, the issue seems to be cost, and comparison of the dynamic performance of a valve as compared with that of an engine or motor. The gain in each system will be limited by the time lags that are present. A by-pass system will not necessarily be better than a variable-speed drive unless the bandwidth of the valve-positioning equipment is greater than that of the variable-speed drive. In many types of flow-control processes, especially where high pressures are involved and the liquids rather than the gases are involved, the time lag of the process τ_p may be considerably smaller than the time lag of either valve-positioning equipment or speed-control equipment.

Sometimes the relative power losses may be the factor which determines which type of flow control to use. In the by-pass scheme, the fluid power losses are the product of the by-pass flow Q_{BP} multiplied by R_{BP}^2, the square of the resistance of the path. The losses in the variable-speed type of control must account for both the pump and the motor losses.

10. PRESSURE REGULATION

Thus far in this section, the emphasis has been upon flow control. The objective has been to study regulators whose purpose is to maintain a constant fluid into or through a process, despite changes in process pressure or changes in process impedance. Now the related problem of pressure regulation will be considered, where the object will be to keep the pressure in a vessel constant despite variations in throughput, temperature, reaction rate, and other variables that can bring about pressure changes.

One way to regulate the pressure in a vessel is to adjust the resistance R_v of the throttle valve in the outflow pipe from the vessel, as shown in Fig. 2.14c. The pressure P is measured and the measured value P_m is compared against a reference pressure P_{ref}. The error in pressure ε_p is used to manipulate the throttle valve located in the outflow pipe-line. The variations in the outflow Q_o counteract changes of the inflow Q, and consequently regulate the pressure.

The dynamic behavior of the process is described by

$$P(s) = \left(\frac{K_p}{\tau_p s + 1}\right)[Q_i(s) + K_1 X_v(s)] \qquad (2.117)$$

in which

$$\tau_p = \frac{C}{K_2} \qquad (2.118)$$

$$K_p = \frac{1}{K_2} \qquad (2.119)$$

$$K_1 = \left(\frac{\partial Q_o}{\partial X_v}\right)_{P=\text{constant}} \qquad (2.120)$$

$$K_2 = \left(\frac{\partial Q_o}{\partial P}\right)_{X_v=\text{constant}} \qquad (2.121)$$

The volume capacity C of the process serves, to some extent, to act as a muffler or pulsation damper, but at the same time the adjustment of the throttle valve brings about counteracting manipulations that can drop or raise the pressure P in the vessel suddenly, provided the valve stem can be positioned rapidly.

The block diagram for the regulator can be drawn by inspection, as shown in Fig. 2.21. The transfer function $K_C G_C(s)$ defines the controller, $K_D G_D(s)$ defines the valve-positioning mechanism, and $K_m G_m(s)$ defines the pressure-measuring element.

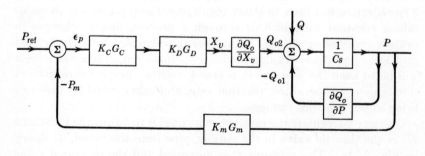

Fig. 2.21. Block diagram of pressure regulator.

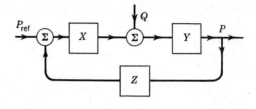

Fig. 2.22. Block diagram simplification—pressure regulator.

The open-loop characteristic of the regulatory system becomes:

$$\frac{P_m(s)}{\mathcal{E}_p(s)} = K_c K_p K_D K_m \left(\frac{1}{\tau_p s + 1}\right) G_c(s) G_D(s) G_m(s) \qquad (2.122)$$

$$= KG(s) \qquad (2.123)$$

$$= X(s)\, Y(s)\, Z(s) \qquad \text{(see Fig 2.22)} \qquad (2.124)$$

The general behavior of the pressure regulator can be predicted by the relationships

$$\left.\frac{P_m(s)}{P_{\text{ref}}(s)}\right|_{Q=0} = \frac{KG(s)}{1 + KG(s)} \qquad (2.125)$$

$$\left.\frac{P(s)}{P_{\text{ref}}(s)}\right|_{Q=0} = \frac{KG(s)}{1 + KG(s)} \frac{1}{Z(s)} \qquad (2.126)$$

$$\left.\frac{P(s)}{Q(s)}\right|_{P_{\text{ref}}=0} = \frac{Y(s)}{1 + X(s)\, Y(s)\, Z(s)} \qquad (2.127)$$

$$\left.\frac{P(s)}{Q(s)}\right|_{P_{\text{ref}}=0} = \left(\frac{KG(s)}{1 + KG(s)}\right)\left(\frac{1}{X(s)\, Z(s)}\right) \qquad (2.128)$$

$$\left.\frac{P(s)}{Q(s)}\right|_{P_{\text{ref}}=0} = \left[\left(\frac{P_m(s)}{P_{\text{ref}}(s)}\right)_{Q=0}\right]\left(\frac{1}{X(s)\, Z(s)}\right) \qquad (2.129)$$

To make pressure P in the vessel insensitive to flow fluctuations calls for the ratio $\dfrac{P(j\omega)}{Q(j\omega)}$ to be zero or nearly zero over the entire frequency range $0 < \omega < \infty$. The requirement that the regulator hold with reasonable accuracy the set point or reference level P_{ref} indicates that the ratio $\dfrac{P(j\omega)}{P_{\text{ref}}(j\omega)}$ must be unity or approximately unity. Therefore the operator $X(j\omega)\, Z(j\omega)$ must have a large magnitude over the low-frequency range.

Unfortunately, valve positioners, controllers, amplifiers, and pressure detectors exhibit magnitude characteristics which attenuate as the frequency ω increases. Thus the static precision of a pressure regulator can be poor, because of the lags in the control equipment. The phase lags in the transfer function $X(j\omega)\, Z(j\omega)$, added to those of the process itself, will affect the stability of the regulator.

An illustrative study of pressure regulator design is too extensive a task to be given a full treatment in this book. However, the method of analyzing the problem can be readily understood. First, the open-loop function $KG(j\omega)$, as defined in eq. 2.124, is plotted. Secondly, the closed-loop response $\dfrac{KG(j\omega)}{1 + KG(j\omega)}$ is formed from the open-loop response $KG(j\omega)$. Next, the regulator performance $\dfrac{P(j\omega)}{Q(j\omega)}$ is determined by modifying the response $\dfrac{KG(j\omega)}{1 + KG(j\omega)}$ as indicated by eq. 2.128. Finally, to study the various modes of control which can improve the regulator performance, the open-loop characteristic KG is modified by different compensation schemes and the whole graphical study is repeated for each compensation.

Numerical Example. Consider that a process has a time lag $\tau_p \simeq 9$ sec. The valve positioner has a time constant $\tau_v \simeq 0.02$ sec and a damping ratio $\tau_v \simeq 0.4$. If a $-45°$ phase-margin criterion is used for selecting the closed-loop gain of the pressure regulator, the value of the gain will be determined by the location of the break frequency $\omega_v = 1/\tau_v = 50$ rad/sec relative to the break frequency $\omega_p = 1/\tau_p = \frac{1}{9}$ rad/sec. Therefore

$$K_{\text{loop}} \simeq 20 \log_{10} (\tfrac{1}{9}) - 20 \log_{10} 50$$

$$\simeq -20 \log_{10} 450$$

$$\simeq 53 \text{ decibels}$$

The addition of one stage of undercompensated integral such that the transfer function

$$G_C(j\omega) = \frac{\tau j\omega + 1}{\alpha \tau j\omega + 1}$$

has a zero at $1/\tau = \omega = \frac{1}{10}\tau_p$, and $\alpha = 10$ gives the compensated system the loop gain

$$K_{\text{loop}} \simeq -[20 \log_{10} \alpha + 20 \log_{10} 450]$$

$$\simeq 73 \text{ decibels}$$

11. PULSATION DAMPERS

Flow and pressure throughout a process may have fluctuating components superimposed upon their steady values, especially when the positive-displacement type of pumps and compressors push fluid periodically into pipelines. Despite the fact that flow and pressure regulators can be built to regulate the individual variables, it may be more advantageous to design pulsation dampers to eliminate the pulsating components flow so that it does not interfere with process operation. Pulsation dampers are designed by arranging resistance, capacitance, and inertance elements into hydraulic networks capable of absorbing and dissipating the energy found in the fluctuating component of the flow.

The waveform of the flow $Q(t)$ shown in Fig. 2.23b is typical of the flow from positive-displacement pumps and high-pressure gas compressors. A Fourier analysis of the wave $Q(t)$

$$Q(t) = a_0 + a_1 \cos \omega t + a_2 \cos 2\omega t \cdots \qquad (2.130)$$
$$+ b_1 \sin \omega t + b_2 \sin 2\omega t \cdots$$

provides definition of the steady component a_0 and the harmonic components $a_1, a_2 \cdots$ and $b_1, b_2 \cdots$ present in the wave. The coefficients indicate the relative amount of each harmonic present in the total flow $Q(t)$. The vector form of the Fourier analysis

$$Q(t) = c_0 + c_1 e^{j\omega t} + c_2 e^{j 2\omega t} + c_3 e^{j 3\omega t} \cdots \qquad (2.131)$$

gives the relative importance of the components in the wave in terms of the magnitudes of the complex coefficients c_1, c_2, etc. The graph of c_j versus ω of Fig. 2.24 shows that the higher-frequency components present in $Q(t)$ are not important, but the first few harmonics may be large enough to cause appreciable fluctuation in process variables.

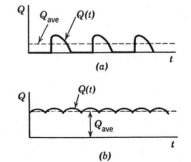

Fig. 2.23. (a) Single-piston pump flow; (b) Multi-piston pump flow.

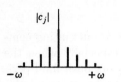

Fig. 2.24. Typical harmonic distribution in a flow wave.

To design vibration dampers which reduce pump pulsations, the problem is to select a circuit of fluid resistance, inertance, and volumetric capacity with proper attenuation versus frequency characteristic so that the particular frequencies present in a wave can be selectively attenuated.   A single frequency, a band of frequencies, or all the frequencies above or below a specific "break" frequency can be attenuated.

A pulsating flow through a resistance element causes the pressure drop across the resistance to fluctuate *in phase* with and *in proportion* to the magnitude of the flow.   The pressure $P(t)$ will contain all harmonics present in the flow in the same proportion as they occur.

However, if a pulsating flow passes into a tank of volume capacity C, the tank will attenuate the high frequencies contained in the flow in proportion to their frequency.   The relationship between $\Delta P(j\omega)$ and $\Delta Q(j\omega)$

$$\frac{\Delta P(j\omega)}{\Delta Q(j\omega)} = \frac{1}{j\omega C} \tag{2.132}$$

shows that the change in pressure for a change in flow will be small for large values of ω.   Thus a surge tank, the volume capacity of the process, or the volume capacity of its pipelines serves to attenuate high-frequency pulsations.

A tank alone may not constitute an adequate damper, nor may the single tank be selective.   Resistance elements must be used in conjunction with capacity to produce filters.   Combinations of more than one tank in a pipeline, with the correct-diameter pipes interconnecting, can have the proper inertance, resistance, and capacitance to produce a *tuned damper*.

Table 2.3 shows a few pulsation dampers.   The physical schematic, the hydraulic network, and the attenuation characteristic for each damper are given.

The limitations on Table 2.3 require a few words of explanation. First, both the attenuation and the phase characteristics of any fluid filter will be influenced by its termination impedance and the impedance of the source which drives it.   Table 2.3 has been developed using a resistance termination R_o for all of the filters. It is possible to convert each filter design so that a general impedance termination Z_o and a source impedance Z_s can be considered. However, a table for general filter design is not practical, because each filter could have an unlimited number of attenuation and phase characteristics. My aim is to have Table 2.3 serve as a guide for design.

The filters chosen are those most useful to the process engineer. The first is a tank in a pipeline. The purpose of the tank is to eliminate high-frequency pulsations by means of the volume capacity of the tank. Pure-capacity filters, however, rarely exist. Tanks empty through throttle valves or resistance to flow. The attenuation characteristic of the resistance-capacitance filter has a slope sequence of zero decibels per decade and -20 decibels per decade. The break frequency is located at the value $\omega = 1/\tau = 1/CR$. The tank capacity C and the valve resistance R determine the frequency-selective properties of the single-tank filter.

The second item is a surge tank connected to the main pipeline by means of a small-diameter branch line. This type of filter has an attenuation characteristic which has zero slope at low frequencies and at high frequencies. At the normalized frequency $\omega = 1$, the surge tank attenuates pressure pulsations by the amount $(1 + R_o/R)$ in decibels. The maximum attenuation is not a function of the capacity of the surge tank, but rather the relative resistance between the pipe going to the surge tank and that of the process resistance R located downstream. The value of the capacity C of the tank, and the value of the inertance M of the branch line determine the frequency at which the filter shows maximum attenuation.

The low-pass filter, made up of two tanks and an interconnecting pipe of resistance and inertance, has zero attenuation until the frequency $\omega = (RMC^2)^{-3}$ is reached. Then the slope changes to -60 decibels per decade. The high-pass filter has zero attenuation at high frequency, and the particular construction of filter shown in the table has an attenuation characteristic of 80 decibels per decade at low frequencies.

In the high-pass, band-pass, and band-elimination filters, it is important to note that diaphragms are used to transmit the compressional energy from one section of the filter to the next in the system. The diaphragm design must be carefully considered.

Pulsation dampers should be of minimum physical dimensions and maximum filtering ability. This keeps their cost low, and it minimizes the effects of their dynamics upon other phases of the process control and regulation problem. The design of pulsation dampers first

TABLE 2.3. PULSATION DAMPERS AND WAVE FILTERS TERMINATED WITH RESISTANCE R_o

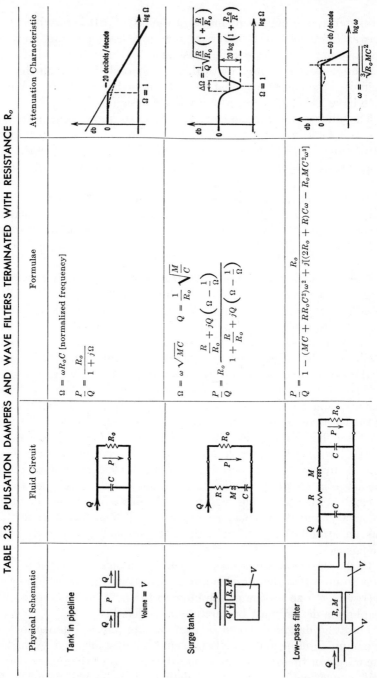

Physical Schematic	Fluid Circuit	Formulae	Attenuation Characteristic
Tank in pipeline		$\Omega = \omega R_o C$ [normalized frequency] $$\frac{P}{Q} = \frac{R_o}{1 + j\Omega}$$	−20 decibels/decade, $\Omega = 1$
Surge tank		$\Omega = \omega\sqrt{MC} \qquad Q = \frac{1}{R_o}\sqrt{\frac{M}{C}}$ $$\frac{P}{Q} = R_o\,\frac{\dfrac{R}{R_o} + jQ\left(\Omega - \dfrac{1}{\Omega}\right)}{1 + \dfrac{R}{R_o} + jQ\left(\Omega - \dfrac{1}{\Omega}\right)}$$	$\Delta\Omega = \frac{1}{Q}\sqrt{\frac{R}{R_o}\left(1 + \frac{R}{R_o}\right)}$ $20\log\left(1 + \frac{R_o}{R}\right)$, $\Omega = 1$
Low-pass filter		$$\frac{P}{Q} = \frac{R_o}{1 - (MC + RR_oC^2)\omega^2 + j[(2R_o + R)C\omega - R_oMC^2\omega^3]}$$	−60 db/decade, $\omega = \dfrac{1}{\sqrt[3]{R_oMC^2}}$

102

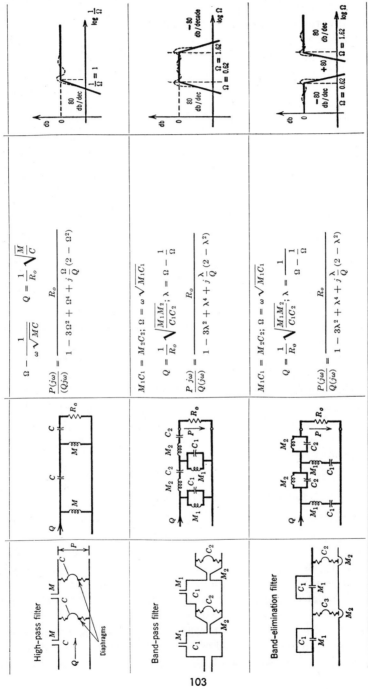

High-pass filter

$$\Omega = \frac{1}{\omega\sqrt{MC}} \qquad Q = \frac{1}{R_o}\sqrt{\frac{M}{C}}$$

$$\frac{P(j\omega)}{Q(j\omega)} = \frac{R_o}{1 - 3\Omega^2 + \Omega^4 + j\,\dfrac{\Omega}{Q}(2 - \Omega^2)}$$

Band-pass filter

$$M_1C_1 = M_2C_2; \quad \Omega = \omega\sqrt{M_1C_1}$$

$$Q = \frac{1}{R_o}\sqrt{\frac{M_1M_2}{C_1C_2}}; \quad \lambda = \Omega - \frac{1}{\Omega}$$

$$\frac{P(j\omega)}{Q(j\omega)} = \frac{R_o}{1 - 3\lambda^2 + \lambda^4 + j\,\dfrac{\lambda}{Q}(2 - \lambda^2)}$$

Band-elimination filter

$$M_1C_1 = M_2C_2; \quad \Omega = \omega\sqrt{M_1C_1}$$

$$Q = \frac{1}{R_o}\sqrt{\frac{M_1M_2}{C_1C_2}}; \quad \lambda = \frac{1}{\Omega - \dfrac{1}{\Omega}}$$

$$\frac{P(j\omega)}{Q(j\omega)} = \frac{R_o}{1 - 3\lambda^2 + \lambda^4 + j\,\dfrac{\lambda}{Q}(2 - \lambda^2)}$$

103

requires that the circuit configuration be chosen. Next, numerical values of the resistance, capacitance, and inertance must be picked so that the attenuation characteristic of the filter shall meet the requirements. Finally, the particular geometry and size of the vessels and pipelines that make up the filter must be chosen so that they establish the foregoing numerical values for the hydraulic-circuit elements. Simulatneously with this part of the design must go the considerations of physical strength, safety, proper thickness of vessel to combat corrosion, and all the other factors pertinent to plant-equipment design.

Even when adequate precautions are taken that designs be carefully carried out, supported by quantitative calculation, adjustments and tuning of a pulsation damper may be necessary after the equipment has been built. Therefore the volume-capacity, resistance, and inertance values should be kept adjustable, or at least the physical apparatus should have provision made in its design so that the values can be changed without need for rebuilding the damper. This flexibility is necessary for another very important reason: the harmonics present in a pulsating flow can change if new compressors or auxiliary equipment are added to a process.

If the parameters of a filter can be adjusted without the entire structure's being rebuilt or reorganized, the attenuation characteristic of the filter may be sufficiently adjustable to meet the changes in the frequency.

Two things should be pointed out in connection with pulsation damping. First, *pulsations should be eliminated at their source, if possible.* The pumps and compressors should be built with a sufficient number of pistons and the proper internal pathways for flow, and with valving so that pulsations are at a minimum. Secondly, whenever possible, the designer of processes should *choose the process vessels and the pipelines that connect them to the compressors so that the plant is its own pulsation damper.* The last thing to do is to add extra volume capacity.

12. DISTRIBUTED-PARAMETER CIRCUITS

The procedure of representing fluid circuits in terms of lumped-parameter resistance, inertance, and capacitance elements fails to emphasize the fact that compressional waves can be generated which can travel through gases, liquids, and the metal process pipes themselves. Actually, resistance, inertance, and capacitance are distributed throughout the pipes and vessels; so partial differential equations must be written to relate the pressure $P(x, t)$ and the flow $Q(x, t)$ for a compressible fluid distributed throughout one-dimensional fluid circuits. These partial differential equations combine to form the general wave equation. The solution of the wave equation has a unique form that is independent of the process, but the parameters in the solution will depend upon particular lengths and sizes of pipelines, sizes of vessels that terminate pipelines, and types of machinery that are connected to fluid process systems.

Equations for pressure and flow that are functions in both x and t can be Laplace-transformed with respect to the time variable so that the transformed equations become functions of x and s. The transformed equations can be handled as if they were ordinary differential equations. The form of their solutions can be predicted either by the classical procedure or by means of the tables of transform pairs in Appendix II.

The operators in the variables x and s can be studied to determine salient characteristics of the distributed-parameter fluid networks, just as the operators in s were studied for the lumped-parameter circuits. Certain types of fluid-circuit characteristics indicate that a process can exhibit resonance phenomena. The traveling waves bring about "water-hammer" effects. Standing waves may overstress equipment.

Quite often, the dynamic response of distributed types of fluid-handling systems can be readily understood by studying the transfer functions or the frequency characteristics for the pressure and flow relationships in terms of distance x in the system from some datum point and in terms of the variable $j\omega$. However, when transient studies are being made, it is better to leave the operators in the form of the variables x and s.

Since there is a direct analogy between the hydraulic circuit and the electric circuit, it is possible to use equations for hydraulic circuits similar to those for electric transmission lines. Caution must be exercised, however, to use the basic forms of these equations rather than the more common design equations. One of the reasons for this is that pipelines, unlike electric lines, usually begin with flow sources, and they usually terminate in vessels that may be open or closed. Therefore they differ from the long electric line, which generally has a voltage driving source and which may terminate in an open-circuited or short-circuited manner for many of the elementary studies made on electric lines.

Partial Differential Equations for a Distributed-Parameter Line. Two partial differential equations relate the pressure P and the flow Q in a differential length dx of pipeline. The relationship for pressure P along the line is

$$m \frac{\partial Q}{\partial t} + rQ = - \frac{\partial P}{\partial x} \qquad (2.133)$$

and the flow Q is

$$c\frac{\partial P}{\partial t} + 0 = -\frac{\partial Q}{\partial x} \tag{2.134}$$

The parameters which characterize the pipeline are the resistance r, the inertance m, and the capacity c, per unit length.

Equations 2.133 and 2.134 can be transformed by the Laplace transformation. All the terms which are functions of x will transform without change. The terms which are functions of time and derivatives with respect to time are replaced by their equivalent functions of s. Initial conditions appear as in the transformations of the ordinary equations. Thus:

$$(ms + r)Q(x, s) = -\frac{dP(x, s)}{dx} + mQ(x, 0) \tag{2.135}$$

and

$$csP(x, s) = -\frac{dQ(x, s)}{dx} + cP(x, 0) \tag{2.136}$$

Equations 2.135 and 2.136 can be differentiated with respect to x and combined so that the wave-equation form results:

$$\frac{d^2P(x, s)}{dx^2} = [(r + ms)cs]P(x, s) = n^2P(x, s) \tag{2.137}$$

$$\frac{d^2Q(x, s)}{dx^2} = [(r + ms)cs]Q(x, s) = n^2Q(x, s) \tag{2.138}$$

The parameter n is defined as the propagation operator and

$$n^2 = ZY \tag{2.139}$$

where

$$Z = r + ms \tag{2.140}$$

is the impedance per unit length of the line, and

$$Y + 0 + cs \tag{2.141}$$

is the admittance per unit length of the line. Thus

$$n = \sqrt{(ms + r)cs} \tag{2.142}$$

The wave-equation solution can be expressed in terms of functions of the variables s and x. Thus

$$P(x, s) = C_1 e^{-nx} + C_2 e^{nx} \tag{2.143}$$

$$= K_1 \cosh nx + K_2 \sinh nx \tag{2.143a}$$

$$Q(x, s) = C_3 e^{-nx} + C_4 e^{nx} \tag{2.144}$$

$$= [K_4 \sinh nx + K_3 \cosh nx] \tag{2.144a}$$

where $K_1 = C_1 + C_2$, $K_2 = C_2 - C_1$, $K_3 = C_3 + C_4$, and $K_4 = C_4 - C_3$.

The ordinary procedures of inverse transformation can be used on the right-hand side of eq. 2.143 and eq. 2.144 to obtain the time solution, provided the constants C_1, C_2, C_3, and C_4 in the equations are evaluated properly in terms of the initial values $P(x, 0)$, $Q(x, 0)$, and any other boundary conditions needed to completely define the specific problem.

The important parameter to study is n. How the value of n and the constants C_1, C_2, C_3, and C_4 vary with different physical system parameters and boundary values may often reveal the necessary conclusions to many studies.   In fact, it may not be necessary to solve the differential equations and put the result into the form of a time function in order to evaluate transient or frequency-response features of a process.

Long Pipe-Lines. For a long pipeline with r, m, and c per unit length, the general equations, eqs. 2.133 and 2.134, must take into account the nature of the source and the termination.

Case 1: Flow Source—Open Line

At $x = 0$, the flow $Q(0, s)$ is Q_p. At $x = L$, the pressure $P(L, s)$ is zero.   The undetermined coefficients K_1 and K_2 can be found to be

$$K_1 = P(0, s) \tag{2.145}$$

$$K_2 = -K_1 \frac{\cosh nL}{\sinh nL} \tag{2.146}$$

Therefore the flow throughout the line becomes

$$Q(x, s) = Q_p \frac{\sinh n(L - x)}{\sinh nL} \tag{2.147}$$

and the pressure is

$$P(x, s) = P(0, s) \frac{\sinh n(L - x)}{\sinh nL} \tag{2.148}$$

Case 2: Flow Source—Impedance Termination

This is a transmission-line problem frequently encountered in gas-plant layout, chemical reactor termination of pipelines, and in connection with instrumentation where signals are sent through pipelines by means of low-pressure air, and the signals terminate in a relay, valve, or bellows.

At $x = L$, the pressure and the flow are related by

$$P(L, s) = Z_T Q(L, s) \tag{2.149}$$

in particular, for the closed vessel $Z_T = \dfrac{1}{Cs}$, where $C = \dfrac{v}{B}$ For the

pressurized reactor vessel, $Z_T = \dfrac{1}{R_v Cs + 1}$, where $C = \dfrac{v}{B}$ and R_v is the throttle-valve resistance in the outflow line. At $x = 0$, the flow $Q(0, s)$ is Q_p. The undetermined coefficients become

$$K_1 = P(0, s) \tag{2.150}$$

and

$$K_2 = \frac{Q(L, s)Z_T - P(0, s)\cosh nL}{\sinh nL} \tag{2.151}$$

When K_1 and K_2 are used in the general equations and the algebra is simplified, the flow is

$$Q(x, s) = Q_p \frac{\sinh n(L - x)}{\sinh nL} + Q(L, s)\frac{\sinh nx}{\sinh nL} \tag{2.152}$$

$$P(x, s) = P(0, s) \frac{\sinh n(L - x)}{\sinh nL} + Q(L, s)Z_T\frac{\sinh nx}{\sinh nL} \tag{2.153}$$

Without difficulty, the technique used to determine eqs. 2.147, 2.148, 2.152, and 2.153 can be used to find the equations for vessels located in between two long lines, and for combinations of vessels and branched long-lines with different values of the r, m, and c parameters for each line.

Setting up the equations and determining the values of the undetermined coefficients is not the difficult part of the work. The solution of the transcendental characteristic equations so that a time solution can be obtained for specific situations is the more difficult aspect of the problem.

Short-Pipeline Formulae. The long-line equation is not always needed, once the general form of the long line equation is known and the wavelength of the sound traveling in the gaseous medium can be determined. *When the length of the pipe is short compared to the wave-length of sound traveling in the fluid, the hyperbolic form of solution to the wave equation can be approximated by allowing the cosine hyperbolic and the sine hyperbolic functions to be expanded in their infinite-series forms.* Then, if the first few terms in each series are taken, and if the remainder term and the convergence rate in the series is checked in terms of the parameter n as it depends upon the value of the line length L, it is possible to develop pressure and flow equations which are short-line approximations to the long line. The short-line equations can be developed as follows:

$$P(x, s) = K_1 \cosh nx + K_2 \sinh nx \tag{2.154}$$

$$Q(x, s) = K_3 \cosh nx + K_4 \sinh nx \tag{2.155}$$

but

$$\cosh nx = 1 + \frac{n^2 x^2}{2!} + \frac{n^4 x^4}{4!} \cdots \simeq 1 + \frac{n^2 x^2}{2!} \tag{2.156}$$

$$\sinh nx = nx + \frac{n^3 x^3}{3!} \cdots \simeq nx \tag{2.157}$$

Therefore

$$P(x, s) = K_1 \left(1 + \frac{n^2 x^2}{2!}\right) + K_2(nx) \tag{2.158}$$

$$Q(x, s) = K_3 \left(1 + \frac{n^2 x^2}{2!}\right) + K_4(nx) \tag{2.159}$$

are the short-line equations which are valid for $nx \ll 1$.

Velocity of Sound Propagation. The solution to the one-dimensional wave equation

$$\frac{\partial^2 P}{\partial x^2} = n^2 \frac{\partial^2 P}{\partial t^2} \tag{2.160}$$

has the traveling-wave form

$$P = f_1 \left(x - \frac{t}{n}\right) + f_2 \left(x + \frac{t}{n}\right) \tag{2.161}$$

The quantity n in eq. 2.160 has the units of reciprocal velocity. The value n is defined by

$$\frac{1}{n^2} = \frac{g\phi P_0}{\rho_0} \tag{2.162}$$

where $1/n$ is the velocity at which sound propagates through an unbounded gas of density ρ_0 and pressure P_0 under adiabatic conditions of compression (ϕ = specific heat ratio).

A similar result can be derived for the velocity of sound or wave propagation in the fluid contained in a pipe or tube with resistance r per unit length *zero*, but inertance m and capacitance c per unit length. Thus, in terms of the inertance m and the capacity c, the velocity of propagation becomes

$$\frac{1}{n} = \frac{1}{\sqrt{mc}} = \frac{1}{\sqrt{\left(\dfrac{\rho}{gA}\right)\left(\dfrac{v_o}{\gamma L P_0}\right)}} \tag{2.163}$$

Sound propagates in a tube or pipe with the same velocity as it does in unbounded or free-gas space, provided the wavelength of the sound with respect to the pipe diameter (that is, the ratio $\lambda : D$) is large. This will generally be true for industrial pipelines.

When liquid is used, the inertance m and the capacity c per unit length will differ, but these values can be put into the equation for velocity of propagation, and the result becomes

$$\frac{1}{n} = \frac{1}{\sqrt{mc}} = \frac{1}{\sqrt{\dfrac{\rho}{gA} \cdot \dfrac{v}{BL}}} = \sqrt{\frac{B}{\rho/g}} \tag{2.164}$$

where B is the bulk modulus of compression of the liquid, and ρ is the density of the fluid.

Characteristic Impedance. If the resistance r equals zero in an infinitely long pipeline, the characteristic impedance of the line becomes $Z_o = \sqrt{\dfrac{m}{c}}.$ When the signal which drives the line is a sinusoidally varying pressure or flow, the ratio of the pressure $P(x)$ to the flow $Q(x)$ at any point along the line is equal to the characteristic impedance.

Reflections

As long as the impedance of the line ahead of a wave is Z_o, the characteristic impedance, the wave will continue to move as if the pipeline were infinite in length, regardless of the nature of the equipment which actually initiates and terminates the line.

However, when the line is terminated in Z_T, which is not equal to the characteristic impedance Z_o, the incident wave will be reflected.

The reflection coefficient becomes

$$\mathcal{R} = \frac{\text{amplitude of reflected wave}}{\text{amplitude of incident wave}} = \frac{Z_T - Z_o}{Z_T + Z_o} \qquad (2.165)$$

Another form useful in calculations gives the termination impedance in terms of the reflection coefficient

$$Z_T = \left(\frac{1 + \mathcal{R}}{1 - \mathcal{R}}\right) Z_o \qquad (2.166)$$

When the reflection coefficient $\mathcal{R}$ is not zero (and it rarely will be for the types of pipelines and terminations found in industrial plants), standing waves can occur upon the lines; in particular, when the length of the line is an integer multiple of the half-wave length $\lambda/2$.

Reflections from a Tank. A typical termination to a pipeline is the tank or reactor vessel with volume capacity C beyond which is a valve with resistance R_v. The impedance is $Z_T = \dfrac{R_v}{j\omega\tau + 1}$, where $\tau = CR_v$. The reflection coefficient

$$\mathcal{R} = \frac{\dfrac{R_v}{Z_o} - 1 - j\omega\tau}{\dfrac{R_v}{Z_o} + 1 + j\omega\tau} \qquad (2.167)$$

obviously is not zero. The conclusion to be reached is: Volume capacity and a resistance termination will always give wave reflection. In fact, few industrial pipelines, flow sources, and terminating vessels can give $\mathcal{R}$ equal to zero.

13. SOME REMARKS ABOUT PLANT LAYOUT

The material presented in this chapter can be interpreted so that it has much bearing both upon the design of process equipment for plants *and* upon the layout of the plants themselves.

First, in the movement and handling of incompressible fluids, the dimensions of the tanks and vessels, the particular manner in which the vessels are interconnected by pipelines and the characteristics of the pumps and control valves and their specific location in the process determine the dynamic behavior of the processes.

Secondly, when compressible fluids are being processed, the dynamic response of pressure and flow regulation systems becomes especially influenced by the volume capacity of the process vessels and the inertance of the fluid in the pipelines. The volume capacity of the plant vessels and pipes ultimately limits the performance of the closed-loop control systems. Interaction of volume capacity and inertance in certain types of processes can give rise to resonance conditions which no automatic regulators can eliminate.

Thirdly, in processes and plants, gases and liquids constitute a continuous medium which has distributed resistance, volume capacity, and inertance. Unless particular attention is given the acoustic problems, traveling waves can be generated in the pipelines and they may reflect from the process vessels. Standing waves can occur. It becomes important to determine whether or not the harmonics generated in pumps and compressors will be troublesome. Provided the frequencies of periodic disturbances remain essentially constant, one can visualize that the layout of plants should be made so that the vessels and principal pieces of apparatus are located at the proper fractions of wavelengths from each other to cause the harmonics, standing waves, and traveling waves to disappear.

It appears safe to say that the cost of automatic control equipment in many plants might be considerably reduced if proper attention were given to the design of the process vessels and the manner of their interconnection. In fact, a saving in plant capital investment might be effected.

BIBLIOGRAPHY

Dynamical Analogies, Harry F. Olsen, D. Van Nostrand Co., New York, 1943.
Acoustics, Leo L. Beranek, McGraw-Hill Book Co., New York, 1954.
Analysis of Unsteady Fluid Flow Using Direct Electrical Analogs, S. E. Isakoff, *Ind. Eng. Chem.*, Part I, 413–421 (Mar. 1955).
M.I.T. Staff, Mechanical Engineering Dept., "Fluid Power Control." Notes prepared for a Special Summer School Course 1956. (To be published by Technology Press, John Wiley and Sons, Cambridge, Mass.)

CHAPTER 3

Forming, Propulsion, and Guidance

1. INTRODUCTION

The operations of extrusion and casting, as well as the purely mechanical actions of propelling and guiding various filaments and webs through industrial processes constitute another phase of processing. Molten material may be extruded through a sharp-edged orifice, chilled as it emerges, and propelled through further operations—such as heat treating, drawing, perforating, or twisting (as in the case of thread or cable winding). Solid granular materials and highly viscous liquids are frequently formed into filaments and sheets upon which mechanical work is done until a hardened web or filament results.

Web and filament materials generally obey Hooke's law of elastic deformation when they are being stretched under the action of forces. However, plastic flow may take place if the force level becomes high enough to exceed the shear strength of the material. Permanent deformations of the stressed material may appear. The deformation may be deliberate in drawing operations.

Moving webs, and certainly moving filaments, have little mass compared with the mass of the rolls which drive them. Consequently, tension control constitutes a problem in the mechanics of elastically coupled inertia members. Several different speed or position regulators may be coupled together by an elastic web which passes through a cascade of processes. The stabilization of web propulsion systems requires that special attention be given to the generation and the application to the web of damping forces.

Webs move sidewise as they are propelled through industrial operations, because of the imperfections in the rolls which guide them, because of the variable tension in the web materials, and because of the processing action taken upon the webs. The sidewise drift of a web can be canceled by proper manipulatory action taken on pivot rolls or rolls which are themselves capable of sidewise movement. The control action in itself, however, may not bring about the stability of the web in lateral movement in a multi-roll guiding system, unless the guiding system itself has the possibility of inherent dynamic mechanical stability, or unless special types of damping forces can be generated and put into action.

Thorough study of the field of forming, guiding, and deforming of materials cannot be undertaken in this book. A survey of the problems is made, and a discussion is made of extrusion, propulsion of webs, tension control, and web guidance. The subjects of plastic flow, rolling, and drawing are not treated. The mathematical description of the transient and dynamic aspects of these subjects cannot be presented because, to my knowledge, the physics itself is not sufficiently well known. This chapter should be regarded as an introduction to a subject which requires considerably more study.

2. EXTRUSION AND CASTING

Many industrial processes involve the formation of a continuous filament or web of material—such as glass, aluminum, or plastic. A supply of raw material is maintained in a proper environment in a hold-up reservoir. Flow from the reservoir passes through orifices or dies to form the filaments or webs.

When hydraulic pressure forces the material to flow through the die, the process is called extrusion. Casting, on the other hand, generally involves the flow of molten material in shaping dies, under the action of gravity. When ingots are cast, the operation is a batch process. Continuous casting takes place when the molten material is continuously poured and the solidified "ingot" is continuously removed. Both solid flow and liquid flow enter extruders; but when a material is cast, the flow is liquid.

The thermal processes associated with extrusion and casting are hard to treat in a quantitative mathematical way, because of the difficulty in expressing exactly what goes on in the material. A screw extruder may heat a solid material by sufficient frictional energy dissipation within the material to make it melt by the time it passes down the screw and enters a die. Alternatively, a molten material in a highly viscous state may enter the screw and leave the die as a free-flowing fluid, to be chilled immediately afterward by a quenching bath.

Dies are frequently heat exchangers. External heat may be applied to the screw and the die. In the process of casting, the die heat exchanger may have to remove heat from the cast object so that flow can come out of the die as a solid. Material which is cast, for example, in the continuous casting of metal must be sufficiently chilled in the die so that the emerging material has a solid surface. However, the core of the material may frequently be still molten.

Heat exchange in dies must take place rapidly enough to insure the melting or the solidification of the material. Generally the melting of solids to form liquids must be total, but the solidification of liquids to form solids need be only at the surface, to a depth enough to hold the body of the material in shape. The middle of a continuously cast section may remain molten and require a considerable amount of additional heat extraction before the whole object becomes solid.

Figure 3.1 shows typical screw extrusion, pressure extrusion, single-roll casting, and continuous die casting.

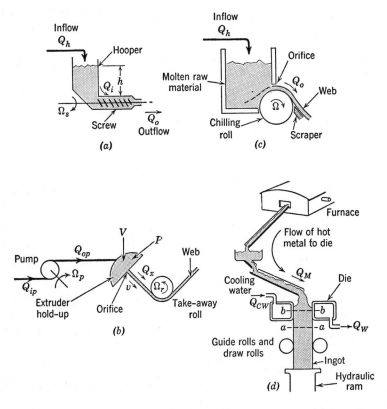

Fig. 3.1. (a) Screw extruder; (b) Pressure extruder; (c) Single-roll casting; (d) Continuous metal casting.

Screw Extruders. Screw extruders generally do not have much hold-up of raw material in the threads of the screw   Mechanical work delivers a supply of raw material from the intake end of the screw to the die.   The power lost in the screw because of mechanical inefficiency may serve to heat the fluid which is carried along in the threads toward the die.

Table 3.1 shows three arrangements of screw extruders.   The screw is the same in each case.   In item 1, the screw extruder is fed with a flow Q_i, has no hold-up, and delivers a flow Q_o through the die.   The

TABLE 3.1.   SCREW EXTRUDERS

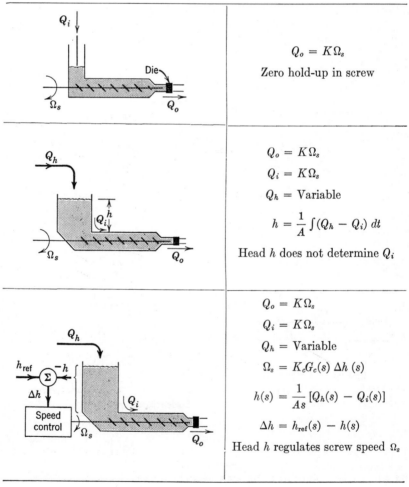

$$Q_o = K\Omega_s$$

Zero hold-up in screw

$$Q_o = K\Omega_s$$
$$Q_i = K\Omega_s$$
$$Q_h = \text{Variable}$$
$$h = \frac{1}{A} \int (Q_h - Q_i)\, dt$$

Head h does not determine Q_i

$$Q_o = K\Omega_s$$
$$Q_i = K\Omega_s$$
$$Q_h = \text{Variable}$$
$$\Omega_s = K_c G_c(s)\, \Delta h\,(s)$$
$$h(s) = \frac{1}{As} [Q_h(s) - Q_i(s)]$$
$$\Delta h = h_{\text{ref}}(s) - h(s)$$

Head h regulates screw speed Ω_s

delivery of material through the die will be proportional to the speed of the screw. Thus

$$Q_o = K\Omega_s \tag{3.1}$$

The second item shows a reservoir of material prior to the screw feed point. A flow Q_h goes into the hold-up. The flow into the screw is Q_i, and the flow through the die is Q_o. If the head h in the hold-up does not in any way influence the hydrodynamics of the flow through the die (and it rarely does), once again the outflow Q_o is proportional to the speed of the die Ω_s. However, the head h will build up or decline as the inflow to the hopper Q_h exceeds the inflow Q_i to the screw, or vice versa. The variation in h is an inventory matter and has nothing to do with extrusion itself, except that the variation in the hold-up may interfere with the rate of melting of the material prior to the flow into the screw, in some types of liquid-feed extruders.

The third item in the table shows a level control used as a speed adjustment on the screw. The level h in the hold-up reservoir is measured, compared with a reference, and the incremental change in head Δh is used to energize the speed control which drives the screw. In this type of system the flow through the die is a function of the head. Actually, the process turns out to be a first-order type of lag process which has already been discussed.

Ordinarily, liquid-level control cannot be used to control the flow from a screw extruder if the caliper of the material coming from the screw is important. However, there are many industrial applications where the screw extruder converts a bulk raw material into a filament or web which can be more readily handled and processed. The filament dimensions may be of no importance. Therefore, to keep the extruder running smoothly and without stoppage, the liquid level may fluctuate and cause the screw to speed up or slow down accordingly.

Precision extrusion requires that the dimensions of the extruded material be kept accurate. The dimension which determines the caliper may have to be measured and control the speed of extrusion as well as the thermal and viscosity aspects of the extrusion operation.

Pressure Extrusion. Extrusion of a material takes place through a die because of hydraulic pressure which is maintained ahead of the die in a flow process. Figure 3.1b shows a pump which operates at a speed Ω_p, taking up a flow Q_{ip}, and delivering a flow Q_{op} to an extruder. The volume in the extruder V contains the material to be extruded. The vessel may be of steel; nevertheless, it may exhibit elastic expansion. The material to be extruded may have compressibility, so that the bulk modulus of compression is B.

The flow Q_x through the orifice determines the outflow from the pressure vessel. The flow Q_{op} comes into the extruder. The extruder pressure varies as

$$V_o \left(\frac{1}{B+K} \right) \frac{dP}{dt} = Q_{op} - Q_x \tag{3.2}$$

Equation 3.2 accounts for the compression of the material to be extruded and for the elastic effects in the extruder vessel. The term K may be regarded as an equivalent coefficient of volumetric expansion. The flow Q_x out of the orifice is a function of the pressure. However, the flow will be laminar, since the material is highly viscous, so that the relationships for Q_x can be linearized as in Chapter 2, section 2. Thus

$$Q_x = K_o P \tag{3.3}$$

and combining eq. 3.3 with eq. 3.2 gives the differential equation

$$V_o \left(\frac{1}{B+K} \right) \frac{dP}{dt} + K_o P = Q_{op} \tag{3.4}$$

which expresses how the pressure in the extruder varies as a function of the flow to the extruder.

Beyond the orifice the flow is generally "pulled away," but the flow Q_x is generally not a function of the take-away velocity v of the web or filament except when the take-away velocity becomes great enough to "neck the material down" as it emerges from the orifice. Thus the outflow stream does not disturb the extruder operation. However, fluctuations or transients in the inflow alter the pressure $P(t)$ and do interfere with the smoothness of operation of the extruder. According to eq. 3.4, the time constant for the extruder is

$$\tau = \frac{V_o}{K_o(B+K)} \tag{3.5}$$

This time constant determines the extent to which fluctuations in the inflow Q_{op} will be attenuated as they pass through the filtering action of the volume capacity of the extruder. With unregulated pressure in the extruder, it will be necessary for the extruder to have a relatively large time constant in order that the fluctuations in pump flow shall be sufficiently muffled so that they do not cause "corrugating" effects in the extrusion.

Ordinarily when a non-Newtonian material, such as a plastic, is extruded through a sharp-edged orifice, the final dimension of thickness or diameter may not be the same as the minimum dimension at the orifice. There tends to be a viscous-elastic effect: Before extrusion, the pressure compresses the material; after extrusion, the material relaxes to its dimensions at atmospheric pressure. The relaxation is not necessarily instantaneous.

The rate at which the web is taken away from the orifice will influence the final caliper of the material, provided the chilling of the web does not take place so rapidly as it emerges from the die or orifice that the material solidifies before the process of drawing can influence the thickness. The extremes would be to have the material pulled away so rapidly and with such force that the web ruptures just outside the die; or to have the take-away so slow that the material drops freely into a chilling vat without being drawn at all, because it is under a condition of zero tension.

The first extreme must be avoided, but the second is used as a practical extrusion operation in many processes. A good practice is to have the take-away roll, as shown in Fig. 3.1b, rotate at a speed Ω_r which will remove the web material as rapidly as it can be solidified in the chilling vat, and will exert only a small amount of forward tension on the solidifying material. Coordinated speed control, extrusion, and melting may be required.

Practically no quantitative information is available to describe the dynamic nature of plastic flow. Therefore, a study of drawing in conjunction with extrusion will not be attempted. In sections 3 and 6 later in this chapter the information available about rolling and drawing material will be discussed and evaluated.

Casting. Certain kinds of material are cast upon rotating drums. Figure 3.1c shows a reservoir of materials which is so arranged that an outflow takes place on a rotating drum at the bottom of the reservoir. The side of the reservoir serves as the top edge of the orifice; the rotating drum is the bottom edge. The material is carried out of the hold-up tank on the drum, and is scraped free by a knife blade a short distance beyond the point at which the flow emerges.

The drum may chill the emerging web, or the web which is freed from the drum may drop into a reservoir of cold liquid so that the web solidifies. To some extent, the removal of viscous fluid by means of the rotating drum is a matter of scraping the molten layer from a chilled layer that is in contact with the drum. The process appears to be more a process of "drag flow" in contact with the roll than of orifice extrusion. Therefore, the flow out of a roll extruder will be approximately proportional to the peripheral speed of the drum. The head of fluid in the reservoir will have little influence on the outflow unless the orifice dimensions are large.

Another arrangement of casting liquid frequently encountered in the metals-processing industry is shown in Fig. 3.1d. A furnace delivers molten metal, such as aluminum, to a small reservoir through a cermaic or asbestos pipe. From the small reservoir, a regulated flow goes to a die. The die is a heat exchanger which extracts sufficient heat from the molten material to chill its surface so that the solid surface will retain the molten interior. As the surface solidifies, a hydraulic ram or equivalent device slowly moves the metal through the die. At the bottom of the die, at line aa in Fig. 3.1d, there is a solid-surface section of cast material moving out of the die which contains a molten core. At the top, at point bb, a molten pool of material receives a continuous flow of molten material.

Two casting procedures can be followed. After a specified length of extruded metal has been obtained, the molten liquid metal flow to the die can be stopped or diverted to another die, and an ingot can be obtained. · Alternatively, the continuous casting of the molten metal is possible. Once the flow has started, and the energing solid can be mechanically handled, the hydraulic ram can be moved away and drive rolls can be brought into contact with the sides of the emerging section. The velocity of take-away from the die can be adjusted by the rolls so that the rate of removal will be correct in relation to the flow of molten metal to the die and the rate of heat exchange between the metal and the cooling water.

Regulation of continuous casting requires simultaneous control over fluid flow and heat exchange. The unusual physical properties that molten metals exhibit when they are being handled as fluids in a flow system cause the regulation problem to be difficult. The thermal-process lags generally tend to be very great compared to the dynamic effects of the flow process. Nevertheless, the regulation of flow to the die, the removal of material from the die, and the heat exchange control can be accomplished with relatively simple control and regulatory equipment.

The critical aspects of process control and regulation over casting relate to our knowledge of the dynamics of the metallurgical process, especially the cooling and solidification dynamics. The design of heat-exchange dies to give optimum rates of heat transfer at the surface contact between the molten metal, the metal of the die, and the cooling water, must be given considerable attention if tight continuous control is to be obtained over continuous casting, especially if the casting is to take place at high speeds.

3. WEB PROPULSION

After filaments and webs have been formed, they are propelled. Through some processing operations they must move at constant velocity, despite external forces or disturbances imparted to them. For other processing operations, special time-varying speed patterns may be required. Variable web speed is often desirable so that the throughput of one process can be matched with the throughput of another process in a cascade system.

Starting and stopping the movement of a web can be an important phase of propulsion. A coordinated action is required between the web-forming operation and the propelling-machinery control. Stopping a web for any length of time requires that the extruder which forms the web must stop. Starting a web in motion may require that extrusion begin first; and that after a successful web has been formed, the web must be threaded through a sequence of guiding rolls and propelling equipment.

The winding-up of rolls of finished or partly finished product, the transporting of the rolls to another point in a process, and the unwinding of them are a frequently encountered intermittent operation. For example: In the manufacture of corrugated board, three sheets of paper arrive at the corrugating machine in the form of tightly wound rolls, each of which may weigh a ton or more. The two surface sheets unwind and pass into the machine above and below the central sheet, which goes through a crinkling die and gluing operation. The corrugating operation must be started, run, and stopped as the rolls of paper are used up.

Propulsion is brought about by engaging with the web of material, drive rolls—generally called pinch rolls. These rolls are connected to motors whose speed can be varied and whose torque and power level can be adjusted so that the motors can accelerate, decelerate, or continuously propel the web or filament. Sometimes several consecutive sets of pinch rolls are needed in a large process. The different sets of drive rolls are maintained in speed synchronism for propulsion. They may have a speed gradient for combined propulsion and rolling or drawing.

A section of slack web between the rolls may hang loosely in processing baths or soaking pits such as might be found in textile dyeing operations or in steel strip cleaning. Weighted rolls may be attached to webs so that the webs remain taut as they move forward. Except for extreme conditions of acceleration and deceleration, weighted rolls produce tension in webs proportional to a fraction of the dead weight of the roll. Dancer rolls are also used to hold a web in a taut condition as it is propelled through various machines.   The object of the dancer roll is to prevent the web from bouncing, vibrating, or snapping into a taut condition from a slack one.   Both the weighted roll and the dancer roll tend to be self-regulating tension schemes (whose performance is rather limited) superimposed upon the propulsion system.

Register is another problem related to web propulsion.   In printing,

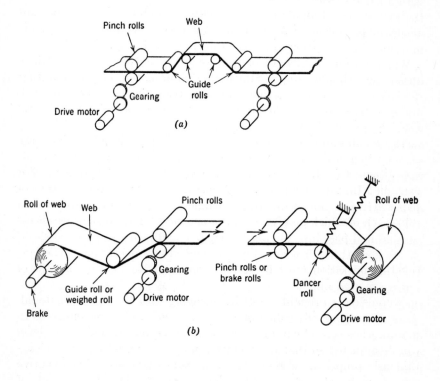

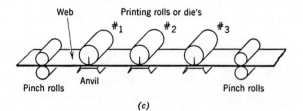

Fig. 3.2.   (a) Pinch rolls and guide rolls in a web-propulsion system; (b) Unwind and upwind systems; (c) Illustration of the register problem.

especially where multi-color operations occur, the exact position of a web may be required to synchronize in time with the positions of consecutive printing rolls or dies which strike the web. Speed-control machinery alone is generally not adequate for providing good register control. A positional type of supervisory control is often needed to coordinate and reset the action of the speed regulators.

As a roll is wound up at the terminal end of a process, the roll starts with a small core diameter. As the diameter increases, the tension in the web of material will tend to increase also. Should the web in the machine suddenly break or for some reason become slack, the prime mover which is winding the roll will tend to accelerate.

When a roll of material is being unwound in a steady throughput condition, and the process is suddenly stopped, the moment of inertia of the roll of web will cause the roll to continue to unwind. Often a brake is put on an unwind roll to regulate the forward motion of the web. Transients in process throughput can cause the unwind roll to accelerate, in which case the web may become slack in the guide-roll system. Then, if the brake is applied to the unwind roll with improper time phase, the unwind roll can stop suddenly, with the result that the web will snap against the guide roll and possibly break under the condition of severe tension which develops.

Figure 3.2 shows the rudimentary schematic drawings which define propulsion of webs, winding and unwinding, and register.

4. SPEED REGULATION

Propelling machinery, pinch rolls, and wind-up reels must maintain their speed constant under fluctuating loads, or they must adjust their speed to accomplish time-varying patterns of production. The yields of a process, and hence the costs of production, may be contingent upon the continuity of production, so that start-up and shutdown must be brought about with optimum acceleration patterns to minimize the down-time.

A variety of speed regulators can be used in web-propelling operations. Electric, mechanical, and hydraulic machinery, as well as various combinations of all three, make up speed controllers and regulators. The speed regulation can be open-loop control in which the self-regulating properties of the motors are used to regulate the speed of the web or to prevent the speed from drifting under slight changes in tension and consequent load on the motors. However, the feedback type of speed regulator becomes superior in performance where rapid as well as precise adjustment of speed and tension conditions is necessary.

To obtain precision regulation of speed generally requires an integral

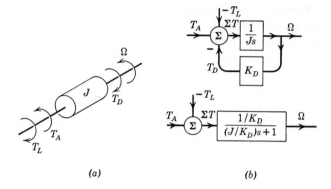

Fig. 3.3.   Self-regulation of speed.   (a) Fly wheel with damping; (b) Block diagram of applied torque and load torque.

and quantitative design of the propelling machinery and the process. Both optimum static and optimum dynamic features of performance must be sought.

Self-Regulation of Speed.   Consider that a flywheel with moment of inertia J represents the rotating member whose speed Ω is to be regulated.   The only way that the flywheel speed can change from initial angular velocity Ω_o will be as the result of a manipulative torque T_A, a load-disturbance torque T_L, or a friction torque T_D applied to the flywheel.

The transfer function $\dfrac{\Omega(s)}{\Sigma T(s)}$ for the flywheel is an integration $1/Js$. A flywheel characterized as an integration will experience a runaway in speed for a sustained torque unbalance.   However, the presence of a damping torque in motors, engines, or the mechanical member which includes the flywheel, tends to establish a negative-feedback type of damping action upon the flywheel speed and prevents it from experiencing great speed changes under sustained unbalanced torques.   The lag operator $\dfrac{1}{\tau s + 1}$, where $\tau = J/K_D$ characterizes the response of a flywheel of inertia J whose motion is opposed by a viscous-friction torque $T_D = K_D \Omega$.   The damping torque T_D serves to *self-regulate* the flywheel against speed changes under the action of load disturbances T_L.

According to the block diagram of Fig. 3.3b, the applied torque T_A is opposed by both the load torque T_L and the damping torque T_D. The net torque ΣT accelerates the flywheel.   The damping torque is a negative feedback, a degenerative torque component in ΣT. However, because the magnitude of K_D tends to be small in most efficient prime movers, self-regulation of flywheel speed Ω under the action of damping torques T_D will not be very good.

For the self-regulated speed system, the dynamic response is determined by

$$\Omega = \left[\frac{1/K_D}{\tau s + 1}\right](T_A - T_L) \tag{3.6}$$

The static response is determined when $s \to 0$. Thus

$$\Omega = \frac{1}{K_D} T_L \tag{3.7}$$

Since K_D is small, $1/K_D$—which is called the *static sensitivity* of speed change to load-torque change—tends to be large. Thus the flywheel speed Ω *is* sensitive to disturbance T_L.

Figure 3.4 shows the dynamic response $\Omega(t)$ for a step function of load disturbance applied to the self-regulated flywheel. The transient

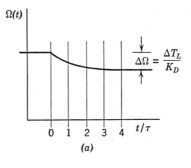

(a)

Fig. 3.4.   (a) Response of a self-regulated speed system; (b) Static "droop" of a self-regulated speed system.

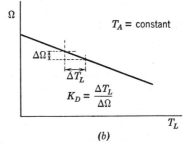

(b)

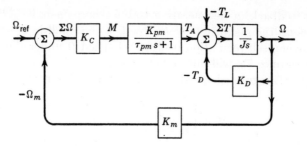

Fig. 3.5. Block diagram for feedback-type speed regulator.

response $\Omega(t)$ is typical of the first-order system. The time constant $\tau = J/K_D$ governs the locus of the curve.

Self-regulation of speed by means of the damping torque T_D has two limitations. First, a power loss is associated with the damping torque, and hence there is a detraction from the efficiency of the prime mover. Secondly, speed regulation under the action of damping torques is not very effective, and it can be uncertain. The precision of regulation depends upon the magnitude of the damping constant K_D. Since K_D tends to be a function of the friction and losses in a machine, it is subject to variation which may give erratic control of the machine speed.

Feedback Regulation of Speed. Next consider that a closed-loop speed regulator is developed. The speed Ω is measured by a speed detector. The signal Ω_m is fed back and compared with a reference speed Ω_{ref}. The error in speed ε_Ω energizes whatever control mechanisms exist for producing the manipulation M on the engine or motor which drives the flywheel. The manipulation M may be a voltage, in the case of an electric-motor drive; it may be steam pressure in the steam chest, in the case of a steam engine; it may be the stroke setting on the variable-displacement pump of a variable-speed hydraulic drive.

The manipulation M produces the torque T_A, which adjusts the speed Ω. The block diagram for the closed-loop speed regulator is shown in Fig. 3.5. On the assumption that instantaneous measurement of speed can be made, and that amplifiers—regardless of their type—can be made to have rapid response compared with that of the mechanical member, we may assume that the measured speed Ω_m and the actual speed Ω are identical. Thus the speed-detector sensitivity $K_m = 1$.

The manipulation signal M generated per unit of the error ε_Ω can be defined by a constant K_C which designates that the manipulation

M is proportional to the error in speed. However, a *time lag* will be associated with the generation of torque T_A in any type of prime mover. This lag cannot be avoided. It originates in the internal energy storage and losses of the prime mover. The relationship between the manipulating signal M and the torque T_A becomes, in general,

$$\frac{T_A(s)}{M(s)} = \frac{K_{pm}}{\tau_{pm}s + 1} \tag{3.8}$$

If the time constant τ_{pm} of the prime mover is small compared with the time constant of the mechanical member $\tau_m = J/K_D$, the dynamic response of the regulator becomes

$$\Omega(s) \simeq \left[\frac{\left(\dfrac{K_C K_{pm}}{K_D + K_C K_{pm}}\right)}{\dfrac{\tau_m}{\left(1 + \dfrac{K_C K_{pm}}{K_D}\right)}s + 1} \right] \Omega_{\text{ref}}(s)$$

$$- \left[\frac{\dfrac{1}{K_D + K_C K_{pm}}}{\dfrac{\tau_m}{\left(1 + \dfrac{K_C K_{pm}}{K_D}\right)}s + 1} \right] T_L(s) \tag{3.9}$$

$$\Omega(s) \simeq \left(\frac{K_o}{\tau_o s + 1}\right) \Omega_{\text{ref}}(s) - \left(\frac{\dfrac{K_o}{K_C K_{pm}}}{\tau_o s + 1}\right) T_L(s) \tag{3.10}$$

Equation 3.10 indicates that the flywheel speed Ω will change as a function of the load torque T_L and as a function of the reference signal Ω_{ref}. The first term in eq. 3.10 indicates the speed *control* action; the second term, the speed *regulation*.

Speed regulation can be studied by arbitrarily assuming that the reference level is $\Omega_{\text{ref}} = 0$ or a constant. A study of small changes $\Delta\Omega$ in speed for small changes ΔT_L in the torque T_L shows how well the regulator can hold the speed constant. If a sustained load-torque increment ΔT_L is applied as a step disturbance to the system, the speed will change by the increment $\Delta\Omega$ according to the relationship

$$\Delta\Omega(s) = -\left(\frac{\dfrac{K_o}{K_C K_{pm}}}{\tau_o s + 1}\right)\left(\frac{\Delta T_L}{s}\right) \tag{3.11}$$

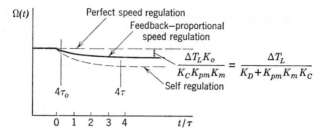

Fig. 3.6. Comparison of the dynamic response for feedback and self-regulation of speed.

In the steady state the speed of the flywheel will droop under a load torque linearly according to a straight-line relationship

$$\frac{\Delta\Omega}{\Delta T_L} = -\frac{K_o}{K_C K_{pm}} = -\left[\frac{1}{K_D\left(1 + \dfrac{K_C K_{pm}}{K_D}\right)}\right] \qquad (3.12)$$

Figures 3.6 and 3.7 show the dynamic transient response and the static response of the feedback regulator compared with the self-regulating scheme.

Proportional Types of Speed Regulators Always Have Drooping Speed under Load. Both their static and their dynamic performance show some improvement over the self-regulated speed system. However the loop gain can rarely be made high enough for good proportional regulation to result.

The performance of the simple speed regulator can be studied by means of frequency response plotted as asymptote magnitude and phase versus frequency graphs. On the coordinates of decibels versus

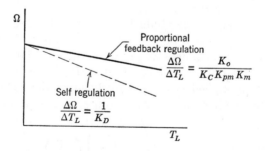

Fig. 3.7. Comparison of static response feedback and self-regulation of speed.

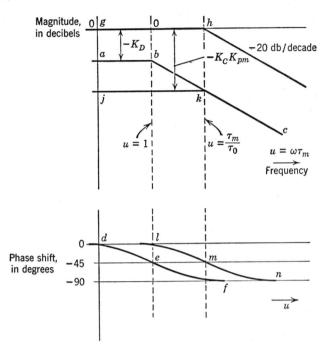

Fig. 3.8. Asymptote study of speed regulator with a single time lag $\tau_0 = J/K_D$.

frequency ju, in Fig. 3.8, the curve abc represents the open-loop unregulated characteristic $\dfrac{\Omega(ju)}{T_L(ju)}$. When the loop is closed, curve ghi—having slope sequence 0 and -20 decibels per decade—represents the follow-up response $\dfrac{\Omega(ju)}{\Omega_{\text{ref}}(ju)}$.

When the gain K_cK_{pm} is known, the curve for the speed variation under load disturbance $\dfrac{\Omega(ju)}{T_L(ju)}$ offsets, from the curve ghi, a negative-decibel distance K_cK_{pm}. This produces curve jkc, which is the closed-loop regulatory response under load disturbance.

The asymptote study shows that the unregulated response has a perfection of static performance determined by the magnitude of the damping coefficient K_D. The closed-loop speed regulator has a static precision of regulation determined by the gain K_cK_{pm}, which is the gain of the mechanisms between the error signal and the torque signal in the closed loop. A general rule develops from this observation which is applicable to all closed-loop speed control: The gain between the error and the point of application of the load must be high in order to have good static speed regulation.

In this particular study, since there is only one lag, the gain $K_C K_{pm}$ can be increased theoretically without limit. However, the fact that a second time constant generally occurs in the prime mover will basically limit the gain that can be used in the proportional type of speed regulator.

The phase curve *def* in Fig. 3.8 is an arc-tangent function. The value $\tan^{-1} u\tau$ progresses from zero phase shift to -90 degrees over the frequency range $0 < u < \infty$. The phase curve indicates that at low frequencies the speed responds in phase agreement with periodic load disturbances, but that at high frequencies the speed changes will lag 90 degrees behind the torque wave. When the closed-loop gain is increased, the shape of the phase curve does not change, but the -45-degree point changes to the frequency $u = 1/\tau_o$ rather than remaining at the frequency $u = 1/K_D$ for the unregulated system.

If the time constants τ_{pm} and τ_m are *comparable in magnitude*, the open-loop transfer function for the feedback regulator becomes

$$\frac{\Omega(s)}{\mathcal{E}_\Omega(s)} = K_C K_{pm} \frac{1}{K_D} \left(\frac{1}{\tau_{pm}s + 1}\right)\left(\frac{1}{\tau_m s + 1}\right) \tag{3.13}$$

The fact that the open loop is characterized by two time lags means that the closed loop will be characterized by a quadratic function. Thus the closed-loop dynamic response is

$$\left.\frac{\Omega(s)}{T_L(s)}\right|_{\Omega_{\text{ref}}=0} = -\frac{\left(\dfrac{\dfrac{1}{K_D}}{\tau_m s + 1}\right)}{1 + K_C K_{pm} K_D^{-1}\left(\dfrac{1}{\tau_{pm}s + 1}\right)\left(\dfrac{1}{\tau_m s + 1}\right)} \tag{3.14}$$

which can be written in terms of the parameters τ and ζ as

$$\frac{\Omega(s)}{T_L(s)} = -\frac{\left(\dfrac{1}{K_C K_{pm}}\right)(\tau_{pm}s + 1)}{\tau^2 s^2 + 2\zeta\tau s + 1} \tag{3.15}$$

where

$$\tau = \left[\frac{\tau_{pm}\tau_m}{1 + \dfrac{K_C K_{pm}}{K_D}}\right]^{1/2} \tag{3.16}$$

$$\zeta = \frac{\tau_{pm} + \tau_m}{2\left[1 + \dfrac{K_c K_{pm}}{K_D}\right]^{\frac{1}{2}} [\tau_{pm}\tau_m]^{\frac{1}{2}}} \qquad (3.17)$$

The damping ratio ζ will be limited in value, because a speed regulator of the feedback type should not exhibit a prolonged transient in the speed resulting from a sudden application of load torque. The practical range for damping ratio ζ for most designs of speed regulators would be $0.5 < \zeta < 1.5$. The value of ζ along with the values of τ_{pm} and τ_m determines approximately the gain $K_c K_{pm}/K_D$ that can be used in the closed-loop system characterized by two lags.

An asymptote study can be developed for the speed control which has two lags. It is shown in Fig. 3.9. Curve $abcd$ is the asymptote for the open-loop magnitude $\Omega(ju)/\mathcal{E}(ju)$ with unity gain. At point b the frequency u_1 is the reciprocal of the mechanical time constant τ_m. At point c, the frequency u_2 is the reciprocal of the prime-mover time constant τ_{pm}. The phase curve efg represents the $-\tan^{-1} u\tau_m$. The $-45°$ value lies at the break frequency u_1. The phase curve hij

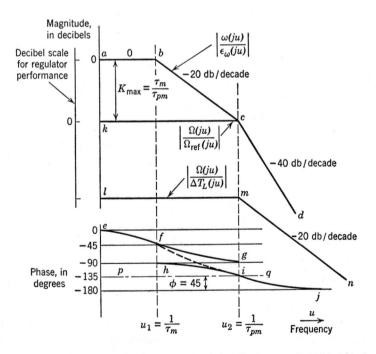

Fig. 3.9. Asymptote study for speed regulator with two time lags and proportional-action.

represents $-\tan^{-1} u\tau_{mp}$ and is symmetrical about the second break frequency u_2. The total phase curve $efij$ is the sum of the phase curves efg and hij. The phase curve $efij$ is the mate to the magnitude asymptote curve $abcd$.

The line pq, which corresponds to a phase margin of 45 degrees, intersects the phase curve $efij$ at the frequency $u \simeq 1/\tau_{pm}$. The projection of the intersection point i to the magnitude curve $abcd$ at point c, and then horizontally to the left to the decibel ordinant value at point k, determines the maximum gain of the closed loop K_{max}. The value for K_{max} is approximately equal to the ratio of the two time constants: thus, $K_{max} \simeq \tau_m/\tau_{pm}$. The curve kcd represents the closed-loop speed of the output with respect to the reference $\dfrac{\Omega(ju)}{\Omega_{ref}(ju)}$. This curve corresponds to the $\dfrac{KG}{1 + KG}$ form for a closed loop. To modify kcd so that the regulator response can be drawn, it becomes necessary to multiply $\dfrac{KG}{1 + KG}$ by the transfer function which lies between the error point and the torque point. Thus,

$$\frac{\Omega(ju)}{T_L(ju)} = \left[\frac{KG}{1 + KG}\right] \times \frac{(ju\tau_{pm} + 1)}{K_C K_{pm}} \tag{3.18}$$

Thus curve kcd modified by the factor $\dfrac{ju\tau_{pm} + 1}{K_C K_{pm}}$ becomes curve lmn drawn on the asymptote diagram. Curve lmn is lowered from curve kcd, provided the value K_D is small, and $K_C K_{pm}$ is greater than τ_{pm}/τ_m.

The regulator response lmn looks like the follow-up response kcd. However, point l is at a distance down from point k which corresponds to $K_C K_{pm}$ decibels. At high frequencies the response for the regulator attenuates at -20 db per decade, in contrast to the follow-up curve, which attenuates at -40 db per decade.

The magnitude curve lmn in Fig. 3.9 and the curve jkc in Fig. 3.8 are the comparative performance of the speed regulator with one time lag and no limitation on its gain because of stability, in the case of Fig. 3.8, and a speed regulator with two time lags upon which there is a limitation on the maximum closed-loop gain as determined by the 45-degree margin criterion.

For improvement in closed-loop speed regulators, beyond this development—and there will always be improvement needed, because unless the time-constant ratio τ_m/τ_{pm} is very large, the gain in the system will be limited—it will be necessary to employ compensation techniques.

Improvement by Compensation. A speed regulator must have an integration $1/s$ located ahead of the point at which the load T_L disturbs the regulator, if the speed regulator is to exhibit zero speed droop under a sustained load torque. The insertion of an integration $1/s$ ahead of the torque summation point, and after the error measuring point in the speed regulator, shown in Fig. 3.5, puts a zero for $s = 0$ in the numerator of the response function $\Omega(s)/T_L(s)$. Thus

$$\frac{\Delta\Omega}{\Delta T_L} = \frac{\dfrac{1}{K_D}[s(\tau_{pm}s + 1)]}{\left[s(\tau_m s + 1)(\tau_{pm}s + 1) + \left(\dfrac{K_{pm}K_C}{K_D}\right)\right]} \tag{3.19}$$

Equation 3.19 shows that $\dfrac{\Delta\Omega}{\Delta T_L}$ has a value which reduces to zero as $s \to 0$. This condition guarantees zero steady-state speed droop under sustained torque load. In other words, *perfect* static speed regulation results.

However, the insertion of an integration $1/s$ can cause difficulties with regulator stabilization. The integration $1/s$ makes the open-loop transfer function have a pole at the origin of the s-plane in addition to two other poles on the negative real axis caused by the time lags τ_m and τ_{pm}. The amount of loop gain which the system can have is therefore limited. In fact, the specific condition for *absolute stability* is:

$$(\tau_m + \tau_{pm}) - \tau_{pm}\tau_m\left(1 + \frac{K_{pm}K_C}{K_D}\right) \geq 0 \tag{3.20}$$

so that the maximum allowable gain is

$$\frac{K_{pm}K_C}{K_D} \leq \frac{\tau_m + \tau_{pm}}{\tau_{pm}\tau_m} - 1 \tag{3.21}$$

For $\dfrac{\tau_m}{\tau_{pm}} = 10$ and $\tau_m = 1.0$, $\dfrac{K_{pm}K_C}{K_D} \leq 10$, which is definitely not adequate gain, especially if K_D is small, to provide precision regulation of speed under varying load disturbances.

The manipulation can be made to have *proportional-plus-integral* or *undercompensated integral* action with respect to the error signal. Both of these control actions stiffen the speed regulator against load disturbance; yet each can preserve its dynamic stability when it is properly adjusted. Between the error signal and the manipulation signal in the control member, a mechanism can be inserted which has the proportional-plus-integral action. Thus

$$\frac{M(s)}{\mathcal{E}(s)} - K_c G_c(s) = K_1 + \frac{K_2}{s} \tag{3.22}$$

$$= K_3 \left(\frac{\tau_i s + 1}{s} \right) \tag{3.23}$$

When the integral action K_2/s cannot be obtained, the undercompensated-integral action can be used, so that

$$\frac{M(s)}{\mathcal{E}(s)} = K_4 \left(\frac{\tau_c s + 1}{\tau_d s + 1} \right) \tag{3.24}$$

The comparative merits of the compensating procedures are:

(1) The proportional-plus-integral type of compensation puts a pole at the origin of the complex plane for the open-loop transfer function. This pole is located ahead of the torque summation point. Therefore the static performance of this type of regulator will show zero droop under sustained load torque. The fact that the asymptote curve $l'm'a'c'z$ shown in Fig. 3.10 approaches $-\infty$ decibels as $\omega \to 0$ also shows the same condition of static performance.

The loop gain $K_{\max}$ will be the same with proportional-plus-integral compensation as for the uncompensated proportional regulator. Thus, $K_{\max} \simeq \tau_m / \tau_{pm}$.

Provided the break frequency $\omega_3 = 1/\tau_i$ in Fig. 3.10 resulting from the numerator zero in the compensation is located at a frequency which is equal to the first break frequency $\omega_1 = 1/\tau_m$ in the uncompensated open-loop characteristic, or at values smaller than the frequency $\omega = 1/\tau_m$, no difficulty will occur in stabilizing the system. Equations 3.23 and 3.24, which define the two different compensation methods, have an important property in common. Both place a zero in the numerator of the open-loop transfer function. Both place a pole in the open-loop function. The proportional-plus-integration places the pole at the origin of the s-plane. The other places the pole on the negative real axis in the vicinity of the origin, provided the time constant τ_d can be made large. When the time constant of the numerator in each form of compensation is properly chosen, the mechanism magnifies the low-frequency portion of the open-loop response, but does not magnify the high-frequency portion. Consequently, these "integral" compensation mechanisms tend to stiffen the speed regulator

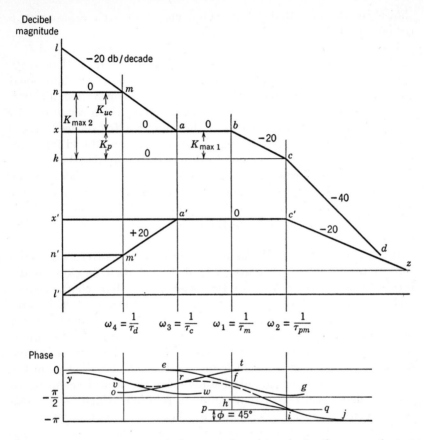

Fig. 3.10. Frequency-response study for a speed regulator, showing the comparative performance between proportional, proportional-plus-reset, and under-compensated integral manipulation.

against low-frequency disturbances. The compensation mechanisms fail to function for high-frequency disturbances. By this procedure the speed-regulator system can be stiffened against static load torques. The flywheel itself regulates against high-frequency load torques.

(2) The undercompensated integral system shows only a limited improvement in the static performance of the regulator. The fact that the undercompensated integral puts a zero and a pole in the open-loop response function, both located on the negative real axis of the s-plane, rather than a pole at the origin and a zero on the negative real axis, means that this form of compensation in the regulator cannot have perfect static performance. The imperfect static performance is

shown by the fact that the response curve $n'm'a'c'z$ approaches a definite decibel value as $\omega \to -\infty$.

However, the loop gain $K_{\max 2}$ is the sum of the gains K_p and K_{uc}, as shown in Fig. 3.10. The portion of the total gain K_p is that which could be obtained by proportional regulating action. The additional gain K_{uc} comes from the action of the undercompensated integral. The value of K_{uc} is determined by the distance which separates the two break frequencies ω_4 and ω_3 of the compensating device. Thus, for $\tau_d/\tau_c = \alpha = 10$, approximately a 20-decibel or a 10-fold improvement in the loop gain can be obtained over the proportional regulator. Thus, curve $n'm'$ begins 20 decibels down from curve $x'a'c'$ for the uncompensated regulator. Sometimes α can be made large—for example, $\alpha = 50$ to 100, so that precision speed regulators can have 50- to 100-fold improvement in the loop gain over that of the under-compensated system.

It is important that the break frequency ω_3, which corresponds to the zero in the undercompensated integral device, shall lie close to the break frequency $\omega_1 = 1/\tau_m$ in the open-loop system characteristic, but not lie to the higher frequency side of ω_1 in a location which interferes with the stability of the system. When the adjustment is made upon an asymptote basis, and using a phase-margin criterion for stability adjustment, a good rule of thumb is to locate the break ω_3 at the break frequency ω_1 or lower in frequency than the break at ω_1 in the curve $xabcd$. An exact graphical study using the decibel versus phase contour charts will reveal that optimum solutions which yield maximum possible gain can be obtained by choosing more exact values for the zeros and poles in the compensation mechanisms.

The compensation technique is outlined by means of the asymptote magnitude and phase curves plotted for the open-loop and the closed-loop transfer functions in Fig. 3.10. Specific curves are identified as follows:

Curve

$xabcd$	Open-loop unity gain response $\dfrac{\Delta\Omega(j\omega)}{\mathcal{E}_\Omega(j\omega)}$ uncompensated system
$efij$	Open-loop phase response—uncompensated system
pq	Phase margin of 45 degrees
$pick$	Construction to determine loop gain $K_{\max}$
$lmabcd$	Open-loop unity gain response $\dfrac{\Delta\Omega(j\omega)}{\mathcal{E}_\Omega(j\omega)}$ for the system with

proportional-plus-integral compensation

orfij   Open-loop phase for system with proportional-plus-integral control

nmabcd   Open-loop unity gain response $\dfrac{\Delta\Omega(j\omega)}{\mathcal{E}_\Omega(j\omega)}$ for the system with undercompensated integral action

yvrfij   Open-loop phase curve for system with undercompensated integral action

$x'a'c'z$ Uncompensated regulator response $\left|\dfrac{\Delta\Omega(j\omega)}{\Delta T_L(j\omega)}\right|$

$l'm'a'c'z$ Regulator response $\left|\dfrac{\Delta\Omega(j\omega)}{\Delta T_L(j\omega)}\right|$ for proportional-plus-integral compensation

$n'm'a'c'z$ Regulator response $\left|\dfrac{\Delta\Omega(j\omega)}{\Delta T_L(j\omega)}\right|$ for the undercompensated integral action

5. VARIABLE-SPEED DRIVES

The variable-speed drive is a very important piece of equipment in conjunction with the speed control of pumps, pinch rolls, take-away rolls, and other machinery. Several schemes yield variable-speed drives. The machinery drive can be electric, hydraulic, or mechanical. Electric variable-speed drives can be Ward-Leonard systems, amplidyne generators driving d-c motors, rototrol generators driving c-d motors. They can also use eddy-current type of clutches. Thyratron and various types of high-current rectifying devices are used from a-c power lines to control d-c motors. Recently the magnetic amplifier coupled with the appropriate circuits of rectifiers has been used to adjust the electric power flow to d-c and a-c machines.

In the hydraulic systems there are two kinds of variable-speed drives. The first uses a hydraulic drive which comprises a variable-displacement pump and a fixed-displacement motor. This "transmission" is generally controlled by a stroking device which adjusts the pump so that its delivery of oil flow to the motor is variable. The hydraulic motor runs at a velocity that is determined by the setting of the pump.

The other type of hydraulic drive consists of a throttle valve modulating the flow of oil from a constant-pressure source to a fixed-displacement motor. This arrangement tends to consume a lot of power in the valve and is not practical for high power levels.

Numerous mechanical variable-speed drives are used. They include: belts operating on cones, and special arrangements of rotating cones and spheres engaging with each other. Mechanical variable-speed drives can be built for high horsepower. Belt drives and various schemes for continuously changing gear ratios have been known to the mechanical-engineering world for a long time. They are now used and find certain advantages in that the maintenance of them is low, they have no electrical parts to be concerned with in connection with explosion hazards, and they tend to be very rugged and easy to maintain. However, they have a limited dynamic speed of response.

An ideal variable-speed drive would have the speed-to-manipulation relationship $\dfrac{\Omega}{M} = K$. However, the internal losses, elastic effects, inductance, and inertia of the machines cause them to have imperfect response.

6. TENSION IN A WEB OF MATERIAL

Webs of material are moved through cascades of processing operations—such as drying, cutting, perforating, spray painting, and applying of tin plate. The webs are driven by pinch rollers which positively engage the web. Various kinds of motors are geared to the pinch rolls; they propel the web at an average speed through the process; they must also maintain the proper tension in the web so that it does not rupture nor go slack.

To keep the tension in a web constant requires that the web shall neither elongate nor contract with respect to time. If two consecutive sets of pinch rolls rotate in identical *positional synchronism*, and if they remain positively engaged with a web at all times, then the web tension will not change unless the properties of the section of web between the pair of pinch rolls changes as the web is exposed to a disturbing environment such as drying, chemical treatment, or mechanical deformation.

When processing actions are taken upon webs, the webs become subject to a variety of manipulating forces that tend directly or indirectly to deform the webs so that their tension changes. The manipulating forces sometimes affect the speed of the drive mechanisms. This in turn brings about changes in the web tension.

Nature of the Web. Webs can be considered as ideal elastic materials, provided they are not being drawn. Also the section of a web between pairs of drive rolls has a small mass compared to the moment of inertia of the drive rolls.* When no drawing takes place

---

* Steel webs may require a treatment which considers the web mass to be distributed and not negligible.

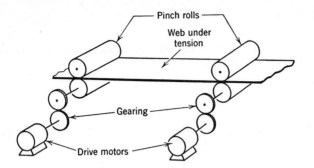

Fig. 3.11.   Web under tension.

between consecutive pairs of drive rolls, Hooke's law applies, and the web extends in direct proportion to the force applied to it.   Of course, there are variations in this idealized condition: The nonhomogeneity of the web material or variations in the thickness may give rise to variations in the elastic deformation.

Figure 3.11 shows a typical arrangement of two pairs of pinch rolls and two motors which drive them.   The connecting web has zero mass but elastance.   The tension T in the web is the variable to be controlled.   As the motor speeds Ω_1 and Ω_2 vary, the positional synchronism of the pinch rolls changes.   This elongates the web.   The tension and elongation are related according to Hooke's law.

The linear stress-strain relationship for a material is defined by the equation

$$\frac{F}{A} = E\frac{\Delta x}{x_o} \tag{3.25}$$

where x_o = free length of the web
Δx = deformation
F = total force of deformation
A = cross-sectional area
E = modulus of elasticity

Therefore, for incremental changes in elongation Δx the incremental changes in the tension ΔT for a web can be determined from the relationship

$$dT = \frac{A}{x_o} E\, dx \tag{3.26}$$

$$= K_w\, dx \tag{3.27}$$

Fig. 3.12.   Dancer roll for tension measurement.

The web tension T is related to positional change of the pinch rolls according to the relationship

$$dT = K_w(dx_1 - dx_2) \qquad (3.28)$$

$$= K_w(r_1 \, d\theta_1 - r_2 \, d\theta_2) \qquad (3.29)$$

where r_1 and r_2 are the respective radii of the rolls.   Since the angles θ_1 and θ_2 are the integrals of the speeds Ω_1 and Ω_2, respectively, the first approximation to the process dynamics is an integration

$$\frac{dT}{dt} = K_w(r_1\Omega_1 - r_2\Omega_2) \qquad (3.30)$$

When plastic material is stretched, and if $r_1 = r_2 = r$, another approximation for the rate of change in tension uses the first two terms in an infinite series expansion (inertia effects assumed equal zero):

$$\frac{dT}{dt} = rK_w(\Omega_1 - \Omega_2) + rK\tau_w\left(\frac{d\Omega_1}{dt} - \frac{d\Omega_2}{dt}\right) \qquad (3.31)$$

where $\tau_w = \dfrac{b}{K_w}$ and b = internal coefficient of viscous friction.

The second term in eq. 3.31 takes into account the viscous shear effect noted in some webs.   The combined right-hand side of the equation permits a study of a web with a visco-elastic property.   Of course, to be strictly correct, $\dfrac{dT(t)}{dt}$ is a nonlinear function of T, Ω, and the derivatives of Ω.

Measurement of Tension.   Tension is generally measured by means of a spring-restrained "dancer" roll, as shown in Fig. 3.12.   The static deflection y of the roll is proportional to the static incremental change in tension T in the web.   The name "dancer," however, is appropriate; it indicates that this means for measuring tension is not stable; the roll exhibits sustained oscillation in the y direction unless the addition of the dashpot d can stabilize the mechanical member.

Provided the moment of inertia of the roll does not impart a component of tension to the web during acceleration or deceleration of the web in the machine direction, and provided $K_w \gg k$, the movement y is related to the tension by the equation

$$\frac{y(s)}{T(s)} = \frac{K}{s^2 + 2\zeta\omega_n s + \omega_n{}^2} \tag{3.32}$$

where

$$\zeta = \frac{d}{2\sqrt{mk}}; \qquad m = \frac{W}{g} \tag{3.33}$$

$$\omega_n = \sqrt{\frac{k}{m}} \tag{3.34}$$

$$K = \frac{2\sin\phi}{m} \tag{3.35}$$

The break frequency of the tension detector is approximately ω_n. Tension T cannot be measured with precision by a *loosely coupled dancer roll* which moves up and down as the web takes up its slack or increases its slack. The measuring means with large m and small k do not have enough bandwidth to procure a measurement of tension fluctuations as functions of time. High-performance types of control and regulatory systems for tension become dependent upon good tension measurement. The basic requirement for a good tension-measuring instrument is that it have minimum mass m, be restrained with a very stiff spring in order to make its natural frequency high, and have a damping ratio $\zeta \simeq 1.0$. To obtain bandwidth, a sacrifice must be accepted in static deflection x per unit of tension T.

Tension Control—Passive Regulation. Regulation of tension can be accomplished to some extent by the weighted roll shown in Fig. 3.13, and the dancer roll shown in Fig. 3.14. This type of regulation is a passive form of tension regulation. The pinch rolls drive the web; the weighted rolls or the dancer roll in contact with the web bring forces to bear upon the web which can alter the tension.

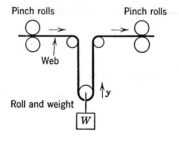

Fig. 3.13.   Dead-weight roll for self-regulation of tension.

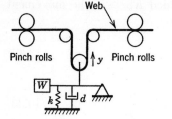

Fig. 3.14. Dancer roll for self-regulation of tension.

Weighted Roll. All friction is assumed zero. The inertia reaction forces of the roll are neglected. The length of web between the pinch rolls is

$$L = \int (v_2 - v_1)\, dt \qquad (3.36)$$

The position of the weighted roll changes in the vertical direction according to the relation $dy = \frac{1}{2} dL$. The tension-to-force relationship is

$$2T = F = \left(\frac{W}{g}\right) \frac{d^2 y}{dt^2} \qquad (3.37)$$

Therefore the tension in the web becomes

$$T = \frac{1}{4} \frac{W}{g} \frac{d}{dt} (v_2 - v_1) \qquad (3.38)$$

$$= \frac{1}{4} \frac{W}{g} (a_2 - a_1) \qquad (3.39)$$

Equation 3.39 shows that the weighted roll permits tension variations proportional to relative acceleration $a_2 - a_1$. Therefore the scheme is good only as a static or steady-state tension regulator. In other words, the weighted roll is *useless* for regulating tension. It only aggravates the variation in tension when speed changes occur at the pinch rolls.

Dancer Roll. If the friction in the bearings and the inertia reaction torques are ignored in the dancer roll, the force-motion equation becomes

$$2T = F = 2ky + d \frac{dy}{dt} + \frac{W}{g} \frac{d^2 y}{dt^2} \qquad (3.40)$$

The transform is

$$T(s) = \frac{1}{2} \left(k + ds + \frac{W}{g} s^2 \right) y(s) \qquad (3.41)$$

The relationship $y = \frac{1}{2}L$ and the relationship between length L and pinch-roll velocity difference $v_2 - v_1$ are substituted in eq. 3.41 and the tension variation for a differential change in speed becomes

$$\frac{T(s)}{v_2(s) - v_1(s)} = \frac{\dfrac{k}{4}(\tau^2 s^2 + 2\zeta\tau s + 1)}{s} \tag{3.42}$$

If eq. 3.42 is looked upon as an attenuation characteristic of the dancer-roll regulator, the regulator attenuates variation in differential speed at -20 decibels per decade for the frequencies below the resonant frequency $\omega = \dfrac{1}{\tau}$. For high-frequency variations in speed, the dancer roll tends to magnify the variations in Δv at $+20$ decibels per decade.

Passive regulation of tension becomes principally a mechanics problem.

7. TENSION CONTROL—FEEDBACK REGULATION

Now consider the problem of feedback control and regulation of tension. Let the Ward-Leonard electric system shown in Fig. 3.15 drive pinch rolls at an angular velocity Ω_1. The rolls, in turn, propel an elastic web of material. A second pair of pinch rolls, located earlier in the process and driven at angular velocity Ω_d, serve as the primary driving rolls. The electric generator and motor are the manipulator. The field current I_f or the voltage E_f causes the manipulator to maintain tension at a constant or nearly constant value in the web.

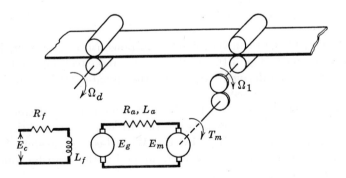

Fig. 3.15. Motor-generator drive of pinch rolls for tension regulation.

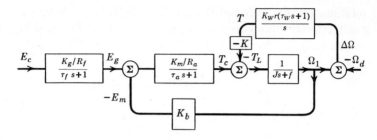

Fig. 3.16.   Block diagram for a motor-generator type of tension manipulation.

The general equations which describe the dynamic behavior of the system shown in Fig. 3.15 are:

$$\frac{dT}{dt} = rK_w(\Omega_1 - \Omega_d) + rK_w\tau_w\left(\frac{d\Omega_1}{dt} - \frac{d\Omega_d}{dt}\right) \quad (3.43)$$

$$T_L = KT \quad (3.44)$$

$$J\frac{d\Omega_1}{dt} + f\Omega_1 = T_c - T_L \quad (3.45)$$

$$T_c = K_m I_a \quad (3.46)$$

$$R_a\left(\tau_a\frac{dI_a}{dt} + I_a\right) = E_g - E_m \quad (3.47)$$

$$E_g = K_g I_f \quad (3.48)$$

$$E_m = K_b\Omega_1 \quad (3.49)$$

Equations 3.43–3.49 can be solved simultaneously.   However, if the reader will refer to Fig. 3.16 and trace cause and effect, he will learn of the benefits to be derived from using the signal-flow diagram in the treatment of complicated systems.

First, a speed variation of the drive Ω_d acts as a disturbance upon the system.   The difference between the drive speed Ω_d and the speed Ω_1 of the pinch rolls driven by the Ward-Leonard system is $\Delta\Omega$. The change in speed $\Delta\Omega$, operated upon by the transfer function $K_w r\left(\dfrac{\tau_w s + 1}{s}\right)$, which describes the dynamics of the web, creates the tension T in the web.   The tension T has an influence back upon the

Ward-Leonard system because, when multiplied by the proper constant K which accounts for roll geometry, gear ratios, and width of web, it produces the load torque T_L.

The load torque T_L is subtracted from the torque T_C developed by the motor at its air gap. The net torque ΣT drives the mechanical member. The mechanical member comprises the total inertia J and the total viscous friction f. The mechanical member changes speed under the application of the net torque. Thus, the tension in the web caused by speed variations in Ω_d reflects a signal back into the torque summing point through a closed loop of cause and effect. The fact that this closed signal path exists means that the web properties are inherently coupled to the properties of the mechanical-electrical drive itself.

A second closed loop relates the mechanical portion of the system to the electrical portion. The signal Ω_1, when multiplied by the back emf constant K_b of the motor, produces the back emf E_m, which opposes the generator voltage E_g. The resultant voltage ΔE forces armature current I_a through the generator and motor and produces the torque T_C. Therefore, the parameters of the motor and the parameters of the generator are coupled through the back emf path, which is typical of the Ward-Leonard or any other type of electric-transmission prime mover.

The fact that the back-emf loop $\Omega_1 - E_m - T_C - \Sigma T - \Omega_1$ and the tension-speed loop $\Omega_1 - \Sigma \Omega - T - T_L - \Omega_1$ interlock, means that the tension control system will have to be designed so that the web dynamics is taken into account.

Current Regulation

Current regulation can be used to bring about tension regulation. The dynamic performance of this type of regulator can be studied by assuming that the armature current I_a in the system shown in Fig. 3.16 can be kept essentially constant. The variation in tension T for changes in drive speed Ω_d gives a measure of the performance quality to be expected from this *indirect* method of tension regulation.

When the armature current in the Ward-Leonard machine is kept essentially constant, no back emf voltage need be considered in the analysis. Thus the signal-flow diagram for the system shown in Fig. 3.15 reduces from the form shown in Fig. 3.16 to the form shown in Fig. 3.17a, where current is the manipulating signal. The simplification of the primitive diagram, Fig. 3.17a, is given in Fig. 3.17b.

For a visco-elastic web and for a motor and machine output member which has viscous friction, the general relationship between tension

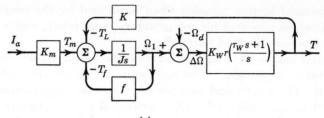

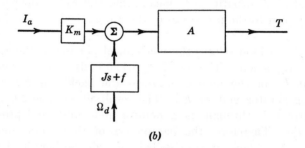

Fig. 3.17. Block diagram for current-type tension regulator. (a) Primitive diagram; (b) Simplified diagram.

$T(s)$ and drive velocity $\Omega_d(s)$ becomes

$$\frac{T(s)}{\Omega_d(s)} = (Js + f)\left[\frac{rK_w\left(\dfrac{\tau_w s + 1}{s}\right)\left(\dfrac{1}{Js + f}\right)}{1 + rKK_w\left(\dfrac{\tau_w s + 1}{s}\right)\left(\dfrac{1}{Js + f}\right)}\right] \quad (3.50)$$

For a purely elastic web, described by $\tau_w = 0$, eq. 3.50 reduces to

$$\frac{T(s)}{\Omega_d(s)} = (Js + f)\left[\frac{rK_w\dfrac{1}{(Js + f)}\cdot\dfrac{1}{s}}{1 + rKK_w\left(\dfrac{1}{s}\right)\left(\dfrac{1}{Js + f}\right)}\right] = (Js + f)A \quad (3.51)$$

$$= \frac{rK_w(Js + f)}{(Js^2 + fs + rKK_w)} \quad (3.52)$$

$$= \frac{\dfrac{f}{K}(\tau_m s + 1)}{(\tau^2 s^2 + 2\zeta\tau s + 1)} \quad (3.53)$$

where

$$\tau_m = \frac{J}{f} \qquad (3.54)$$

$$\tau^2 = \frac{J}{rKK_w} \qquad (3.55)$$

$$2\zeta\tau = \frac{f}{rKK_w} \qquad (3.56)$$

When there is zero damping in the web itself, i.e., $\tau_w = 0$, and the friction in the motor is also zero, so that $f = 0$, since the dynamic damping of back emf is zero, the output member will tend to sustain oscillation. This is predicted by the relationship

$$\frac{T(s)}{\Omega_d(s)} = \frac{\dfrac{J}{K} s}{\left(\dfrac{J}{KK_w}\right) s^2 + 1} \qquad (3.57)$$

The result given in eq. 3.57 indicates that the current type of indirect tension regulation may be applicable to the machinery which handles plastic, textiles, or paper webs, even if not much damping is present in the generator-drive-motor transmission. However, for webs such as steel, which have little or no losses so that $\tau_w = 0$, special attention must be given the stabilization aspects of the tension regulator design.

Voltage Regulation

Tension can also be controlled *indirectly* by means of voltage regulation in the Ward-Leonard system. If E_g is maintained essentially constant, the influence of changes in Ω_d upon the tension will be lessened. The equations which express the system dynamic behavior

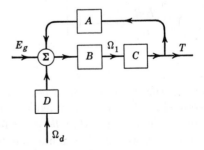

Fig. 3.18. Block diagram showing voltage as manipulating variable for web tension.

are somewhat more complicated than those for current regulation, because the back-emf of the electric transmission is present.

Figure 3.18 shows the general form of the signal-flow diagram which expresses the cause-and-effect relations for the voltage-manipulated tension control system. Tension T is related to generator-voltage E_g and pinch-roll speed Ω_d as follows:

$$T = \left(\frac{BC}{1 + ABC}\right) E_g - \left(\frac{BCD}{1 + ABC}\right) \Omega_d \qquad (3.58)$$

where the transfer functions A, B, C, and D have the definitions:

$$A = \frac{KR_a}{K_m} (\tau_a s + 1) \qquad (3.59)$$

$$B = \frac{\dfrac{K_m/fR_a}{(\tau_a s + 1)(\tau_m s + 1)}}{1 + \dfrac{K_b K_m}{R_a f} \left[\dfrac{1}{(\tau_a s + 1)(\tau_m s + 1)}\right]} \qquad (3.60)$$

$$C = rK_w \left(\frac{\tau_w s + 1}{s}\right) \qquad (3.61)$$

$$D = \frac{1}{B} \qquad (3.62)$$

A study of the operator $\dfrac{BCD}{1 + ABC}$ reveals the influence of Ω_d upon tension. Thus

$$\frac{BCD}{1 + ABC}$$

$$= \frac{rK_w \left(\dfrac{\tau_w s + 1}{s}\right)}{1 + \dfrac{KR_a}{K_m}(\tau_a s + 1) \left[\dfrac{\dfrac{K_m}{fR_a}}{(\tau_a s + 1)(\tau_m s + 1) + \dfrac{K_m K_b}{R_a f}}\right] K_w r \left(\dfrac{\tau_w s + 1}{s}\right)} \qquad (3.63)$$

Since the denominator of eq. 3.63 is a cubic, the possibility for a sustained oscillating system exists. By means of Routh's stability criterion, which states that $bc \geq ad$ for the general cubic $as^3 + bs^2 + cs + d = 0$, we can determine that for

Case 1. $\tau_w \neq 0, f \neq 0$ the inherent stability of the tension regulator is predicted by $bc \geq ad$, where

$$a = \tau_a \tau_m \tag{3.64}$$

$$b = \tau_a + \tau_m + \frac{KK_w}{f} \tau_a \tau_w \tag{3.65}$$

$$c = 1 + \frac{K_m K_b}{R_a f} + \frac{rKK_w}{f}(\tau_a + \tau_w) \tag{3.66}$$

$$d = \frac{rKK_w}{f} \tag{3.67}$$

Case 2. When $\tau_w = 0, f \neq 0$, the stability is predicted by

$$(\tau_a + \tau_m)\left(1 + \frac{K_m K_b}{R_a f} + \frac{rKK_w}{f}\tau_a\right) \geq \frac{\tau_a \tau_m KK_w r}{f} \tag{3.68}$$

Case 3. When $\tau_w = 0, f = 0$, the stability is predicted by

$$\left(\frac{K_m K_b}{R_a} + rKK_w\tau_a\right) \geq \tau_a KK_w Jr \tag{3.69}$$

Case 4. When $\tau_w \neq 0, f = 0$, the stability is predicted by

$$[rKK_w\tau_a\tau_w]\left[\frac{K_m K_b}{R_a} + rKK_w(\tau_a + \tau_w)\right] \geq \tau_a KK_w rJ \tag{3.70}$$

Closed-Loop Tension Regulator

To develop a complete closed-loop tension regulator requires that the tension T be measured by the dancer-roll type of measuring instrument, and that the measured value T_m be compared with the reference tension T_{ref}. The difference, being the error in tension $\mathcal{E}_T$, is multiplied by the transfer function $K_C G_C$ of the controller. The field voltage E_c produces field current I_f, which in turn produces the generator voltage E_g, but not without the time lag of the field τ_f coming into the operation.

The block diagram of Fig. 3.19 shows that the web, the pinch rolls, the armature of the motor, the electric circuit between the generator and the motor, the generator, the field-control coils, and the amplifier combine into a single dynamical unit whose transfer function becomes inherently related to the static and dynamic performance of the tension regulator.

An important fact to be recognized in relation to the design of tension regulators can be noted from the signal-flow diagram in Fig. 3.17. Three signal loops exist: First, there is the loop through the web itself; secondly, there is the degenerative loop through the back emf of the motor-generator which serves to connect the mechanical-electrical members in an interacting fashion; finally, there is the closed loop through the measuring element.

The fact that a cubic equation relates the tension T and the generator voltage E_g means that the loop gain of the regulator cannot be high. It will be limited by the fact that the attenuation curve for $\dfrac{T(j\omega)}{E_g(j\omega)}$ will ultimately reach -60 decibels per decade, and the phase angle for $\dfrac{T(j\omega)}{E_g(j\omega)}$ will progress from zero degrees to -270 degrees.

Should the web be very stiff, the likelihood is that the bandwidth of the motor-generator will limit the regulator gain. For soft webs with low elastic constants, it may be the *web* that limits the gain despite the use of a good motor-generator. Needless to say, a poor detector of tension—that is, a dancer roll with a low natural frequency—might limit the regulator gain regardless of the web modulus of elasticity and the bandwidth of the drive mechanism.

When a web of material is delicate, such as thin plastic or metal foil, practical measures may require that a tension feedback be superposed upon a feedback speed control. The signal-flow diagram shown in Fig. 3.20 illustrates the type of double feedback system.

First, the addition of the speed-control loop merely puts another feedback loop around the motor-generator similar in function to the back emf negative-feedback signal path inherent in the drive mechanism. The speed regulator will not be free from droop. This was

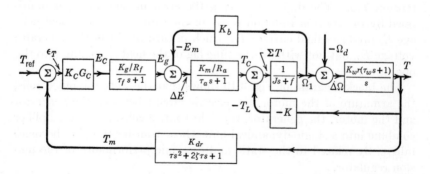

Fig. 3.19. Block diagram for feedback type of tension regulator.

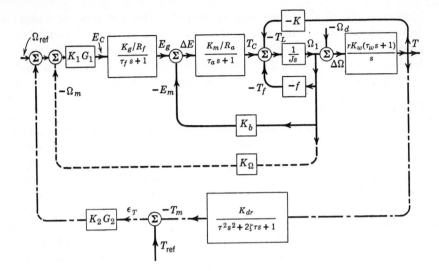

Fig. 3.20. Block diagram for tension regulator in which speed regulator has its command Ω_{ref} adjusted by means of a tension-resetting loop.

proved in section 4, p. 128. However, the presence of the speed loop can tend to make the bandwidth of the speed regulator greater than the bandwidth of the drive mechanism-web combination alone. Ultimately, the performance of the speed loop limits the performance of the tension regulator.

The nature of the resetting action by the tension feedback loop upon the speed reference must be such that "integrating" action is present. Otherwise, tension cannot be kept in simultaneous regulation with the regulation of the speed of the web.

Summary

Tension control is not a simple matter. The fact that webs do not break during starts, stops, and upsets in the running of web-processing plants may simply indicate the strength of the web rather than the dynamic precision of the regulator. The time lags of the propelling equipment figure prominently in the stability of the system; they also determine the static precision of tension regulation.

For continuous webs being propelled through multistand rolling or multiroll printing actions, a lumped-parameter mass-and-elastance combined rotational and translational mechanical system results. For heavy webs, a distributed-mass and lumped-mass loaded elastance system is the more correct representation. This situation can lead to complex problems of vibration; many modes of oscillation can be generated by external disturbances. The disturbances can move back and forth through the web, the drive machinery, and even the structures which take processing action upon the web.

8. WEB GUIDANCE

As webs are propelled through processes, they may tend to move sidewise. The sidewise movement may be a steady "drift" to one side of the guiding rolls, or the webs may weave from side to side. Either type of movement may be severe enough to cause the web to leave the guide rolls. Even when the web does not leave the rolls, the sidewise movement may be sufficient to twist, buckle, or stretch the web beyond its practical limits.

The forces that cause sidewise movement of webs arise from heterogeneous properties of the supposedly uniform and homogeneous web, from the imperfections of mechanical design and construction of the guiding rolls and machine frames, and from processing action—such as drying, wetting, and printing with rapidly drying ink—which stresses the webs nonuniformly as they move through guide-roll systems. Also, rolls of web in the form of raw material may be wound unevenly; so that when they unwind to feed a process, the imperfections in the roll may cause the web to weave from side to side.

Web Movement.   To develop the equations that predict the sidewise movement of webs is a difficult task, because many factors influence the behavior of the web. The physical properties of the web, the nature of the surface of the web, the surface condition of the rolls, and the mechanical rigidity and freedom from vibration of the machine structure are all factors that influence the manner in which the web moves. Also, the subtleties of Coulomb and sliding friction can render worthless an otherwise elaborate and clever analysis and whole sets of equations for predicting the movement of the web. The reader is cautioned to view the material which follows as an introductory approach to the problem of web guidance which may not remain valid when webs respond to severe conditions of stress.

Perfect Roll, Perfect Wrap.   Consider that a web has uneven tension distribution across its width, but that it rolls over a perfectly formed cylindrical guide roll. The web also wraps perfectly on the cylinder, with no wrinkles or trapped air between the web and the cylinder. Under these conditions, no horizontal motion can occur between the web and the roll, regardless of how the tension varies as a function of distance across the web or as a function of time. No

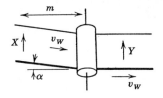

Fig. 3.21.   Web skewed on a perfect roll.

crosswise force component can be established between the web and
the cylindrical surface.   Even when a tension gradient occurs across
the web, the web will keep its position relative to the roll, because the
crosswise force component will remain zero unless the contact line
between the web and the roll becomes skewed with respect to the
rotational axis of the roll.

Perfect Roll, Skewed Wrapping.   When a web moves over a perfect
roll, but the wrap of the web is skewed on the roll so that the contact
line between the web and the surface of the roll is not parallel in space
with the axis of rotation of the roll, the web will move sidewise in a
direction that tends to reduce to zero the unbalanced forces which
act upon the web.   The web tends to "escape from you" in order to
return to equilibrium.   The rate of sidewise movement will be approximately in proportion to the angle of skew and proportional to the forward velocity of the web.   However, a more exact study of the movement can be made with reference to Fig. 3.21.

The rate at which the web moves sidewise to the right of the guide
roll shown in Fig. 3.21 is:

$$\frac{dY}{dt} = v_w \tan \alpha \tag{3.71}$$

$$= v_w \left(\frac{X - Y}{m} \right) \tag{3.72}$$

$$\frac{dY}{dt} + \frac{v_w}{m} Y = \frac{v_w}{m} X \tag{3.73}$$

Therefore the transfer function which relates $Y(s)$ to $X(s)$ is:

$$\frac{Y(s)}{X(s)} = \frac{1}{\tau s + 1} \tag{3.74}$$

where the time lag is:

$$\tau = \frac{m}{v_w} \tag{3.75}$$

Thus, as the web velocity v_w increases, the web position Y will follow more rapidly the web position X. The separation distance m has direct and proportional influence upon the time constant.

Convex-Cone Roll. Convex-cone rolls have long been used for the self-stabilizing of belt drives. The equilibrium position of a belt or web on a double convex-cone roll is at the center line through the cone perpendicular to the axis of rotation. Whenever the web has its center line displaced from the cone center, there will be a stretching of the web on the side which is nearest to the cone center. A sidewise stretching force develops which is proportional to the normal reaction force on the pulley.

Webs need not center themselves perfectly on convex rolls if there is unbalanced tension across the web, but the web will find for itself a position of equilibrium.

Concave-Cone Rolls. In contrast to the self-stabilizing convex-cone rolls, the concave-cone rolls impart inherently unstable movements to webs. They cause the web to drift from the roll toward one side or the other, and there is no possibility of making the web return so that its axis aligns with the center of the roll.

Imperfect Rolls and Deformations. What normally might be expected to be a perfectly cylindrical roll or a slightly convex roll in a static condition, may not remain so in a dynamic condition. During operation, rolls deform and their shafts bend because of the high tension maintained in webs. Bearings may also deform as tension is placed on webs. Uneven bearing deformation on the two ends of the roll may skew a roll. Thus a static cylindrical roll will, under conditions of high web tension, tend to become a concave roll as the roll rotates about a continually deforming axis. Stressed rolls may have an inherently unstabilizing effect upon web guidance systems.

Extraneous Material. Sometimes layers of glue or paint will coat on rolls. A slight change in the shape of a roll is sufficient, if it produces concavity at all, to bring about unstable sidewise movement of a web. Many webs have an edge which has a bead. Thus the web has a nonuniform thickness, especially near the edge. As a web is rolled up into a cylindrical roll, the bead tends to build up so that the central section of the roll of web is smaller in diameter than the two ends. The resulting concave roll may impart instability to a wind-up system.

Regulation. To prevent the sidewise movement of webs, there are two basic procedures for manipulation. The first is the use of a translation roll. A guide roll in tight contact with the moving web, or a roll of web itself, can be designed so that it can be moved in a trans-

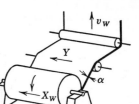

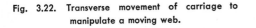

Fig. 3.22. Transverse movement of carriage to manipulate a moving web.

verse direction to the web movement. The movement of the roll brings about a change in the contact line between the web and the guide rolls immediately preceding and following the roll which is translating crosswise. A moving-carriage type of device is shown in Fig. 3.22. An entire roll of web of raw material is placed in a carriage which can be translated crosswise. In this instance there is only one contact line which changes. It is between the web and the guide roll which immediately follows the unwind.

The differential equation which describes the sidewise movement of the web under the action of a disturbance $X_w(t)$, and the manipulation $X_c(t)$ which is the transverse movement of the web roll, is given by

$$\frac{dY}{dt} = v_w \left(\frac{\Delta X - Y}{m} \right) \tag{3.76}$$

but ΔX is the net movement $X_w - X_c$ of the web. Therefore

$$\frac{dY}{dt} = \frac{v_w}{m} (X_w - X_c - Y) \tag{3.77}$$

Equation 3.79 transforms so that

$$Y(s) = \left(\frac{1}{\tau s + 1} \right) [X_w(s) - X_c(s)] \tag{3.78}$$

The time constant τ has the same definition as in eq. 3.75.

The second form of manipulation is the use of a pivot roll to bring about translational movement of the web. A typical pivot roll is shown in Fig. 3.23. The web is taken over a guide roll a, over a pivot roll b, and over a second guide roll c. To translate the web sidewise on guide roll c, as compared with its location on guide roll a, requires that the web be pivoted about the axis NN. The pivoting takes a point on the web over the pivot roll b so that a sidewise increment of movement ΔY occurs as the web moves from point Z_1 to point Z_2.

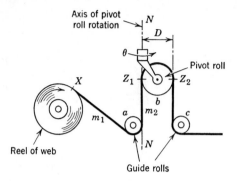

Fig. 3.23.   Pivot roll for manipulating a moving web.

The increment ΔY at point Z_2 is proportional to the angle θ of turn of the pivot roll.

For the system shown in Fig. 3.23, the movement $Y(s)$ at point Z_2, in terms of a web movement X_w at point X and the manipulation angle θ, is:

$$Y_{Z_1}(s) = \left(\frac{1}{\tau_1 s + 1}\right)\left(\frac{1}{\tau_2 s + 1}\right) X_w(s) \qquad (3.79)$$

where

$$\tau_1 = \frac{m_1}{v_w} \qquad (3.80)$$

and

$$\tau_2 = \frac{m_2}{v_w} \qquad (3.81)$$

Therefore

$$Y_{Z_2}(s) = Y_{Z_1}(s) - K\theta(s) \qquad (3.82)$$

$$= \frac{1}{(\tau_1 s + 1)(\tau_2 s + 1)} X_w(s) - K\theta(s) \qquad (3.83)$$

In eq. 3.83, K is a proportionality constant which depends upon the dimensions and the geometry of the pivot roll and its carriage.

BIBLIOGRAPHY

"Edge-Positioning Device Aligns Web in Laminating Operation," Askania Regulator Co., *Boxboard Containers* (Jan. 1953).

"Edge-Position Control," Askania Regulator Company, *Bulletin G-100*.

"Edge-Position Control," Askania Regulator Co., *Bulletin 161*.

"Control of Moving Webs," Askania Regulator Co., *Technical Paper No. 207*.

"*Web Guiding Control*," Stephen E. Amos, *Machine Design* (September 1951).

"Askania Edge Position Controls," Askania Regulator Co., *Instruction Book VG-I*.

CHAPTER 4

Thermal Process Dynamics

1. BASIC THERMAL PROCESSES

The basic thermal processes are: *mixing* of hot and cold fluids; *heat exchange* through contiguous bodies; *generation* of heat by combustion, chemical reaction, or atomic disintegration; *exposure to radiation;* and direct *induction* of heat in material by molecular or atomic agitation. These processes may be used individually in a process, to heat or cool a material, or they may be used in conjunction with the other processing operations, such as materials handling, forming, mass transfer, and chemical reactions. The particular designs of apparatus are numberless.

Figure 4.1 shows several basic thermal processes. In Fig. 4.1a, hot and cold fluid streams enter a hold-up vessel where *mixing* brings about an averaging of the thermal energy. By adjusting the flow rates, or by varying the temperatures of the hot and cold streams, the sensible heat brought into the mixing vessel can be varied so that the temperature of the material in the vessel is manipulated. Thus the temperature or flow variation of the inflow serves to control the thermal energy of the flow leaving the vessel.

The second item, in Fig. 4.1b, shows a shell and tube type of heat *exchanger.* Many different kinds of heat exchangers occur. In some, the fluid flow is concurrent; in other, countercurrent. Still others have baffles and multiple tubes so that cross-flow occurs. Some are used as boilers or evaporators, others as condensers. The principle of the operation of the exchanger is to have the heat from one fluid flow transfer to the other fluid flow. Generally, exchangers are made of metal or other highly conducting material. The heat-exchanging fluids are: liquid to liquid, liquid to gas, and gas to gas. Fluids in the inner tube may receive or give up heat from the liquid in the outer

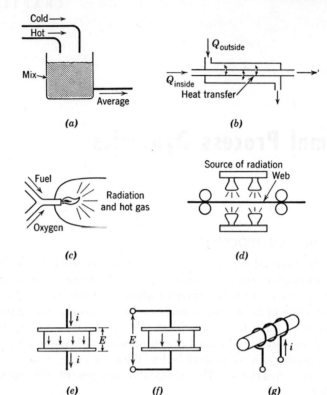

Fig. 4.1. Basic thermal processes; (a) Mixing or convection; (b) Exchange between two fluids; (c) Combustion; (d) Radiation; (e) Electric conduction; (f) Dielectric loss; (g) Induction loss.

tube. However, the heat-transfer direction depends upon the use and the design of the exchanger. In any event, heat transfers from the hotter fluid to the metal, and from the metal to the second fluid. Therefore the heat storage in the metal must be taken into account when the dynamic response of an exchanger is predicted.

Figure 4.1c illustrates how combustion processes control or modulate the release of heat. Pulverized coal or liquid fuel and oxygen are supplied to a nozzle where the mixture burns. At the flame boundary, a partial or a total combustion of the fuel occurs. Radiation is generated in the flame and also by the hot gases which leave the flame boundary. Both the radiation and the sensible heat carried by the hot gases can heat tubes of fluid flowing through the combustion chamber.

The fourth item, Fig. 4.1d, shows direct radiation used to heat a moving web. The process may be that of drying, as encountered in printing or paint drying, or it may be the aging of the web of material. The amount of heat which arrives at the surface of the web will depend upon the temperature of the radiator and the radiation-absorbing properties of the gaseous medium between the source and the web. Of course, conduction and convection occur as well as radiation, since the radiation heats the gaseous medium which surrounds the web.

The remaining types of processes, shown in Figs. 4.1e, f, and g, illustrate electric conduction, dielectric heating, and induction heating. These processes have a certain similarity: They use electrical energy as a means of producing heat energy in a material. In conduction, a voltage gradient is established in the material. The current which flows in the material by virtue of its conductance serves to produce heat in proportion to the I^2R losses.

In dielectric heating, an alternating voltage, generally of high frequency, causes current to flow in the dielectric material. Heating is brought about by the energy losses in the dielectric imperfections.

Magnetic induction is used to heat metals. A coil which is the tank circuit of a high-frequency type of power generator encircles the metal to be heated. The hysteresis and eddy-current losses in the metal tend to make it become hot enough for heat treating and other operations to be accomplished.

2. PHYSICAL CONCEPTS

Heat energy is created during the conversion of energy of other kinds. Mechanical, electrical, and chemical energy conversions produce heat. Combustion is a form of chemical reaction that generally produces heat rapidly, compared with the slower chemical reactions. The nuclear reactions, which involve the disintegration of atoms, produce great quantities of heat. Energy lost in materials exposed to time-varying electric and magnetic fields also produces heat.

The first law of thermodynamics governs the manner in which the heat energy is generated and determines the amount. The second law of thermodynamics governs the direction of the flow of heat.

Heat transmission takes place by *conduction, convection,* and *radiation.* Conduction involves transmission through contiguous bodies; convection involves transmission through transportation and mixing; radiation of heat and radiation of light are the same phenomenon.

The dynamical relationship for the addition or removal of heat from any body of material requires that the summation of heat flow ΣQ shall equal zero. *The rate of change of temperature of a body will be proportional to the total heat energy transferred to or from the body per unit time* by conduction, convection, and radiation. *The temperature of a body is the driving force that causes heat to transfer.*

Conduction within a material takes place according to the relationship

$$H = -K \frac{\partial T}{\partial x} A \qquad (4.1)$$

where H is the heat energy in Btu per unit time flowing opposite to the direction of the temperature gradient $\frac{\partial T}{\partial x}$. The proportionality constant K is the thermal conductivity of the material. A is the area across which heat transfer takes place. When heat transfers from a fluid to a solid, or vice versa, the heat flow can be expressed by the relationship

$$H = hA \, \Delta T \qquad (4.2)$$

where h is the conductance of the film (film coefficient), A is the total area of conduction, and ΔT is the temperature differential across the film. Generally the unit conductance h is a function of the relative velocity between the heat-exchanging media.

Convection takes place as materials of different sensible heat content move among one another. Particles or small volumes of material may mix, with or without the diffusion of heat. Conduction may take place simultaneously with convection. The heat energy carried in a flow stream is

$$H = \rho C_p T Q \qquad (4.3)$$

where Q is the volume flow rate; T, the absolute temperature; C_p, the specific heat; and ρ, the density of the fluid.

As a quantity of material from a hot stream and a cold stream drops into a vessel and is mixed with the contents of the vessel, the particles of higher temperature and lower temperature which flow into the vessel will be distributed among the particles already in the vessel. Adjacent particles may, or may not, give up their heat to one another. The particles near the walls of the vessel may give up heat to the wall. Therefore, the meaning of "average temperature" must be given some thought.

Radiation. Transmission of heat by radiation can be determined according to the Stefan-Boltzmann law, which states that for a perfectly black body,

$$H = \sigma A T^4 \qquad (4.4)$$

where H is the heat energy transfer; A, the area; T, the absolute temperature of the body; and σ, the Stefan-Boltzmann constant. Of course, radiant transfer of heat may take place concurrently with convection and conduction.

Heat storage takes place in all bodies according to the relationship

$$H = \rho C_p V \frac{dT}{dt} \tag{4.5}$$

where H is the heat energy stored per unit time, V is the volume of the body, ρ is its density, C_p is its specific heat, T is temperature, and t is time.

Dynamic Response. Sometimes an elementary approach to the thermal dynamics problem can be made. The rate of rise of temperature of a body is proportional to the total heat added to the body by convection, conduction, and radiation.

$$\rho C_p V \frac{dT}{dt} = H_{CV} + H_{CD} + H_R \tag{4.6}$$

Equation 4.6 is nonlinear; but when only conduction or only convection is involved, a linear equation may result. For example: when only conduction is involved, a volume of material can be assigned a total thermal capacity $C = \rho C_p V$ and a surface-film thermal conductance $G = hA$. The rate of change of the average temperature T of the volume of material will be predicted by the differential equation

$$C \frac{dT}{dt} = G[T_o - T] \tag{4.7}$$

where T_o is the temperature of the external medium. The body will experience thermal transients of the exponential form $e^{-t/\tau}$. The "settling time" for thermal transients is approximately 4τ. The dynamic response of the body is signified by saying that a single-order pole at $s = -1/\tau$ defines the transfer function. The bandwidth over which the body temperature will respond to external temperature variations without attenuation is approximately $\omega_b = \frac{1}{\tau}$. The time constant

$$\tau = \frac{C}{G} = \frac{\rho C_p V}{hA} \tag{4.8}$$

relates the dynamic response to the physical parameters ρ, C_p, V, h, and A.

Should the volume V of material be considered spherical in shape, *the time constant τ would become proportional to the diameter!* Thus, the larger the body, in general, the larger the time constant. Actually, the conductance G is the more important factor in minimizing τ. Any factor that increases h or A without increasing V will make τ smaller.

In convection, the heat balance can be written as

$$\rho C_p V \frac{dT}{dt} = \sum H \qquad (4.9)$$

where ΣH is the sensible heat being added to the process. The heat from ΣH can be made up of incoming sensible heat H_{si} and outflowing sensible heat H_{so}. In general, the sensible heat is given by the product of material flow rate and heat content of the material

$$H_s = \rho' C_p' Q T' \qquad (4.10)$$

The prime values of ρ', C', and T' designate that the material carrying the sensible heat may differ in properties from the material with which it mixes. The throughput Q may be equal for inflow and outflow, or there may occur the build-up or decline of hold-up if $Q_{\text{in}} \neq Q_{\text{out}}$.

Heat-transfer processes should be described by the partial differential equation

$$\frac{C_p \rho}{K} \frac{\partial T}{\partial t} = \nabla^2 T \qquad (4.11)$$

or

$$\frac{C_p \rho}{K} \frac{\partial T}{\partial t} = \left(\frac{\partial^2 T}{\partial x^2} + \frac{\partial^2 T}{\partial y^2} + \frac{\partial^2 T}{\partial z^2} \right) \qquad (4.12)$$

However, partial differential equations can be avoided in many thermal control problems by resorting to an approximate description of the thermal process. The partial differential equations can then be replaced by ordinary differential equations in which the coefficients or parameters represent "lumped" parameter equivalents of the thermal capacities and conductances or the mixing lags. The lumped-parameter approximate treatment of thermal process dynamics makes possible the development of signal-flow diagrams of thermal models.

Electrical analogs can be used to represent the ordinary differential equations which describe heat flow and temperature in a process. Electric sources of voltage or current can drive circuits of electrical resistance and electrical capacity which simulate thermal processes which contain heat sources, sinks, thermal resistance, and thermal capacity. One can even simulate the nonlinearity of the thermal process by choosing variable resistance and variable gain amplifiers that simulate the conditions of film conductivity variation as a function of flow.

3. MANIPULATION OF THERMAL PROCESSES

One has the choice of two basic methods for manipulating thermal processes: first, by controlling the rate at which heat energy is generated during the conversion of other forms of energy; secondly, by controlling the rate at which heat energy transfers from one point to another.

The first method applies to combustion, chemical reaction, nuclear reaction, and to some extent to processes that involve electrical energy conversion. In combustion and chemical reactions, the fuel that brings about the burning or the raw materials which permit the reaction to proceed can be made available in varying quantity. The rate of combustion or reaction will be modulated accordingly. In the catalytic processes, even though the raw materials or fuel are abundant the rate of combustion or the rate of chemical reaction can be varied in proportion to the catalyst concentration.

A limitation, however, can be encountered in the direct modulation of the combustion and chemical processes. The process of combustion or of reaction does not sustain itself over a wide range of variation in the fuel-to-oxygen or the raw-material-to-catalyst ratio. Thresholds exist beyond which combustion or reaction will not occur under any circumstances. At the other extreme, when the reaction rate becomes great, the vessels or combustion chambers are likely to overheat to such an extent that the products of reaction or combustion decompose. Thus there may be the tendency for the decomposition to act as a self-regulating force to prevent further increase in the rate of heat release.

In the nuclear processes the rate of disintegration of atoms depends upon the availability of fuel and the quantity of control material present to absorb the fast neutrons. Once fission occurs, however, the rate of the disintegration of atoms generally cannot be modulated except indirectly by absorption or by reduction of the availability of fuel, which prevents further fission from taking place. In this respect the atomic disintegration tends to be a run-away process. However, this is not basically different from the combustion or the chemical process because these processes would also run away if the fuel for them could be provided in sufficient abundance to make the combustion or reaction sustain itself at an increasing rate.

The second method of manipulation—namely, the controlling of energy transfer in space—applies to mixing and convection processes, to heat exchangers, and to the radiation type of process.

In the mixing process, the sensible heat H_s, which is carried in a gas or liquid flow Q whose material is at a temperature T, is given by

$$H_s = \rho C_p T Q \tag{4.13}$$

Therefore, to vary the amount of sensible heat carried into a process by the stream requires that either the temperature T of the fluid or the flow rate Q be controlled. Little can be done about changing the density ρ or the specific heat C_p, except in unusual situations where the choice of the fluid itself can be varied, or where mixtures are formed specifically to accomplish manipulation.

In the heat-transfer processes the heat transferred is given by

$$H_c = hA\,\Delta T \tag{4.14}$$

To manipulate the heat flow H_c, the temperature differential ΔT can be varied, and the area A can be varied. The conductance h per unit area per degree can also be varied, since it will be a function of the flow rate of the vapor or liquid which is providing the heat. This latter form of manipulation, in which h is a function of flow Q, becomes a parametric type of heat-flow modulation.

Figures 4.2a, b, and c show how thermal mixing or convection processes can be controlled. In Fig. 4.2a a steam line injects steam at a flow rate Q_s into a liquid flow Q_L. The steam is completely condensed, and the liquid flow downstream from the injection point will be heated in proportion to the amount of thermal energy released to the liquid by the steam.

Figure 4.2b shows two fluid streams entering a mixing vessel. When one stream is hotter than the other and the ratio of the two flows is controlled, the average temperature in the hold-up vessel can be manipulated.

Figure 4.2c shows a variation of the former two. A flow of liquid splits: The main stream by-passes a heat exchanger, but a "vernier" stream passes through a heat exchanger or through a mechanism for steam injection. The two streams are brought together after the vernier is heated. The amount of the vernier stream Q_v, added to the main stream Q_m, will bring about a varying temperature in the mixture. This arrangement can be used to add heat energy to a process without changing the flow rate. Also the vernier, by-pass type of heat control tends to be rapid in response.

Next consider the problem of manipulating the exchange of heat between contiguous fluids or objects. In Fig. 4.2d, a heat exchanger of the shell and tube type is shown. The inside flow rate Q_i or the temperature T_i constitutes the disturbance. The sensible heat $\rho C_p Q_i T_i$

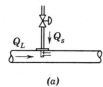

(a)

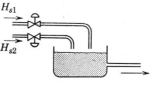

(b)

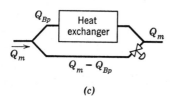

(c)

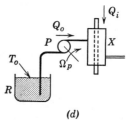

(d)

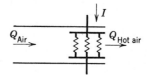

(e)

(f)

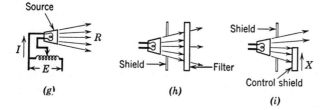

(g)

(h)

(i)

Fig. 4.2. Manipulation of thermal processes; (a) Valve manipulation of direct steam injection; (b) Ratio control over sensible heat flow to a mixing vessel; (c) Split stream—valve control of vernier flow; (d) Variable speed of pump in a flow to an exchanger; (e) Circulating and variable flow through a heat exchanger; (f) Electrical heater in an air stream; (g) Varying radiation-source temperature; (h) Filtering of radiation; (i) Total elimination by shield.

associated with the flow Q_i is to be increased, decreased, or kept constant by heat transfer from the flow Q_o which passes through the shell of the exchanger.   In many exchangers the flow Q_o is pumped from a reservoir by a pump whose speed Ω_p is adjustable.   Thus the flow Q_o can be varied, but the temperature T_o may be essentially constant.

A recirculating type of flow system can be used with the heat exchangers as shown in Fig. 4.2e.   A reservoir R contains hot fluid of temperature T_o.   The flow Q_o is pumped by means of the pump P into the heat exchanger X.   The fluid flow Q_m comes back to the reservoir to be reheated or reprocessed.   Often two stages of heat exchange can occur.   The temperature of the fluid in the reservoir may be controlled by manipulating the heating rate of the reservoir, and the second exchanger controlled by varying the pumping rate Q_o.

Figure 4.2f shows an air flow passing over an electrical heating element.   The current which passes through the heating element produces the electrical energy loss $I^2 R$.   In turn, the heat produced is transferred to the air.   The manipulation can be brought about in two ways: The current in the heater can be maintained constant and the air-flow rate Q_a varied, or the air-flow rate can remain constant and the current be varied.

In the radiation processes, one can manipulate the energy exchange by controlling the radiation at the source, as shown in Fig. 4.2g.   The voltage e_1 applied to the radiator is adjusted.   The radiation can be passed through filters or shut off by shields.   Figure 4.2h shows a filter whose absorbing property can be varied: for example, the amount of CO_2 gas or the quantity of the water vapor in the filter space modulates the radiation.   The absorption may be partial or total, depending upon the property of the filter placed in the path of radiation.   The total filtering, shown in Fig. 4.2i, would be analogous to changing the area of material exposed to the radiation.

Of the many possible ways to manipulate heat processes, only a few have been shown in Fig. 4.2.   The important issue is to recognize when a thermal process has the possibility of being manipulated rapidly, or when its thermal capacity prevents it from being manipulated rapidly.

4. CONVECTION HEATERS

Hot and cold liquid streams can be mixed together in a hold-up vessel or a short pipeline to manipulate the temperature of the mixture.   The vessel is generally stirred to give uniform mixing of the hot and cold fluid inflow with the contents of the vessel.   If the inflow streams have constant temperature and constant flow rates, and if the specific heats of the material are constant, the temperature of the mixture in the hold-up vessel should remain constant.

The thermal equilibrium of the hold-up vessel can become disturbed in many ways. The sensible-heat flows might have a constant average value, but vary momentarily. The temperature of the environment of the tank might change, thus causing the thermal losses to vary. The demand for fluid outflow from the tank can increase or decrease the hold-up in the tank. Consequently, the thermal capacity of the tank will change. Changes in the throughput can change the thermal conductance between the fluid and the walls of the vessel or of the pipe.

To determine the possibilities of temperature regulation and control by means of convection heaters, one must write the heat-balance equations for the process. Several possible variations of the mixing type of heater are enumerated in Table 4.1. The schematic for each system is shown in the first column; the differential equations, in the second column; the Laplace transform of the differential equations, in the third column; and the block diagram that describes the thermal process, in the fourth column.

Vessel Perfectly Insulated. Item 1 in Table 4.1 shows a tank of fluid hold-up of volume V, with good agitation. Two streams of heated fluid enter the tank. The fluid stream with a volumetric flow rate Q_1 has a temperature T_1. The stream with a flow rate Q_2 has the temperature T_2. If the tank is an overflow type, the hold-up is constant and the outflow Q is equal to the sum of the two inflows. Otherwise, if the head empties the tank, the total inflow $Q_1 + Q_2$ can be made to equal the outflow Q when the level is properly regulated.

The temperature T of the outflow is equal to the average temperature throughout the tank, since the fluids are well mixed. The sensible heat H_1 carried in by the stream Q_1 is $\rho_1 C_{p1} T_1 Q_1$; the sensible heat H_2 carried in by the Q_2 stream is $\rho_2 C_{p2} T_2 Q_2$. The sensible heat H_o carried away by the outflow stream will be $\rho_o C_{po} T_o Q_o$. The heat balance in the form of a differential equation

$$\rho_o C_{po} V \frac{dT}{dt} = H_1 + H_2 - H_o \tag{4.15}$$

$$= \rho_1 C_{p1} T_1 Q_1 + \rho_2 C_{p2} T_2 Q_2 - \rho_o C_{po} T_o Q_o \tag{4.16}$$

expresses the average temperature T of the fluid in the mixing tank, provided the tank is sufficiently well insulated so that no heat loss takes place through the tank walls. Since the tank is well agitated, $T = T_o$.

TABLE 4.1. CONVECTION HEATERS

Schematic	Differential Equations	Transfer Functions	Signal-flow Diagram
1. Perfectly insulated and perfectly mixed vessel. Thermal holdup $= \rho_o C_{po} V$	$\rho_o C_{po} \dfrac{dT_o}{dt} = \rho_1 C_{p1} T_1 Q_1 + \rho_2 C_{p2} T_2 Q_2 - \rho_o C_{po} T_o Q_o$ $Q_o = Q_1 + Q_2$ $\dfrac{V}{Q_o}\dfrac{dT_o}{dt} + T_o = \dfrac{\rho_1 C_{p1}}{\rho_o C_{po}} T_1 \dfrac{Q_1}{Q_o} + \dfrac{\rho_2 C_{p2}}{\rho_o C_{po}} T_2 \dfrac{Q_2}{Q_o}$	$T_o(s) = \dfrac{1}{\rho_o C_{po} Q_o \left(\dfrac{V}{Q_o}s + 1\right)}[H_1(s) + H_2(s)] + \rho_o C_{po} V T_o(0^+)$ where $H_1(s) = \mathcal{L}[\rho_1 C_{p1} T_1(t) Q_1(t)]$ $H_2(s) = \mathcal{L}[\rho_2 C_{p2} T_2(t) Q_2(t)]$	
2. Perfectly mixed vessel with conducting, zero thermal capacity wall. $H_2 = hA(T_o - T_x)$	$\rho_o C_{po} V \dfrac{dT_o}{dt} = \rho_1 C_{p1} T_1 Q_1 + \rho_2 C_{p2} T_2 Q_2 - \rho_o C_{po} T_o Q_o - hA(T_o - T_x)$ $\left(\dfrac{V}{Q_o}\right)\left(\dfrac{1}{1 + \dfrac{hA}{\rho_o C_{po} Q_o}}\right)\dfrac{dT_o}{dt} + T_o = K'[H_1(t) + H_2(t) + hAT_x]$ where $K' = \dfrac{1}{\rho_o C_{po} Q_o + hA}$	$T_o(s) = \dfrac{K'}{\tau' s + 1}[H_1(s) + H_2(s) + hAT_x(s)] + \rho_o C_{po} V T_o(0^+)$ where $\tau' = \dfrac{\tau}{1 + \dfrac{hA}{\rho_o C_{po} Q_o}}$	
3. Perfectly mixed vessel, insulated, with finite thermal capacity wall. Thermal holdup in wall $= \rho_m C_{pm} V_m$	$\rho_o C_{po} V \dfrac{dT_o}{dt} = \rho_1 C_{p1} T_1 Q_1 + \rho_2 C_{p2} T_2 Q_2 - \rho_o C_{po} T_o Q_o - h_{fm} A_{fm}(T_o - T_m)$ $\rho_m C_{pm} V_m \dfrac{dT_m}{dt} = h_{fm} A_{fm}(T_o - T_m)$	$\dfrac{\rho_o C_{po} V s + \rho_o C_{po} Q_o + h_{fm} A_{fm}}{H_1(s) + H_2(s) + h_{fm} A_{fm} T_m(s) + \rho_o C_{po} V T_o(0^+)}\,T_o(s) =$ $\dfrac{\rho_m C_{pm} V_m s + h_{fm} A_{fm}}{h_{fm} A_{fm} T_o(s) + \rho_m C_{pm} V_m T_m(0^+)}\,T_m(s) =$	
4. Perfectly mixed vessel with radiation losses from finite thermal capacity wall. $H_3 + H_2$	$\rho_o C_{po} V \dfrac{dT_o}{dt} = \rho_1 C_{p1} T_1 Q_1 + \rho_2 C_{p2} T_2 Q_2 - \rho_o C_{po} T_o Q_o - h_{fm} A_{fm}(T_o - T_m)$ $\rho_m C_{pm} V_m \dfrac{dT_m}{dt} = h_{fm} A_{fm}(T_o - T_m) - h_{mx} A_{mx}(T_m - T_x)$	$[\rho_o C_{po} V s + \rho_o C_{po} Q_o + h_{fm} A_{fm}]T_o(s) =$ $H_1(s) + H_2(s) + h_{fm} A_{fm} T_m(s) + \rho_o C_{po} V T_o(0^+)$ $[\rho_m C_{pm} V_m s + h_{fm} A_{fm} + h_{mx} A_{mx}]T_m(s) =$ $h_{fm} A_{fm} T_o(s) + h_{mx} A_{mx} T_x(s) + \rho_m C_{pm} V_m T_m(0^+)$	

The transfer function $\dfrac{1}{\tau s + 1}$ relates fluid temperature $T(s)$ with the total inflow of sensible heat to the vessel. The form of the operator shows that the process has a first-order thermal lag. The transfer function is characterized by the time constant $\tau = \dfrac{V}{Q}$, *which is the mixing lag for the vessel.* Thus, the time lag τ for the basic convection process is the familiar "hold-up over throughput" ratio that we have found so useful in the case of materials handling and fluids handling, and not a thermal lag at all.

Vessel with Conduction Losses. When the mixing vessel has conduction losses to the outside, but when the material of the vessel itself has zero thermal capacity, the equations in Table 4.1, item 2, show that the time constant for the convection process is

$$\tau' = \frac{V}{Q_o} \left[\frac{1}{1 + \dfrac{hA}{\rho_o C_{po} Q_o}} \right] \tag{4.17}$$

Thus the time lag τ' for the vessel with losses is a modification of τ for the perfectly insulated tank. The time constant τ' will always be smaller than the mixing lag τ, since the term $hA/\rho_o C_{po} Q_o$ will always be a number which is positive and greater than zero. However, the form of the transfer function which characterizes the process does not change.

Vessel with Thermal Capacity. Consider next item 3, in which the metal of the vessel has a thermal capacity C_m. Two cases can be considered: In the first, the thermal capacity of the metal can be taken into account, but the insulation between the metal and the outside can be considered perfect, so that zero losses occur. In the second case, conduction takes place between the metal of the vessel and the outside.

Two simultaneous equations, one expressing the temperature T of the mixture in the vessel, and the other expressing the temperature T_m of the metal, will be needed to describe the process dynamics of the vessel with perfect insulation:

$$\rho_o C_{po} V \frac{dT}{dt} = H_1 + H_2 - H_{fm} - H_o \tag{4.18}$$

$$\rho_m C_{pm} V_m \frac{dT_m}{dt} = H_{fm} \tag{4.19}$$

The differential equations can be transformed and collected into a suitable expression to give either the temperature of the liquid $T(s)$ or the temperature of the metal $T_m(s)$ as functions of the sensible heats $H_1(s)$ and $H_2(s)$.

When thermal systems like this one are encountered, sometimes a signal-flow diagram or block diagram proves to be an effective way of studying the dynamics of the process. Therefore, the interpretation of the signal-flow diagram shown in item 3, Table 4.1, is as follows:

The summation of sensible heat $H_1 + H_2$ entering the vessel has added to it the initial value of heat $\rho_o C_{po} V T_o(0^+)$ which results from the fluid inflow's having an initial temperature $T(0^+)$. The amount of heat H_o that flows out of the vessel is subtracted. The net heat flow ΣH is integrated, $1/s$, and divided by the thermal capacity C of the fluid hold-up. The signal generated after the integration is the fluid temperature T. However, because of the sensible-heat flow H_o carried out of the vessel, the integration $1/Cs$ has a negative-feedback loop $\rho_o C_{po} Q_o$ around it. This establishes a first-order lag between $\Sigma H(s)$ and $T(s)$.

The second component of heat flow H_{fm} from the fluid into the metal of the vessel is also subtracted from the heat flowing into the vessel. The temperature $T(s)$ is compared with the metal temperature $T_m(s)$. The difference ΔT is multiplied by the conductance $h_{fm} A_{fm}$ to produce the heat H_{fm} which is transferred. To the heat H_{fm} there must be added the initial value of heat stored in the metal, $C_m T(0^+)$. When the total heat flowing to or from the metal is established at the heat-summing point for the metal, the net heat flow to the metal $\Sigma H'$, integrated by the operator $1/\rho_m C_{pm} V_m s$, produces the metal temperature $T_m(s)$. The temperature T_m is fed back and enters the comparison point mentioned before.

It is important to note the interlocking loops in the signal-flow diagram. The path defined by T_m back to the summing point with T, and then through the pathway ΔT, H_{fm}, $\Sigma H_m'$, and T_m constitutes a closed pathway. The other closed path from the first summing point through Σ_h, T, ΔT_1, H_{fm}, and back is another closed path. A common member occurs in these two closed paths: namely, the conductance $h_{fm} A_{fm}$. This is reasonable, since the conductance between the two is the only means whereby thermal energy can transfer between the fluid in the vessel and the metal of the vessel.

Vessel with Thermal Capacity and Conduction Losses. To study the dynamic behavior of the vessel which has a thermal capacity of the metal C_m and conduction losses from the metal to the outside, requires that the signal-flow diagram for item 3 in Table 4.1 be extended. The metal temperature T_m has subtracted from it the outside temperature T_x. The difference in temperature, multiplied by the conductance G_{mx} between the metal and the outside environment, produces the heat flow H_{mx} which is lost from the convection heater. The signal representing heat flow H_{mx} must be fed back to the heat-summation point so that the heat flow from the fluid to the metal H_{fm} has subtracted from it the heat flow H_{mx} from the metal to the outside. The difference ΣH_2, when integrated by $1/\rho_m C_{pm} V_m s$, produces the metal temperature T_m.

In the block diagram for item 4, Table 4.1, three interlocking loops appear instead of two, which defined the perfectly mixed vessel with thermal capacity of the metal vessel but zero thermal conduction losses. The three signal loops interlock in such a way that the simplification of the block diagram by the rules outlined in Appendix 1 is somewhat more difficult. Nevertheless, the equations can be solved to predict the temperature of the outflowing fluid T in terms of the heat supplied $H_1 + H_2$. The outside temperature T_x will be a disturbance on the convection heater. Changes in environment temperature will of necessity have to be accounted for in the design of the convection types of thermal regulators.

Frequency - Response Characteristics. The frequency - response characteristics of the convection-type heaters can be studied by noting how the outflow temperature $T(j\omega)$ changes as a function of the total heat supplied to the vessel $H(j\omega)$. For the vessel which is a mixing tank, the frequency characteristic $20 \log_{10} \left| \dfrac{T(j\omega)}{H(j\omega)} \right|$ has a slope sequence of 0, -20 decibels per decade. The break frequency ω is located at the reciprocal of the time constant $1/\tau = Q_o/V$. Therefore the process bandwidth is proportional to the throughput Q, and inversely proportional to the hold-up V.

For the convection heater, which has conduction losses to the outside, but zero thermal capacity, the reciprocal of the time constant τ' determines the break frequency (see Table 4.1, item 2). Since $\tau' < \tau$, the break frequency $\omega' > \omega$. Therefore, the bandwidth of a convection heater with losses will be greater than that of the perfectly insulated vessel. The temperature is less affected by incremental periodic changes in the sensible-heat inflow for the vessel with poor insulation than it is for the perfectly insulated vessel.

The third item in Table 4.1, where the influence of the thermal capacity of the metal vessel must be taken into account when the heater dynamics is being evaluated, presents a more difficult analytical problem. The relationship between the temperature $T(j\omega)$ and the total heat inflow $H(j\omega)$ has the quadratic form

$$\frac{T_o(j\omega)}{H(j\omega)} = \frac{1}{\left[(G_{fm} + G_T)\left(\dfrac{C}{G_T + G_{fm}} j\omega + 1 \right) - \dfrac{G_{fm}}{\left(\dfrac{C_m}{G_{fm}} j\omega + 1 \right)} \right]} \tag{4.20}$$

$$\frac{T_o(j\omega)}{H(j\omega)} = \frac{\left(\dfrac{C_m}{G_{fm}} j\omega + 1 \right)}{(G_{fm} + G_T)\left(\dfrac{C}{G_T + G_{fm}} j\omega + 1 \right)\left(\dfrac{C_m}{G_{fm}} j\omega + 1 \right) - G_{fm}} \tag{4.21}$$

where $C = \rho_o C \rho_o V$, $G_{fm} = h_{fm} A_{fm}$, $G_T = \rho_o C_{po} Q_o$, $C_m = \rho_m C_{pm} V_m$, $\tau_m = \dfrac{C_m}{G_{fm}}$

Then

$$\frac{T_o(j\omega)}{H(j\omega)} = \frac{K''(\tau_m j\omega + 1)}{(\tau_m j\omega + 1)(\tau'' j\omega + 1) - G_{fm} K''} \tag{4.22}$$

where

$$\tau'' = \frac{V/Q_o}{1 + \dfrac{h_{fm} A_{fm}}{\rho_o C_{po} Q_o}} \tag{4.23}$$

and

$$K'' = \frac{1}{\rho_o C_{po} Q_o + h_{fm} A_{fm}} < 1 \tag{4.24}$$

Equation 4.22 shows that the frequency-response characteristic which relates the temperature T to the total sensible-heat flow H has a denominator which will have two poles, and a numerator which gives the function one zero. The two poles in the denominator will lie on the negative real axis of the s-plane. These can never be conjugate complex poles. Also both poles will be negative in value, since a thermal system can neither have a condition of oscillatory heat transfer nor exhibit runaway. The zero in the numerator will lie on the negative real axis of the s-plane between the two poles of the denominator. This indicates that there will be a slope sequence of 0, $+20$ decibels per decade for the numerator factor. Combined they can give various combinations of negative and positive slopes. However, a general algebraic study of the transfer function shows that the denominator will approach a perfect square as the conductivity G_{fm} decreases.

When G_{fm} approaches zero, the vessel is lossless and the thermal capacity C_m will have no significance because there can be no conduction between the fluid and the metal. Therefore, only the first-order mixing lag V/Q has significance.

However, as G_{fm} increases with respect to the quantity $\rho_o C_{po} Q_o$, the factor G_{fm} times K'' approaches unity. Therefore the roots of the quadratic factor will tend to remain always real. The presence of metal in this convection heater will tend to flatten the response of the vessel temperature to sensible-heat flow disturbances.

The convection heater with losses and vessel thermal capacity, described by the fourth item in Table 4.1, has the same general form of transfer function as does the physical system described in Item 3, with the exception that the temperature $T_o(j\omega)$ is a function of two disturbances: the sensible-heat flow $H(j\omega)$ and the external temperature $T_x(j\omega)$. The response equation becomes

$$T_o(j\omega) = \frac{1}{\left[G_{T'}\left(\dfrac{C}{G_{T'}} j\omega + 1\right) - \dfrac{G_{fm}{}^2}{G_{T''}\left(\dfrac{C_m}{G_{T''}} j\omega + 1\right)} \right]} H(j\omega)$$

$$+ \frac{G_{fm} G_{mx} \dfrac{1}{G_{T''}} \left(\dfrac{1}{\dfrac{C_m}{G_{T''}} j\omega + 1}\right)}{\left[G_{T'}\left(\dfrac{C}{G_{T'}} j\omega + 1\right) - \dfrac{G_{fm}{}^2}{G_{T''}\left(\dfrac{C_m}{G_{T''}} j\omega + 1\right)} \right]} T_x(j\omega) \quad (4.25)$$

where

$$G_{T'} = G_T + G_{fm} \quad (4.26)$$

$$G_{T''} = G_{mf} + G_{mx} \quad (4.27)$$

Equation 4.25 simplifies to the form

$$T_o(j\omega) = \left[\frac{K''(\tau''' j\omega + 1)}{(\tau''' j\omega + 1)(\tau'' j\omega + 1) - K'' K''' G_{mf}{}^2} \right] H(j\omega)$$

$$+ \left[\frac{K'' K''' G_{fm} G_{mx}}{(\tau''' j\omega + 1)(\tau'' j\omega + 1) - K'' K''' G_{mf}{}^2} \right] T_x(j\omega) \quad (4.28)$$

where

$$\tau''' = \frac{C_m}{G_{mf} + G_{mx}} = \frac{\tau_m}{1 + \dfrac{G_{mx}}{G_{mf}}} \quad (4.29)$$

$$\tau'' = \frac{C}{G_o + G_{mf}} = \frac{\tau}{1 + \dfrac{h_{mf} A_{mf}}{\rho_o C_{po} Q_o}} \tag{4.30}$$

$$K'' = \frac{1}{G_T + G_{fm}} = \frac{1}{G_{T'}} \tag{4.31}$$

$$K''' = \frac{1}{G_{mf} + G_{mx}} = \frac{1}{G_{T''}} \tag{4.32}$$

5. CONVECTION-TYPE TEMPERATURE REGULATOR

A convection-type temperature regulator is shown in Fig. 4.3.   A constant flow of liquid passes through the hold-up vessel.   Heat is brought into the vessel by a flow of steam which condenses as it bubbles into the liquid.   All the steam is used: that is, no steam escapes from the surface of the liquid.

The amount of steam condensate Q_{sc} is small compared to the liquid throughput Q.   The agitation in the hold-up vessel is perfect, so that the liquid and steam condensate are instantly mixed.

The purpose of the regulator is to maintain constant the temperature of the liquid stream leaving the hold-up vessel.   The disturbances to the thermal process will be variations in the temperature of the inflow liquid stream.   The modulation of the steam flow counteracts the disturbances.   Sometimes fluctuations in steam pressure also create disturbances, but these will not be included here.

A thermal detector located at the exit of the vessel or in the outflow line measures the temperature T_o.   A controller positions a throttle valve in the steam-flow line in proportion to the temperature error $\mathcal{E}_T = T_{\text{ref}} - T_m$.   The signal-flow diagram shown in Fig. 4.4 indicates how the regulator operates.

According to the diagram, the time lag τ_p of the process will be the principal time lag in the system.   The detector time lag τ_d, however,

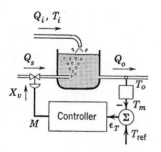

Fig. 4.3.   Convection-type temperature regulator.

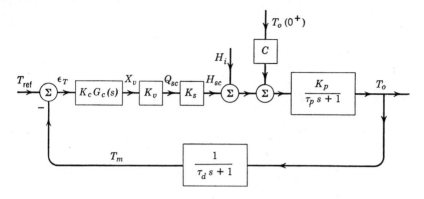

Fig. 4.4. Signal-flow diagram of convection-type temperature regulator—Process vessel perfectly insulated.

may have to be taken into account.   The asymptote magnitude characteristic in Fig. 4.5 shows the exit flow temperature $T_o(j\omega)$ as a function of the controlled heat flow $Q_{sc}(j\omega)$.   Curve $abcd$ is the asymptote which describes the open-loop regulator dynamics for unity gain.   The first break in the curve is located at the frequency $\omega_1 = 1/\tau_p$.   The second break is located at the frequency $\omega_2 = 1/\tau_d$.

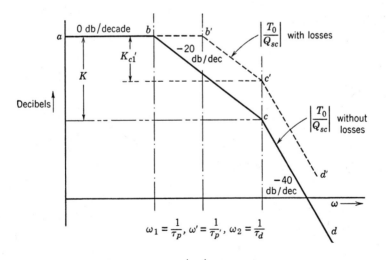

Fig. 4.5. Frequency response characteristic $\left|\dfrac{T_o}{Q_{sc}}\right|$ for convection-type temperature regulator showing the influence of process vessel conduction losses.

If τ_d is very small, a high closed-loop gain K can be obtained for the temperature regulator. The value of the gain $K_c K_v K_s K_p$ will be large in direct proportion to the value of ω_2 or $1/\tau_d$.

Process with Thermal Losses. An interesting change in the regulator performance takes place if the hold-up vessel has conduction losses to the outside. When the tank loses heat by conduction to the outside environment, but the metal of the tank does not have any thermal capacity, the time lag τ_p changes. According to the work in Table 4.1, the value of τ_p' was proved to have the value

$$\tau_p' = \frac{\rho_o C_{po} V}{\rho_o C_{p_o} Q_o + h_{fo} A_{fo}} = \frac{\tau_p}{1 + \dfrac{h_{fo} A_{fo}}{\rho_o C_{p_o} Q_o}} = \alpha \tau_p \qquad (4.33)$$

Conduction from the vessel to the outside decreases the time constant τ_p' of the process. The break frequency b', which corresponds to the new value of process time constant $1/\tau_p'$, lies to the right of point b on the asymptote graph. The curve representing the open-loop attenuation characteristic for the temperature regulator is now $ab'c'd'$. The portion of the curve $b'c'd'$ has asymptotes which are parallel to the asymptotes for the system with zero conduction losses. However, since point b' is to the right of point b, and the point c' has not changed its location in the frequency scale because the detector time constant remains unchanged, the maximum permissible gain in the closed loop will be less for the process with losses than that for the process without losses. Here we have the anomaly: The static gain of the regulator decreases, but the bandwidth of the process member has been improved.

Addition of Metal Thermal Capacity

In contrast to the former study, if the thermal capacity of the tank must be taken into account, in the convection type of regulator, but the losses to the outside remain zero, further limitations are forced upon the gain and the bandwidth of the system. Figure 4.6 shows the signal-flow diagram. There is a heat transfer from the fluid to the metal H_{fm}. Upon integration of this heat flow, the metal temperature $T_m(s)$ is obtained. The metal temperature is compared with the fluid temperature $T_f(s)$, and the difference in temperature ΔT becomes the true driving force which modulates the heat transfer from the fluid through the area of contact between the fluid and the metal into the metal. The signal-flow diagram can be simplified successively as shown to give the relationship between the temperature of the fluid

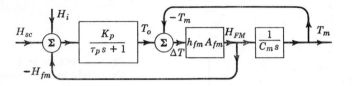

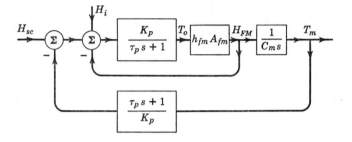

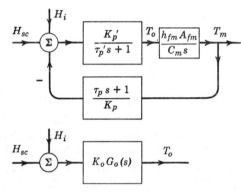

Fig. 4.6. Signal-flow diagram development for convective-type temperature regulator–vessel has thermal capacity but zero conduction losses.

$T(s)$, the heat supplied by the steam condensate H_{sc}, and the heat brought in by the inflowing stream H_i.

The transfer function $K_o G_o$ will be:

$$\frac{T_o(s)}{\mathcal{E}H(s)} = \frac{K_p'\dfrac{h_{fm}A_{fm}}{C_m}}{\tau_p's^2 + \left(1 + \dfrac{K_p'h_{fm}A_{fm}}{K_pC_m}\tau_p\right)s + \dfrac{K_p'h_{fm}A_{fm}}{K_pC_m}} \qquad (4.34)$$

The quadratic-function break frequency will *not* be equal to the time constant τ_p of the process.

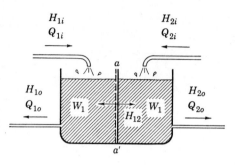

H_{1i}
Q_{1i}

H_{2i}
Q_{2i}

H_{1o}
Q_{1o}

H_{2o}
Q_{2o}

W_1

W_1

H_{12}

a

a'

Fig. 4.7. Two convection heaters placed side by side to form heat exchanger.

In Fig. 4.6, $K_p = 1/\rho_o C_{po} Q_o$, $\tau_p = V/Q_o$,

$$\tau_p' = \frac{V/Q_o}{1 + \dfrac{h_{fm} A_{fm}}{\rho_o C_{po} Q_o}} \tag{4.35}$$

$$K' = \frac{1}{\rho_o C_{po} Q_o + h_{fm} A_{fm}} \tag{4.36}$$

6. TWO CONVECTION HEATERS AS A SIMPLE HEAT EXCHANGER

Two convection heaters can be placed side by side so that their common boundary becomes a heat-exchanging surface as shown in Fig. 4.7. Liquid flow Q_{1i} enters the first convection heater, and liquid flow Q_{1o} leaves. The sensible heat flows are H_{1i} and H_{1o}. The hold-up W_1 is adjacent to the surface aa' through which there is a heat exchange H_{12}. On the other side of the barrier, the second convection heater has a liquid inflow Q_{2i}, a liquid outflow Q_{2o}, sensible-heat flows H_{2i} and H_{2o}, and a hold-up W_2.

A variety of cases can be studied for the "double convection" exchanger. Perfect mixing for each hold-up vessel, zero losses to the outside, and zero thermal capacity in dividing surface can be assumed. The barrier thermal capacity C_m can exist even though perfect mixing and zero losses occur. Finally, the metal of vessels themselves can have thermal capacities, the barrier can have thermal capacity, and losses can occur to the outside.

The basic differential equations which describe the average temperature of the fluid in the vessel on the left and the vessel on the right for: (1) perfect mixing in both hold-ups, (2) zero losses to the outside, and (3) zero thermal capacity in barrier, are:

$$\rho_1 C_{p1} V_1 \frac{dT_1}{dt} = H_{1i} - H_{1o} - H_{12} \tag{4.37}$$

$$= \rho_1 C_{p1} T_{1i} Q_{1i} - \rho_1 C_{p1} T_1 Q_{1o} - h_{12} A (T_1 - T_2) \tag{4.38}$$

$$\rho_2 C_{p2} V_2 \frac{dT_2}{dt} = H_{2i} - H_{2o} + H_{21} \tag{4.39}$$

$$= \rho_2 C_{p2} T_{2i} Q_{2i} - \rho_2 C_{p2} T_2 Q_{2o} - h_{12} A (T_2 - T_1) \tag{4.40}$$

From eqs. 4.37 and 4.39 the signal-flow diagram development shown in Fig. 4.8 can be made for the simple exchanger in which the metal has zero thermal capacity. Two heat-summing points are required—one in which all of the heat adding to or subtracting from the vessel on the left-hand side must be directed, and the second one where all the heat adding to or subtracting from the vessel on the right-hand side must be directed. The temperature T_1 is the average temperature of the fluid in the vessel on the left, and the temperature T_2 is the average temperature of the fluid in the vessel on the right. Their difference, multiplied by the conductance G_{12} and multiplied by the area of the surface through which heat is transferring, gives the heat transfer H_{12} which takes place between the vessel on the left and the vessel on the right.

The disturbance to the system is H_{2i}, the heat flow into the second vessel. The manipulation variable becomes H_{1i}, the heat flow to the first vessel. The initial temperatures $T_1(0^+)$ and $T_2(0^+)$ appear as external signals.

The relationship between the temperature T_2, which is also the temperature of the outflow Q_{2o}, and the heat H_{1i} and the heat H_{2i} is given

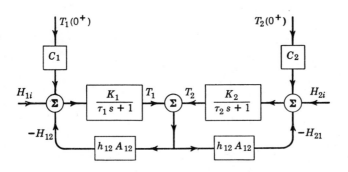

Fig. 4.8. Signal-flow diagram for the double convection heater used as a simple heat exchanger.

by

$$T_2(s) = \left[\frac{\dfrac{(h_{12}A)K_1'K_2'}{(\tau_1's + 1)(\tau_2's + 1)}}{1 - \dfrac{(h_{12}A)^2K_1'K_2'}{(\tau_1's + 1)(\tau_2's + 1)}} \right] H_{1i}(s)$$

$$+ \left[\frac{\dfrac{K_2'}{\tau_2's + 1}}{1 - \dfrac{(h_{12}A)^2K_1'K_2'}{(\tau_1's + 1)(\tau_2's + 1)}} \right] H_{2i}(s) \quad (4.41)$$

The temperature T_1 is given by a similar relationship:

$$T_1(s) = \left[\frac{\dfrac{K_1'}{(\tau_1's + 1)}}{1 - \dfrac{(h_{12}A)^2K_1'K_2'}{(\tau_1's + 1)(\tau_2's + 1)}} \right] H_{1i}(s)$$

$$+ \left[\frac{\dfrac{(h_{12}A)K_1'K_2'}{(\tau_1's + 1)(\tau_2's + 1)}}{1 - \dfrac{(h_{12}A)^2K_1'K_2'}{(\tau_1's + 1)(\tau_2's + 1)}} \right] H_{2i}(s) \quad (4.42)$$

If there is perfect mixing in both vessels and there are zero losses to the outside, but the metal has thermal capacity C_m, three simultaneous equations are needed to describe the process.

$$\rho_1 C_{p1} V_1 \frac{dT_1}{dt} = H_{1i} - H_{1o} - H_{1m} \tag{4.43}$$

$$= \rho_1 C_{p1} T_{1i} Q_{1i} - \rho_1 C_{p1} T_1 Q_{1o} - h_{1m} A_{1m}(T_1 - T_m) \tag{4.44}$$

$$\rho_m C_{pm} V_m \frac{dT_m}{dt} = H_{m1} - H_{m2} \tag{4.45}$$

$$= h_{1m} A_{1m}(T_1 - T_m) - h_{m2} A_{m2}(T_m - T_2) \tag{4.46}$$

$$\rho_2 C_{p2} V_2 \frac{dT_2}{dt} = H_{2i} - H_{2o} + H_{m2} \tag{4.47}$$

$$= \rho_2 C_{p2} T_{2i} Q_{2i} - \rho_2 C_{p2} T_2 Q_{2o} + h_{m2} A_{m2}(T_m - T_2) \tag{4.48}$$

The response equations can be determined by solving the set of simultaneous equations.   Determinants can also be used.

7. DERIVATION OF GENERAL EQUATIONS FOR CONVECTIVE HEAT TRANSFER

The partial differential equations which describe heat exchange between two fluids separated by a conducting barrier can be formulated.   However, these equations become very complex unless certain assumptions are made about the physics of the problem.   To simplify the mathematical study, assume: (1) that according to Fig. 4.9, one fluid flows inside a tube which is surrounded by another fluid environment; (2) that radial temperature distributions are averaged and the only space variable is the distance x in the direction of flow measured from the inlet of the tube; (3) that the effects of buoyancy are negligible, only forced convection, as opposed to natural or free convection, being considered; (4) that heat conduction in the direction of flow is negligible both in the fluid and in the tube wall; (5) that effects of radiation and radial conduction are included in the over-all local heat-transfer coefficient; (6) that the specific heats are constant; (7) that the density of an incompressible fluid is constant; (8) that convective heat-transfer coefficients are functions of temperature and velocity for a given apparatus; (9) that the mechanical energy (kinetic and potential) is negligible compared with thermal energy.

The variable U can be used to define a specific property of the fluid inside the tube.   The quantity V can be used to define the energy, mass, or momentum carried through the tube by the inner fluid.   The variable V is in proportion to U and to the volume element under consideration.   In the differential section between x and $x + dx$, the general conservation relationship, accumulation = gain − loss, can be applied.

At time t, the quantity V stored in the volume element $A\,dx$ is $k_o U A\,dx$, where A is cross-section of the slice and k_o is the constant of proportionality relating U and V.   At time $t = t + dt$, the quantity

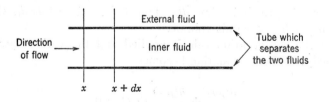

Fig. 4.9.   Single-tube heat exchanger.

stored is $k_o \left(U + \dfrac{\partial U}{\partial t} \, dt \right) A \, dx$. The quantity accumulated in time

dt is the net increase in the quantity stored: $k_o \dfrac{\partial U}{\partial t} A \, dx \, dt$.

At x, the quantity carried in (or gained) in time dt is $k_1 U A \, dt$, where k_1 is a constant depending on the flow rate.   At $x = x + dx$, the quantity carried out (or lost) in time dt is $k_1 \left(U + \dfrac{\partial U}{\partial x} \, dx \right) A \, dt$.

According to a law of transfer, the quantity lost from the slice, in the time dt, other than by transport, is $f(U) A \, dx \, dt$.   By combining these terms in the conservation equation, the partial differential equation which describes the thermal process is:

$$k_o \frac{\partial U}{\partial t} + k_1 \frac{\partial U}{\partial x} + f(U) = 0 \tag{4.49}$$

When $f(U)$ is a linear function and k_o and k_1 are independent of U, eq. 4.49 is a linear partial differential equation which can be solved for given boundary conditions by either classical or transform method of mathematics.

Conservation of Energy

The general equation, eq. 4.49, can be applied specifically to the study of energy.   At time t, the energy stored in the element $A \, dx$ is $\rho u A \, dx$, where ρ is the density and u is the internal energy of the fluid.

The energy accumulated in time dt in the slice dx is $\dfrac{\partial(\rho u)}{\partial x} A \, dx \, dt$.

The energy passing a point x in time dt is $\rho e v \, A \, dt$, where e is the enthalpy and v is the velocity of the fluid.   The net energy lost from the slice dx in time dt due to transport is $\dfrac{\partial(\rho e v)}{\partial x} A \, dx \, dt$.

A law of energy transfer defines the energy lost through the tube wall over a length dx in time dt.   Thus the loss is $Q A \, dx \, dt$, where Q is the energy flux per unit volume.

When the conservation rule is applied and the various parts are combined, the energy equation becomes

$$\frac{\partial(\rho u)}{\partial t} + \frac{\partial(\rho e v)}{\partial x} + Q = 0 \tag{4.50}$$

Conservation of Mass

A similar study can be made for the mass. At time t, the mass stored in the volume element $A\,dx$ is $\rho A\,dx$. The mass accumulated in time dt in $A\,dx$ is $\dfrac{\partial \rho}{\partial t} A\,dx\,dt$. The mass passing a point x in time dt is $\rho v A\,dt$. The net mass lost from the volume element $A\,dx$ in time dt due to transport is $\dfrac{\partial(\rho v)}{\partial x} A\,dx\,dt$. Since no mass can be transferred through the tube wall, the mass equation becomes:

$$\frac{\partial \rho}{\partial t} + \frac{\partial(\rho v)}{\partial x} = 0 \tag{4.51}$$

Conservation of Momentum

According to Newton's law, $F = \dfrac{d}{dt}(mv)$, where F is force, m is mass, and v is velocity. When the $\Sigma F = 0$ are set up for the volume element, two forces must be considered. First, there is a force due to the viscous drag between the tube walls and the fluid. This is a friction force or viscosity force. Secondly, there is the force due to the pressure difference between the two ends of the element $A\,dx$.

At x, the pressure force is AP, where A is the area and P is the pressure. At $x + dx$, the pressure force is $-A\left(P + \dfrac{\partial P}{\partial x} A\,dx\right)$.

The viscosity force in three dimensions is given by*

$$F_\mu A\,dx = A\,dx \left\{ \mu \left(\frac{\partial^2 v_x}{\partial x^2} + \frac{\partial^2 v_x}{\partial y^2} + \frac{\partial^2 v_x}{\partial z^2} \right) + \frac{\mu}{3} \frac{\partial}{\partial x} \left(\frac{\partial v_x}{\partial x} + \frac{\partial v_y}{\partial y} + \frac{\partial v_z}{\partial z} \right) \right\} \tag{4.52}$$

where μ is the viscosity and v_x, v_y, and v_z are the velocity components along the coordinate axes. If the fluid is incompressible, eq. 4.52 reduces to the form $\dfrac{\partial v_x}{\partial x} + \dfrac{\partial v_y}{\partial y} + \dfrac{\partial v_z}{\partial z} = 0$. The velocity components, v_x and v_z, can be chosen zero. The velocity in the direction of flow can be taken as the average velocity v_x with respect to radial distance from the tube axis. Thus the derivatives of v_x with respect to y and z can be eliminated from the expression for the friction force. Thus,

* *Heat Transfer*, vol. I, M. Jacob, John Wiley & Sons, Inc., 1949, p. 18.

for an incompressible fluid, the friction force is given by

$$\mu \frac{\partial^2 v}{\partial x^2} A \, dx \qquad\qquad (4.53)$$

For a compressible fluid, the friction force is

$$\frac{4}{3} \mu \frac{\partial^2 v}{\partial x^2} A \, dx \qquad\qquad (4.54)$$

The friction force can be considered the same, with and without heat transfer, except that the viscosity and density must be assigned values consistent with the operating temperature of the system. If the flow is laminar, the friction force is $8\pi\mu v \, dx$. If the flow is turbulent, experimental measurement[*] has shown that the viscosity force is: $0.1243(N_{Re})^{0.75}\mu v \, dx$, where $N_{Re} = vD\rho/\mu$ = Reynold's number, and D is the tube diameter. Equations 4.53 and 4.54 apply only to smooth tubes. For rough tubes, the friction force is given by[†]

$$\frac{\pi}{2} f N_{Re} \mu v \, dx \qquad\qquad (4.55)$$

where f is the friction factor, which is an experimentally determined function of Reynold's number and the degree of roughness of the tube. Thus, the general viscous force is $F_\mu A \, dx$, where F_μ is the friction force per unit volume.

The rate of change of momentum of an element of mass of the system must next be found. An element of mass dx changes momentum because of the change in its velocity. Since the velocity is a function of time and distance, the rate of change must be expressed as a total derivative. Thus:

$$\frac{dv}{dt} = \frac{\partial v}{\partial t} + \frac{\partial v}{\partial x} \frac{dx}{dt} = \frac{\partial v}{\partial t} + v \frac{\partial v}{\partial x} \qquad\qquad (4.56)$$

The element of mass can be expressed in terms of the density as $dm = \rho \, A dx$. The resulting force balance provides the equation of conservation of momentum for the system:

$$\rho \frac{\partial v}{\partial t} + \rho v \frac{\partial v}{\partial x} + g \frac{\partial P}{\partial x} = F_\mu \qquad\qquad (4.57)$$

The general equations for the conservation, mass, and momentum can now be combined with the equation of state: $P = \phi(\rho, T)$ to pro-

[*] *Ibid.*, p. 433.
[†] *Ibid.*, p. 434.

vide sets of partial differential equations which can express the heat transfer between various combinations of gases and liquids in a single tube exchanger.

8. EQUATIONS FOR LIQUID AND VAPOR HEAT EXCHANGERS

The energy, mass, and momentum equations which were developed for convective heat exchange in section 7 can be applied to the study of various types of liquid and gas heat exchangers. For example: The heat transfer to a tube which passes through a well-mixed medium can be studied. The environment temperature may be constant or variable in time, but invariant in distance along the tube. Both liquids and gases may be considered. The tube may or may not have thermal capacity. To complicate the problem, thermal conduction may take place axially in the fluid, in the tube, or in both. For a "thick-walled" tube, the radial gradient of temperature within the tube itself must be considered. Some problems may involve condensing vapors or boiling liquids.

Variable-environment temperature studies are more important to consider than are the ones for constant-environment temperature. Concentric tubes with various gas or liquid combinations in concurrent or countercurrent flow become the ultimate problem to be studied. How various physical effects influence the dynamics of heat exchange in convective heat transfer, is the issue.

Liquid Element: Transfer to or from a Liquid

The energy equation and the law of convective heat transfer can be applied to both the liquid and the tube wall. For the liquid, the heat flux $\dfrac{\text{Btu/hr}}{\text{ft}^3}$ is given by $\dfrac{\pi D}{A} h_{fw}(T_f - T_w)$, where πD is the wall perimeter, h_{fw} is the film coefficient, fluid to wall, T_f is the liquid temperature, T_w is the wall temperature, and A is the cross-sectional area of liquid flow.

The internal energy and the enthalpy are essentially the same for an incompressible fluid. Therefore the internal energy and the enthalpy of the fluid are given by

$$u_f = e_f = c_f T_f \tag{4.58}$$

where c_f is the specific heat of the liquid.

The energy equation for the liquid becomes:

$$\frac{\partial(\rho_f c_f T_f)}{\partial t} + \frac{\partial(\rho_f c_f T_f v)}{\partial x} + \frac{\pi D}{A} h_{fw}(T_f - T_w) = 0 \tag{4.59}$$

On the exchange tube wall, $v = 0$, so that the enthalpy term in the energy equation disappears. The internal energy of the tube wall is given by

$$u_w = c_w T_w \tag{4.60}$$

where c_w is the specific heat of the wall. The net heat flux from the wall is given by

$$\frac{h_{we}}{x_w} (T_w - T_e) - \frac{h_{fw}}{x_w} (T_f - T_w) \tag{4.61}$$

where x_w is wall thickness, h_{we} is film coefficient, wall to environment, T_e is environment temperature.

The energy equation for the exchange tube wall becomes:

$$\frac{\partial(\rho_w c_w T_w)}{\partial t} + \frac{h_{we}}{x_w} (T_w - T_e) - \frac{h_{fw}}{x_w} (T_f - T_w) = 0 \tag{4.62}$$

The remaining equations are the mass and momentum equations. Since the fluid is incompressible, the density is constant and the mass equation becomes $\dfrac{\partial v}{\partial x} = 0$. The momentum equation can be written as:

$$\rho_f \frac{\partial v}{\partial t} + g \frac{\partial P}{\partial x} = F_\mu \tag{4.63}$$

Specifically, for a single tube filled with an incompressible fluid as the flowing medium, the equations which describe the heat flow to or from the element are:

$$\frac{\partial T_f}{\partial t} + v \frac{\partial T_f}{\partial x} + \frac{\pi D h_{fw}}{A \rho_f c_f} (T_f - T_w) = 0 \tag{4.64}$$

$$\frac{\partial T_w}{\partial t} + \frac{h_{we}}{\rho_w c_w x_w} (T_w - T_e) + \frac{h_{fw}}{\rho_w c_w x_w} (T_w - T_f) = 0 \tag{4.65}$$

$$\frac{\partial v}{\partial x} = 0 \tag{4.66}$$

$$\rho_f \frac{\partial v}{\partial t} = F_\mu - \frac{\partial P}{\partial x} \tag{4.67}$$

where T_f = liquid temperature, °F

$\quad T_w$ = tube wall temperature, °F

$\quad T_e$ = environment temperature, °F

$\quad h_{fw}$ = film coefficient, liquid to wall, $\dfrac{\text{Btu}}{\text{hr °F ft}^2}$

h_{we} = film coefficient, wall to environment, $\dfrac{\text{Btu}}{\text{hr °F ft}^2}$

ρ_f = density of liquid, lb/ft^3

ρ_w = density of tube wall, lb/ft^3

c_f = specific heat of liquid $\dfrac{\text{Btu}}{\text{lb °F}}$

c_w = specific heat of tube wall, $\dfrac{\text{Btu}}{\text{lb °F}}$

πD = perimeter of tube wall, ft

x_w = thickness of tube wall, ft

A = flow cross-section of tube, ft^2

Gas Element: Transfer to or from a Gas

The heat flux from the gas is given by

$$\frac{\pi D}{A} h_{gw}(T_g - T_w) \tag{4.68}$$

where T_g is the gas temperature, h_{gw} is the film coefficient, gas to tube wall. The internal energy of an ideal gas is given by $u_g = c_v T_g$, where c_v is the specific heat of the gas at constant volume $\dfrac{\text{Btu}}{\text{lb °F}}$. The enthalpy of an ideal gas is given by $e_g = c_p T_g$, where c_p is the specific heat of the gas at constant pressure.

The energy equation for the gas becomes:

$$\frac{\partial(\rho_g c_v T_g)}{\partial t} + \frac{\partial(\rho_g c_p T_g v)}{\partial x} + \frac{\pi D h_{gw}}{A}(T_g - T_w) = 0 \tag{4.69}$$

The energy equation for the exchange tube wall is identical with eq. 4.69, except that h_{fw} is replaced by h_{gw} and T_f by T_g. Thus

$$\frac{\partial T_w}{\partial t} + \frac{h_{we}}{\rho_w c_w x_w}(T_w - T_e) - \frac{h_{gw}}{\rho_w c_w x_w}(T_g - T_w) = 0 \tag{4.70}$$

The mass and momentum equations are:

$$\frac{\partial \rho_g}{\partial t} + \frac{\partial(\rho_g v)}{\partial x} = 0 \tag{4.71}$$

$$\rho_g \frac{\partial v}{\partial t} + \rho_g v \frac{\partial v}{\partial x} + g \frac{\partial P}{\partial x} = F_\mu \tag{4.72}$$

$$P = \rho_g R_o T_g \tag{4.73}$$

where R_o is the specific gas constant for the gas being considered. Thus, when the flowing medium is a compressible gas, and the geometry of the single tube exchanger is the same as for the liquid element, the equations of the element are:

$$c_v \frac{\partial(\rho_g T_g)}{\partial t} + c_p \frac{\partial(\rho_g T_g v)}{\partial x} + \frac{\pi D h_{gw}}{A}(T_g - T_w) = 0 \qquad (4.74)$$

$$\frac{\partial T_w}{\partial t} + \frac{h_{we}}{\rho_w c_w x_w}(T_w - T_e) + \frac{h_{gw}}{\rho_w c_w x_w}(T_w - T_g) = 0 \qquad (4.75)$$

$$\frac{\partial \rho_g}{\partial t} + \frac{\partial(\rho_g v)}{\partial x} = 0 \qquad (4.76)$$

$$\rho_g \frac{\partial v}{\partial t} + \rho_g v \frac{\partial v}{\partial x} + g \frac{\partial P}{\partial x} = F_\mu \qquad (4.77)$$

$$P = \rho_g R_o T_g \qquad (4.78)$$

where T_g = gas temperature
$\quad h_{gw}$ = film coefficient, gas to tube wall
$\quad \rho_g$ = gas density
$\quad c_v$ = specific heat of gas at constant volume
$\quad c_p$ = specific heat of gas at constant pressure
$\quad R_o$ = specific gas constant, ft-lb/°F-lb

Condensing or Vaporizing Element: Transfer from a Condensing Vapor or to a Boiling Liquid

To determine the relative proportion of vapor and liquid at a point x in the tube, let a be the mass of liquid contained in a unit volume, and b be the mass of vapor contained in a unit volume. In addition:

v_f = velocity of liquid, ft/sec
v_v = velocity of vapor, ft/sec
A = tube cross-section, ft^2
ρ_f = liquid density, lb/ft^3
ρ_v = vapor density, lb/ft^3
G = *total* mass flow rate, lb/sec-ft^2

The volumes occupied by the liquid and the vapor become:

$$\text{Liquid volume} = \frac{aA\,dx}{\rho_f} \qquad (4.79)$$

$$\text{Vapor volume} = \frac{bA\,dx}{\rho_v} \qquad (4.80)$$

Therefore

$$\frac{aA\ dx}{\rho_f} + \frac{bA\ dx}{\rho_v} = A\ dx \qquad (4.81)$$

Or $\dfrac{a}{\rho_f} + \dfrac{b}{\rho_v} = 1$ can be defined as $y = \dfrac{a/\rho_f}{\dfrac{a}{\rho_f} + \dfrac{b}{\rho_v}} = \dfrac{a}{\rho_f} =$ liquid fraction

of total volume. At the inlet of the vaporizer, $y = 1$. Always, $0 < y < 1$.

The mass flow of the liquid is av_f and the vapor is bv_v. Therefore $av_f + bv_v = G$. The proportion of liquid flow is

$$z = \frac{av_f}{av_f + bv_v} = \frac{av_f}{G}.$$

For condensation, $z = 0$ at the inlet; for vaporization, $z = 1$ at the inlet. Always, $0 < z < 1$.

The variables a, b, v_f, and v_v become:

$$a = \rho_f y \qquad (4.82)$$

$$b = \rho_v(1 - y) \qquad (4.83)$$

$$v_f = \frac{G}{\rho_f}\left(\frac{z}{y}\right) \qquad (4.84)$$

$$v_v = \frac{G}{\rho_v}\left(\frac{1-z}{1-y}\right) \qquad (4.85)$$

The energy passing a point x in time dt is $(e_f v_f a + e_v v_v b)A\ dt$. The net energy lost from a differential slice dx in time dt due to transport is $\dfrac{\partial}{\partial x}(e_f v_f a + e_v v_v b)A\ dx\ dt$. The energy stored at time t in a differential slice dx is $(u_f a + u_v b)A\ dx$. The energy accumulated in time dt in a differential slice dx is $\dfrac{\partial}{\partial t}(u_f a + u_v b)A\ dx\ dt$. The energy lost in time dt in a differential slice dx due to heat transfer is $h_{vw}(T_v - T_w)\ \pi D\ dx\ dt$, where T_v is the boiling or condensing temperature and h_{vw} is the film coefficient from condensing or vaporizing fluid to exchange tube wall. The energy balance yields the equation:

$$\frac{\partial}{\partial x}(e_f v_f a + e_v v_v b) + \frac{\partial}{\partial t}(u_f a + u_v b) + \frac{\pi D}{A} h_{vw}(T_v - T_w) = 0 \qquad (4.86)$$

The mass passing a point x in time dt is $(av_f + bv_v)A\ dt$. The mass lost from a differential slice dx in time dt due to transport is $\dfrac{\partial}{\partial x}(av_f + bv_v)\,A\,dx\,dt$. The mass stored at time t in a differential slice is $(a + b)A\,dx$. The mass accumulated in time dt in a differential slice dx is $\dfrac{\partial}{\partial t}(a + b)A\,dx\,dt$. The mass balance yields the equation:

$$\frac{\partial}{\partial t}(a + b) + \frac{\partial}{\partial x}(av_f + bv_v) = 0 \qquad (4.87)$$

For the momentum equation, the force balance gives

$$dF = \frac{dv_f}{dt}\,dm_f + \frac{dv_v}{dt}\,dm_v \qquad (4.88)$$

where $dF = -\dfrac{\partial P}{\partial x}A\,dx + F_\mu A\,dx$. From the force balance,

$$a\frac{\partial v_f}{\partial t} + b\frac{\partial v_v}{\partial t} + av_f\frac{\partial v_f}{\partial x} + bv_v\frac{\partial v_v}{\partial x} = F_\mu - \frac{\partial P}{\partial x}g \qquad (4.89)$$

An energy balance applied to the exchange tube wall gives

$$\frac{\partial T_w}{\partial t} + \frac{h_{vw}}{\rho_w c_w x_w}(T_w - T_v) - \frac{h_{we}}{\rho_w c_w x_w}(T_e - T_w) = 0 \qquad (4.90)$$

The expressions for a, b, v_f, and v_v can be substituted into eqs. 4.88, 4.89, and 4.90 to form the general energy, mass, and momentum equations for a condensation or vaporization element. Thus:

$$\frac{\partial}{\partial x}\{G[(e_f - e_v)s + e_v]\} + \frac{\partial}{\partial t}\{(\rho_f u_f - \rho_v u_v)y + \rho_v u_v\}$$
$$+ \frac{\pi D}{A}h_{vw}(T_v - T_w) = 0 \qquad (4.91)$$

$$\frac{\partial}{\partial t}\{(\rho_f - \rho_v)y + \rho_v\} + \frac{\partial G}{\partial x} = 0$$

$$\rho_f y\frac{\partial}{\partial t}\left(\frac{Gz}{\rho_f y}\right) + \rho_v(1 - y)\frac{\partial}{\partial t}\left[\frac{G}{\rho_v}\left(\frac{1 - z}{1 - y}\right)\right] + Gz\frac{\partial}{\partial x}\left(\frac{Gz}{\rho_f y}\right)$$
$$+ G(1 - z)\frac{\partial}{\partial x}\left[\frac{G}{\rho_v}\left(\frac{1 - z}{1 - y}\right)\right] = F_\mu - \frac{\partial P}{\partial x}g \qquad (4.92)$$

where T_v = vapor temperature
  G = total mass velocity based on tube cross-section, lb/ft^2 – sec
  e_f = enthalpy of liquid
  e_v = enthalpy of vapor
  u_f = internal energy of liquid
  u_v = internal energy of vapor
  ρ_f = density of liquid
  ρ_v = density of vapor
  h_{vw} = over-all film coefficient, vapor to tube wall
  z = ratio of liquid mass velocity to total mass velocity
  y = ratio of liquid volume to total volume

9. DYNAMIC RESPONSE OF HEAT EXCHANGERS

The purpose in writing the general equations which describe convective-heat transfer between two fluids was to establish a basis for predicting the dynamic response of the heat exchangers. The cause-and-effect relationships between the physical variables which describe the two fluids must be known before manipulation over exchangers to counteract disturbances can be considered upon a quantitative basis.

Unfortunately, the general equations given in section 7 and the more specific equations given in section 8 are nonlinear. Unless the sets of equations can be uncoupled and rendered quasi-linear or linear, little hope exists for a quantitative evaluation of the dynamic response of heat exchangers. The work of Gould* established the extent to which the general equations of section 7 could be linearized so that the performance of simple heat exchangers could be studied from an automatic-control point of view. This work showed that the impulse transient characteristics and the frequency-response characteristics of simple exchanger forms could be predicted.

For liquid exchangers, provided the flow does not vary greatly, and provided the temperature does not vary over wide ranges, the equations can be linearized. The gas exchangers present a somewhat more difficult problem. Finally, to linearize the equations which describe exchangers with condensing vapors and boiling liquids becomes a very difficult problem.

To linearize the conservation and state equations requires that the parameters in the equations which are functions of time and distance be replaced by constants which are either invariant with both time and distance or independent of time and variant linearly with distance.

---

* L. A. Gould, "The Dynamic Behavior and Control of Heat Transfer Processes," Sc.D. Thesis, Dept. of Electrical Engineering, M.I.T., 1953.

Since the equations to be solved, even though linearized, are partial types, transcendental functions of complex variables must be handled. These transcendental forms are difficult to work with; it is especially difficult to determine the solutions to the equations and to prepare inverse Laplace transformations that will yield transient behavior of the exchangers to disturbances or manipulations. Studies in frequency response become complex and difficult to interpret.

One way to simplify the problem is to convert the linearized partial-differential equations into linear equivalent ordinary differential equations. These equations can be treated as rational functions in the complex variable which respond to the ordinary direct and inverse Laplace transformation techniques.

Response of a Single Tube Exchanger in a Perfectly Mixed Shell

The dynamic nature of the heat exchange between the fluid in a single tube and a perfectly mixed surrounding fluid can be found.

The set of equations which describe the heat exchange of the liquid element in the tube and the surrounding environment are nonlinear because: the film coefficient h_{fw} is a function of temperature T_f and velocity G; the friction force F_μ is also a function of the temperature and velocity; and the velocity can be a function of viscosity, which in turn becomes a function of temperature. However, the equations of primary interest are:

$$\rho_f \frac{\partial T_f}{\partial t} + G \frac{\partial T_f}{\partial x} + \frac{\pi D h_{fw}}{A c_f}(T_f - T_w) = 0 \qquad (4.93)$$

$$\frac{\partial T_w}{\partial t} + \frac{h_{we}}{\rho_w c_w x_w}(T_w - T_e) + \frac{h_{fw}}{\rho_w c_w x_w}(T_w - T_f) = 0 \qquad (4.94)$$

where G is $\rho_f v$, which is the mass velocity. Equations 4.93 and 4.94 become linear if neither the stream velocity G nor the variations in temperature are so great that the heat-transfer coefficient h_{fw} is a function of temperature or flow.

For a liquid element with constant mass flow rate G, variable environment temperature T_e, but constant environment side film coefficient h_{we}, the equations which described the dynamic response can be completely linearized.

$$C_f \frac{\partial T_f}{\partial t} + G_f \frac{\partial T_f}{\partial x} + g_{fw}(T_f - T_w) = 0 \qquad (4.95)$$

$$C_w \frac{\partial T_w}{\partial t} + g_{we}(T_w - T_e) - g_{fw}(T_f - T_w) = 0 \qquad (4.96)$$

where

$$C_f = \rho_f c_f A \tag{4.97}$$

$$C_w = \rho_w c_w x_w \pi D \tag{4.98}$$

$$G_f = GAc_f \tag{4.99}$$

$$g_{fw} = \pi D h_{fw} \tag{4.100}$$

$$g_{we} = \pi D h_{we} \tag{4.101}$$

To explore the cause-and-effect nature of the heat exchange for control applications, eqs. 4.95 and 4.96 can be expressed as Laplace transforms.
In eqs. 4.93 and 4.94, let

$$b_1 = h_{fw}/C_f \tag{4.102}$$

$$b_2 = h_{we}/C_w \tag{4.103}$$

$$b_3 = h_{fw}/C_w \tag{4.104}$$

$$b_4 = G_f/C_f \tag{4.105}$$

Also, if each temperature is considered to be the steady-state value T_{ss} and a variable portion T', the differential equations become:

$$\frac{\partial T_f'}{\partial t} + b_4 \frac{\partial T_f'}{\partial x} + b_1(T_f' - T_w') + b_4 + b_1 = 0 \tag{4.106}$$

$$\frac{\partial T_w'}{\partial t} + b_2(T_w' - T_e') + b_2 + b_3(T_w' - T_f') + b_3 = 0 \tag{4.107}$$

By definition, the differential steady-state terms in each equation must equal zero. The initial value of the variable portion of each temperature can be made as zero. The Laplace-transformed equations become

$$(s + b_1)T_f'(x, s) + b_4 \frac{\partial T_f'(x, s)}{\partial x} = b_1 T_w'(x, s) \tag{4.108}$$

$$(s + b_2 + b_3)T_w'(x, s) = b_3 T_f'(x, s) + b_2 T_e'(x, s) \tag{4.109}$$

Next, $T_w'(x, s)$ is eliminated and the ordinary differential equation

$$b_4 \frac{dT_f'(x, s)}{dx} + \left[\frac{s^2 + (b_1 + b_2 + b_3)s + b_1 b_2}{s + b_2 + b_3} \right] T_f'(x, s)$$
$$= \left(\frac{b_1 b_2}{s + b_2 + b_3} \right) T_e'(x, s) \tag{4.110}$$

results.

To simplify eq. 4.110, let

$$\alpha(s) = \frac{s^2 + (b_1 + b_2 + b_3)s + b_1 b_2}{s + b_2 + b_3} \qquad (4.111)$$

$$= s + b_1 - \frac{b_1 b_3}{s + b_2 + b_3} \qquad (4.112)$$

$$\beta(s) = \frac{b_1 b_2}{s + b_2 + b_3} \qquad (4.113)$$

Equation 4.110 can be Laplace transformed a second time with respect to the variable x.

$$[b_4 p + \alpha(s)]T_f'(p, s) = \beta(s)T_e'(p, s) + b_4 T_f'(0, s) \qquad (4.114)$$

The environment temperature $T_e'(p, s)$ becomes the manipulation variable. The temperature $T_f'(0, s)$ of the fluid entering the tube at $x = 0$ is the disturbance.

When the environment fluid is perfectly mixed, the temperature $T_e'(p, s)$ is independent of the distance x along the tube. The transform of $T_e'(p, s)$ becomes $\frac{1}{p} T_e'(s)$. The temperature of fluid any where in the tube can be expressed in terms of transfer function form:

$$T_f'(p, s) = \left[\frac{\beta(s)}{b_4 p + \alpha(s)}\right]\left(\frac{1}{p}\right)T_e'(s) + \left[\frac{b_4}{b_4 p + \alpha(s)}\right]T_f'(0, s) \qquad (4.115)$$

The transfer function

$$H_1(p, s) = \frac{\beta(s)}{b_4 p + \alpha(s)} \qquad (4.116)$$

determines the relationship between the temperature of the fluid $T_f'(p, s)$ anywhere in the tube $0 < x < L$ and the manipulation $T_e'(s)$ for $T_f'(0, s) = 0$.

The transfer function

$$H_2(p, s) = \frac{b_4}{b_4 p + \alpha(s)} \qquad (4.117)$$

relates the outflow to inflow temperature in the tube for a constant temperature environment.

The solution to eq. 4.116 is obtained by expanding the first term on the right-hand side into a partial fraction and then taking the inverse

Laplace transform term by term. The fluid temperature becomes

$$T_f'(x, s) = \frac{\beta(s)}{\alpha(s)} [1 - e^{-\frac{\alpha(s)}{b_4}x}]T_e'(s) + [e^{-\frac{\alpha(s)}{b_4}x}]T_f'(0, s) \quad (4.118)$$

The temperature of the fluid emerging from the tube at $x = L$ is

$$T_f'(L, s) = \frac{\beta(s)}{\alpha(s)} [1 - e^{-\frac{\alpha(s)}{b_4}x}]T_e'(s) + [e^{-\frac{\alpha(s)}{b_4}x}]T_f'(0, s) \quad (4.119)$$

Thus, the partial differential equations for the single tube exchanger have been solved in such a way that transfer functions $H_1(s)$ and $H_2(s)$ relate the temperatures $T_f'(L, s)$, $T_e'(s)$ and $T_f'(0, s)$.

The function

$$H_2(s) = e^{-\frac{\alpha(s)L}{b_4}} \quad (4.120)$$

also has the form

$$H_2(s) = e^{-t_d s} \cdot e^{-t_d b_1} \cdot e^{t_d \left(\frac{b_1 b_3}{s+b_2+b_3}\right)} \quad (4.121)$$

where t_d is the "dead time" L/b_4 related to the flow in the tube over the length L.

The transfer function

$$H_1(s) = \frac{\beta(s)}{\alpha(s)} [1 - e^{-\frac{\alpha(s)L}{b_4}}] \quad (4.122)$$

can be expressed in terms of the transfer function $H_2(s)$.

$$H_1(s) = \frac{\beta(s)}{\alpha(s)} [1 - H_2(s)] \quad (4.123)$$

Figure 4.10 shows the signal flow diagram which can be drawn for

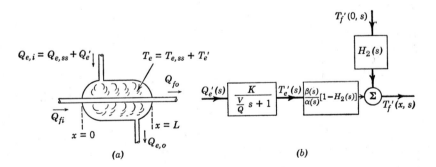

(a)   (b)

Fig. 4.10. Simple heat exchanger: A tube passing through a perfectly mixed shell (a) Physical arrangement; (b) Signal-flow diagram.

the single tube passing through a perfectly mixed shell. The convection mixing lag V/Q for the shell must be included.

Impulse Response

If $T_{fo}'(0, s)$ is a unit impulse and $T_e'(s) = 0$, the impulse response $h_2(t)$ corresponding to $H_2(s)$ can be found by expanding $H_2(s)$ in an infinite series and inverse-transforming term by term.

The last exponential in the expression for $H_2(s)$ can be expanded so that the form of $H_2(s)$ is

$$H_2(s) = e^{-b_1 t_d} e^{-t_d s} \left[1 + \sum_{n=1}^{\infty} \frac{1}{n!} \left(\frac{b_1 b_3 t_d}{s + b_2 + b_3} \right)^n \right] \quad (4.124)$$

The inverse transformation of eq. 4.124 is

$$h_2(t) = e^{-b_1 t_d} \left([\delta(t - t_d)] + \left[\sum_{n=1}^{\infty} \frac{1}{n!} \mathcal{L}^{-1} \left\{ \left(\frac{t_d b_1 b_3}{s + b_2 + b_3} \right)^n e^{-t_d s} \right\} \right] u(t - t_d) \right) \quad (4.125)$$

where $u(t - t_d)$ is a unit step at $t = t_d$, and $\delta(t - t_d)$ is a unit impulse at $t = t_d$. The inverse Laplace transform in eq. 4.125 can be found. Thus,

$$\mathcal{L}^{-1} \left\{ \left(\frac{t_d b_1 b_3}{s + b_2 + b_3} \right)^n e^{-t_d s} \right\} = e^{-(b_2 + b_3)(t - t_d)} \left[\frac{(b_1 b_3 t_d)^n (t - t_d)^{n-1}}{(n - 1)!} \right] \quad (4.126)$$

The impulse response $h(t)$ corresponding to $H(s)$ is given by:

$$h_2(t) = e^{-b_1 t_d} \left([\delta(t - t_d)] + \left[s^{-(b_2 + b_3)(t - t_d)} \sum_{n=1}^{\infty} \frac{(b_1 b_3 t_d)^n (t - t_d)^{n-1}}{n!(n - 1)!} \right] u(t - t_d) \right) \quad (4.127)$$

For an arbitrary variation of the inlet temperature, the outlet temperature variation is given by the superposition integral:

$$T_{fL}'(t) = \int_0^{\infty} h_2(x) T_{fo}'(t - x) \, dx \quad (4.128)$$

Similarly, if $T_e'(s)$ is a unit impulse and $T_f'(0, s) = 0$, the impulse response $h_1(t)$ corresponding to $H_1(s)$ can be found.

$$H_1(s) = \left\{ \frac{b_1 b_2}{s^2 + (b_1 + b_2 + b_3)s + b_1 b_2} \right\} [1 - H_2(s)] \quad (4.129)$$

$$= \left[\frac{K_1}{s - s_1} + \frac{K_2}{s - s_2} \right] [1 - H_2(s)] \quad (4.130)$$

where K_1 and K_2 and the roots s_1 and s_2 must be determined for the specific parameters b_1, b_2, and b_3.

The forms $\dfrac{K_1}{s - s_1}$ and $\dfrac{K_2}{s - s_2}$ can be inversely transformed directly. However, the terms containing $H_2(s)$ have the form typical of transforms which lead to Bessel functions.   Thus

$$H_1(s) = \phi_1(s) + \phi_2(s) + \phi_3(s) \quad (4.131)$$

$$\phi_1(s) = \frac{K_1}{s - s_1} - \frac{K_2}{s - s_2} \quad (4.132)$$

$$\phi_2(s) = -K_e{}^{-b_1 t_d} e^{-t_d s} \frac{1}{s - s_1} e^{\frac{c_o}{s + c_1}} \quad (4.133)$$

$$\phi_3(s) = +K e^{-b_1 t_d} e^{-t_d s} \frac{1}{s - s_2} e^{\frac{c_o}{s + c_1}} \quad (4.134)$$

The term $\phi_1(s)$ can be inversely transformed directly.   Except for the time delay $e^{-t_d s}$ both $\phi_2(s)$ and $\phi_3(s)$ have the form

$$\frac{1}{s + a} e^{\frac{c_o}{s + c_1}} \quad (4.135)$$

The inverse transform of $\phi_2(s)$ becomes

$$\phi_2(t) = -K e^{-b_1 t_d} e^{-c_1(t - t_d)} \sum_{v=0}^{\infty} \beta_1{}^v c_o{}^{-\frac{v}{2}} (t - t_d)^{\frac{v}{2}} I_v(2 \sqrt{c_o(t - t_d)})$$

$$(4.136)$$

where $\beta_1 = (s_1 + c_1)$.   The impulse response $h_1(t)$ becomes

$$h_1(t) = K(e^{s_1 t} - s^{s_2 t}) \quad \text{for} \quad 0 < t < t_d \quad (4.137)$$

and

$$h(t) = K(e^{-s_1 t} - e^{s_2 t}) + K e^{-b_1 t_d} e^{-c_1(t - t_d)} \quad (4.138)$$

$$\sum_{v=0}^{\infty} \left(\frac{\beta_2{}^v - \beta_1{}^v}{c_o{}^{v/2}} \right) (t - t_d)^{v/2} I_v(2 \sqrt{c_o(t - t_4)}) \quad (4.139)$$

for $t > t_d$. Thus, the impulse response becomes a series of Bessel functions.

If the exponent $\dfrac{\alpha(s)}{b_4} L$ is investigated for order of magnitude of numerical coefficients, the approximation

$$H_2(s) = e^{-\frac{\alpha(s)L}{b_4}} = 1 - \frac{\alpha(s)L}{b_4} + \frac{\alpha(s)^2 L^2}{2 b_4{}^2} \cdots \qquad (4.140)$$

$$[1 - H_2(s)] = 1 - e^{-\frac{\alpha(s)L}{b_4}} = \frac{\alpha(s)L}{b_4} - \frac{\alpha(s)^2 L^2}{2 b_4{}^2} + \frac{\alpha(s)^3 L^3}{2.3 b_4{}^3} \qquad (4.141)$$

can be used. Thus

$$H_1(s) \simeq \beta(s) \frac{L}{b_4} \qquad (4.142)$$

$$\simeq \left(\frac{L}{b_4} b_1 b_2\right) \left[\frac{1}{s + (b_2 + b_3)}\right] \qquad (4.143)$$

and the impulse response becomes

$$h_1(t) = \left(\frac{L}{b_4} b_1 b_2\right) e^{-(b_2 + b_3)t} \qquad (4.144)$$

Finally the superposition integral permits the fluid temperature $T_f{}'(L, t)$ to be expressed for combined disturbance and manipulation.

$$T_f{}'(L, t) = \int_0^\infty h_2(x) T_f{}'(0, t - x)\, dx + \int_0^\infty h_1(y) T_e{}'(t - y)\, dy \qquad (4.145)$$

Response of a Concentric Tube Exchanger

Consider next the heat exchange between two fluids that flow in concentric tubes as shown in Fig. 4.11. The differential equations can be derived for the temperature $T_1(x, t)$ and $T_2(x, t)$ in the fluids from the energy equation. The temperature $T_w(x, t)$ of the separating wall can be expressed by a third energy equation so that the ther-

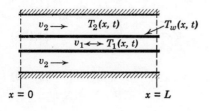

Fig. 4.11. Concentric tube exchanger.

mal capacity of the separating wall can be included in the analysis. When necessary, one additional equation can be written to express the heat loss from the outer tube to the surrounding environment.

Four situations occur: First, in the two tubes the fluid flow may be steady and *concurrent;* secondly, the flows may be steady but *counter-current;* finally, either one or both of the flows may be variable with respect to time. The steady flow cases lead to linear partial differential equations; the variable flow cases, to nonlinear partial differential equations. For restricted conditions of time variations in the flow, the nonlinear equations can be linearized.

In this section the heat exchange dynamics for steady concurrent and counter-current flow will be studied. The losses to the environment from the outer tube will be neglected. The wall temperature will be considered an average value without gradient. In general, the conditions for analysis stated in section 7, hold.

$$\rho_1 c_1 \frac{\partial T_1}{\partial t} + \rho_1 c_1 v_1 \frac{\partial T_1}{\partial x} + \frac{\pi D}{A_1} h_1 (T_1 - T_w) = 0 \qquad (4.146)$$

$$\rho_w c_w \frac{\partial T_w}{\partial t} + \frac{h_2}{x_w} (T_w - T_2) - \frac{h_1}{x_w} (T_1 - T_w) = 0 \qquad (4.147)$$

$$\rho_2 c_2 \frac{\partial T_2}{\partial t} + \rho_2 c_2 v_2 \frac{\partial T_2}{\partial x} + \pi D \frac{h_2}{A_2} (T_2 - T_w) = 0 \qquad (4.148)$$

for $v_1 = $ constant and $v_2 = $ constant and $T = T_{ss} + T'$

$$\frac{\partial T_1'}{\partial t} + d_4 \frac{\partial T_1'}{\partial x} + d_1 (T_1' - T_w') = 0 \qquad (4.149)$$

$$\frac{\partial T_w'}{\partial t} + d_2 (T_w' - T_2') + d_3 (T_w' - T_1') = 0 \qquad (4.150)$$

$$\frac{\partial T_2'}{\partial t} + d_5 \frac{\partial T_2'}{\partial x} + d_6 (T_2' - T_w') = 0 \qquad (4.151)$$

where

$$d_1 = \frac{\pi D h_1}{C_1} \qquad (4.152) \qquad\qquad d_4 = v_1 \qquad (4.155)$$

$$d_2 = \frac{h_2}{C_w} \qquad (4.153) \qquad\qquad d_5 = v_2 \qquad (4.156)$$

$$d_3 = \frac{h_1}{C_w} \qquad (4.154) \qquad\qquad d_6 = \frac{\pi D h_2}{C_2} \qquad (4.157)$$

Equations 4.149, 4.150, and 4.151 can be Laplace transformed first with respect to t.

$$d_4 \frac{\partial T_1'(x, s)}{\partial x} + (s + d_1)T_1'(x, s) = d_1 T_w'(x, s) \qquad (4.158)$$

$$(s + d_2 + d_3)T_w'(x, s) = d_2 T_2'(x, s) + d_3 T_1'(x, s) \qquad (4.159)$$

$$d_5 \frac{\partial T_2'(x, s)}{\partial x} + (s + d_6)T_2'(x, s) = d_6 T_w'(x, s) \qquad (4.160)$$

The wall temperature variation $T_w'(x, s)$ can be eliminated so that

$$d_4 \frac{\partial T_1'(x, s)}{\partial x} + \lambda_1(s)T_1'(x, s) = \psi_1(s)T_2'(x, s) \qquad (4.161)$$

$$d_5 \frac{\partial T_2'(x, s)}{\partial x} + \lambda_2(s)T_2'(x, s) = \psi_2(s)T_1'(x, s) \qquad (4.162)$$

where

$$\lambda_1(s) = s + d_1 - \frac{d_1 d_3}{s + d_2 + d_3} \qquad (4.163)$$

$$\lambda_2(s) = s + d_6 - \frac{d_6 d_3}{s + d_2 + d_3} \qquad (4.164)$$

$$\psi_1(s) = \frac{d_1 d_2}{s + d_2 + d_3} \qquad (4.165)$$

$$\psi_2(s) = \frac{d_6 d_3}{s + d_2 + d_3} \qquad (4.166)$$

A second transformation with respect to x gives the general set of equations in p and s for the concentric tube exchanger. However, the boundary conditions must be chosen to distinguish between concurrent and counter-current fluid flow.

Concurrent Flow

When the two streams flow concurrently, the boundary conditions become: $x = 0$, $T_1'(x, s) = T_1'(0, s)$, $T_2'(x, s) = T_2'(0, s)$. Thus the transformed equations become:

$$d_4 p + \lambda_1(s)T_1'(p, s) = \psi_1(s)T_2'(p, s) + d_4 T_1'(0, s) \qquad (4.167)$$

$$d_5 p + \lambda_2(s)T_2'(p, s) = \psi_2(s)T_1'(p, s) + d_5 T_2'(0, s) \qquad (4.168)$$

Equation 4.167 and 4.168 can be solved for the temperatures $T_1'(p, s)$ and $T_2'(p, s)$.

$$T_1'(p, s) = \frac{d_5\psi_1(s)T_2'(0, s) + d_4T_1'(0, s)}{\{[d_4p + \lambda_1(s)][d_5p + \lambda_2(s)] - \psi_1(s)\psi_2(s)\}} \quad (4.169)$$

$$T_2'(p, s) = \frac{d_4\psi_2(s)T_1'(0, s) + d_5T_2'(0, s)}{\{[d_5p + \lambda_1(s)][d_4p + \lambda_2(s)] - \psi_1(s)\psi_2(s)\}} \quad (4.170)$$

The characteristic equation in p

$$d_4d_5p^2 + [d_4\lambda_2(s) + d_5\lambda_1(s)] + [\lambda_1(s)\lambda_2(s) - \psi_1(s)\psi_2(s)] = 0 \quad (4.171)$$

can be simplified and factored to obtain two roots, p_1 and p_2, both of which are functions of the variable s. The roots of the characteristic equation are

$$p_1 \text{ and } p_2 = -\frac{d_4\lambda_2 + d_5\lambda_1}{2d_4d_5}$$

$$\pm j\frac{1}{2d_4d_5}\sqrt{(d_4\lambda_2 + d_5\lambda_1)^2 - 4d_4d_5(\lambda_1\lambda_2 - \psi_1\psi_2)} \quad (4.172)$$

$$= -m(s) \pm n(s) \quad (4.173)$$

Counter-Current Flow

When the two fluids flow counter-currently, the boundary conditions are: $x = 0$, $T_1'(x, s) = T_1'(0, s)$, but $T_2'(x, s) = T_2'\left(\frac{v_2}{v_1}L, s\right)$. When the velocities of the two streams are equal so that $v_1 = v_2$ $T_2'(x, s) = T_2'(L, s)$. The transformed equations become

$$d_4p + \lambda_1(s)T_1'(p, s) = \psi_1(s)T_2'(p, s) + d_4T_1'(0, s) \quad (4.174)$$

$$d_5p + \lambda_2(s)T_2'(p, s) = \psi_2(s)T_1'(p, s) + d_5T_2'(L, s) \quad (4.175)$$

Equations 4.174 and 4.175 will have the same form of solution as eqs. 4.167 and 4.168. The characteristic equation in p will be the same as for concurrent flow. However, the sign of the coefficients which contain v_1 and v_2 must be chosen to indicate that $v_1 = -v_2$ or $v_1 = -\alpha v_2$.

When the stream velocities $v_1 = v_2$ for concurrent flow, $d_4 = d_5$. The roots of the characteristic equation become

$$p_1, p_2 = -\frac{1}{2d_4}(\lambda_2 + \lambda_1) \pm j\frac{1}{2d_4}\sqrt{(\lambda_2 + \lambda_1)^2 - 4(\lambda_1\lambda_2 - \psi_1\psi_2)}$$

$$\quad (4.176)$$

$$= -m(s) \pm jn(s) \quad (4.177)$$

$$m(s) = \frac{1}{2d_4}\left[2s + d_1 + d_6 - \frac{d_1 d_3 + d_6 d_3}{s + d_2 + d_3}\right] \qquad (4.178)$$

$$n(s) = \frac{1}{2d_4}\left[\frac{1}{s + d_2 + d_3}\right]\sqrt{F(d_1, d_2, d_3, d_6)} \qquad (4.179)$$

The roots p_1 and p_2 will be conjugates. Since the value under the radical is minus the j will disappear:

$$p_1 = -m(s) + n(s) \qquad (4.180)$$

$$p_2 = -m(s) - n(s) \qquad (4.181)$$

$$p_1 - p_2 = 2n \qquad (4.182)$$

$$p_2 - p_1 = -2n \qquad (4.183)$$

The exponential portion of the solution for eqs. 4.174 and 4.175 is

$$e^{p_1 x} = e^{-mx+nx} = e^{-mx} \cdot e^{nx}$$

$$e^{-mx} = e^{-\frac{s}{d_4}x} \cdot e^{-\frac{d_1+d_6}{2d_4}x} \cdot e^{\frac{1}{2d_4}\left(\frac{d_1 d_3 + d_6 d_3}{s + d_2 + d_3}\right)x} \qquad (4.184)$$

$$e^{+nx} = e^{-\frac{1}{2d_4}\left(\frac{1}{s + d_2 + d_3}\right)x} \cdot e^{\sqrt{F(d_1 d_2, d_3, d_6)x}}$$

Thus the term $e^{-\frac{s}{d_4}x}$, a *transport lag*, factors out of solution.

When the stream velocities $v_1 = -v_2$ for countercurrent flow, $d_4 = -d_5$. The roots p_1 and p_2 become

$$p_1, p_2 = -\frac{1}{2d_4}(\lambda_2 - \lambda_1) \pm j\frac{2}{2d_4}\sqrt{(\lambda_2 - \lambda_1)^2 + 4(\lambda_1\lambda_2 - \psi_1\psi_2)} \qquad (4.185)$$

$$= -m'(s) \pm jn'(s) \qquad (4.186)$$

$$m'(s) = d_6 - \frac{d_6 d_3}{s + d_2 + d_3} - d_1 + \frac{d_1 d_3}{s + d_2 + d_3} \qquad (4.187)$$

$$n'(s) = \frac{1}{2d_4}\frac{1}{s + d_2 + d_3}\sqrt{F'(d_1, d_2, d_3, d_6)} \qquad (4.188)$$

Thus for countercurrent flow, no transport lag term factors from the general solution.

For concurrent flow a transportation lag lies between both the disturbance $T_1'(0, s)$ and the manipulation $T_2'(0, s)$ and the point of temperature measurement $x = L$ at the exit of the exchanger.

For counter-current flow, the manipulation and disturbance will be separated by the length L of the exchanger. A transportation distance L will lie between the point of temperature measurement at $x = L$ and either the manipulation or the disturbance, but not between both. The transportation lag in the equations will depend upon which tube of fluid is manipulating and which is the process that is being disturbed.

A Simplified Approach

It is apparent that the distributed-parameter approach requires lengthy and laborious calculations. From a practical engineering point of view, one may well inquire under what conditions a lumped-parameter, linearized treatment may be used to give answers of sufficient accuracy. A study by Mozley (see Bibliography, p. 207) of a concentric pipe heat exchanger showed that it is possible to approximate the ratio of outlet temperature of one fluid to the inlet temperature of the other fluid by a simple second-order lag. This approximation is fairly good over a range of frequencies that extend to the frequency at which the true phase lag is 180°. At higher frequencies the approximation deteriorates rapidly. It should be noted that the particular exchanger investigated had a length-to-volume ratio of 71 ft/ft³. Since many commercial heat exchangers have a smaller ratio, the lumped-parameter approach has considerable potential value.

The same study by Mozley also showed that for flow variations with magnitudes up to 50 per cent of mean flow, the response of the exchanger may be linearized.

Parameter Variation

In the equations for heat exchange described in section 9, the parameters in the transformed equations b_1, b_2 $\cdots$ and the parameters d_1, d_2 $\cdots$ can be expressed in terms of the "steady-state" design parameters that are commonly used for calculating heat exchange performance.

In particular

$$b_1 = \frac{h_{fw}}{C_f} = 0.092 P_R^{\frac{1}{3}} \mu_f^{0.2} \left(\frac{1}{\rho_f}\right)\left(\frac{G^{0.8}}{D^{1.2}}\right) \tag{4.189}$$

$$b_2 = \frac{h_{ew}}{C_w} = \xi b_1 \tag{4.190}$$

$$b_3 = \frac{h_{fw}}{C_w} = 0.023 \left(\frac{2S}{P}\right)\left(\frac{C_f}{\rho_w C_w}\right) P_R^{\frac{1}{3}} \mu_f^{0.2} \left(\frac{G^{0.8}}{D^{1.2}}\right) \tag{4.191}$$

$$b_4 = \frac{G}{\rho_f} \tag{4.192}$$

in which the definitions of the symbols are:

D = diameter of the tube

πD = perimeter of the tube

P = pressure in the tube

S = stress in the tube

P_R = Prandtle's Number

ρ_f = density of the fluid

ρ_w = density of the wall

μ_f = fluid kinematic viscosity

C_w = Thermal capacity of wall volume per unit length

C_f = thermal capacity of fluid volume per unit length

c_{pw} = specific heat of the wall

c_{pf} = specific heat of the fluid

ξ = Ratio of heat transmission: outside to inside

Thus the dynamic response of the various forms of heat exchangers can be related to the nature of materials which flow in them, the physical dimensions of the pipes, and the characterizing Prandtle's and Reynold's numbers.

10. THERMAL CIRCUITS

Circuits of thermal resistance and thermal capacity can be drawn to represent the various configurations of equipment used in heat exchange. For example: in Fig. 4.12, a furnace with molten metal is heated with hot gas. Two layers of firebrick contain the metal. The heat is supplied to the space between the metal surface and the top of the furnace. The gas temperature T_g is the driving thermal force in the furnace. It drives heat H_m into the metal and heat H_w into the walls above the metal. There is radiation resistance R_R between the red-hot metal and the firebrick. There is also conduction resistance R_G. The radiation and conduction occurs below the metal surface and also where the gas radiates directly to the walls and is in contact with the walls above the metal surface. The temperature of the metal will be determined by the amount of heat that flows to the metal H_m. The metal has thermal capacity C_m. The inner layer of the brick in contact with the metal has capacity C_{B1}, and the outer layer of brick has a capacity C_{B2}. Between the metal and the first layer of brick is a resistance R_{MB1} and likewise a resistance between the two layers of brick R_{B1B2}. Between the outside layer of brick and the outside air there is a resistance R_{B20}. The bottom portion of the thermal circuit terminates in a source which represents the air temperature T_o. The gas heats the wall above the metal surface through two resistances

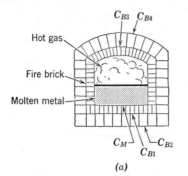

(a)

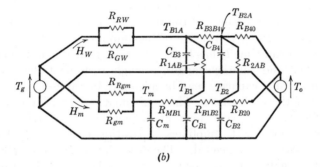

(b)

Fig. 4.12. Equivalent thermal circuit for a furnace. (a) Section through furnace; (b) Thermal
circuit.

R_{RW} and R_{GW}. The first is the radiation resistance; the second is the
resistance due to the film of hot gas in contact with the wall. The
temperature T_{B1A} is across the capacitance C_{B3}, which represents the
thermal capacitance of the top part of the inner layer of firebrick.
However, the temperature T_{B1A} may differ from T_{B1}. If it does, a flow
of heat will pass from the upper to the lower portions of the particular layer of brick. This heat flow can be indicated by a resistance
R_{AB1} connecting the nodes which represent the temperatures T_{B1A}
and T_{B1} in the equivalent circuit. Similarly in the outer layers of
firebrick, the temperature nodes T_{B2A} and T_{B2} can be connected by a
resistance, which indicates that there will be heat flow from the upper
to the lower portion of the brick. Finally, the upper portion of the
circuit terminates in the external temperature source T_o through a
resistance R_{B40}. Thus, thermal circuits to represent the heat flow
and temperature relationships for various types can almost be drawn
by inspection by people who have a good background in circuit theory.

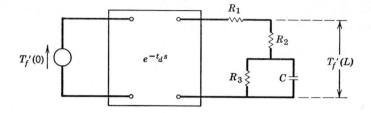

Fig. 4.13. Thermal circuit for simple, concurrent-flow, shell-and-tube heat exchanger.

However, provision must be made so that the transportation lag or dead time can be put into the equivalent circuits. Unless this is done the dynamic response of the thermal network may not bear close resemblance to the performance of the equipment.

After the dead time t_d has been extracted, as it was in the equation for the shell and tube exchanger, a single section of thermal resistance and thermal capacity may be adequate to represent the dynamic behavior of the exchanger. The equivalent circuit is shown by Fig. 4.13. To represent very long exchangers, four or five resistance-capacity sections with amplifiers separating each section from the preceding one may be needed. The dead-time operator can be placed ahead of the entire network or part of it can be included in the amplifiers which separate the R-C sections. When more than one section of resistance and capacity are necessary to represent the exchanger because of its length, the resistance and capacitance values in each section may be different. The sections can be isolated by "buffer" amplifiers.

Gould was able to show that when the heat carried by the fluid along the axis of flow in a unit length of heat exchanger is approximately equal to the heat transferred perpendicularly through the unit length of the exchange surface, the heat exchanger can be approximated by the extracted dead time and a single section of lumped-thermal resistance and capacity circuit. This fact is borne out by the form of the transfer function $H(s)$ in eq. 4.121 when $n = 1$. Therefore, the combined transport delay and exponential time-lag form of operator

$$\frac{e^{-as}}{\tau s + 1} \tag{4.193}$$

is suitable for prediction of the performance of certain simple exchangers. The next approximation has a delay function e^{-as} and two R-C sections. Ultimately, for typical industrial exchangers, seldom more than about five R-C sections will be needed to express the dynamic behavior of the exchanger.

11. CONCLUSION

This chapter emphasized the dynamics of thermal processes in terms of the configurations of equipment and materials of construction. The response of many elementary thermal processes can be represented adequately by linear differential equations with constant coefficients. The dynamic response of the theoretically perfect thermal equipment can be modified so that the influence of the materials of construction and geometry of configurations can be noted. Convection heaters are characterized by mixing lags. Long heat exchangers exhibit transportation type of lags. Only the most elementary form of exchangers can be represented by a combination of dead time and a first-order time lag operator. The more complex problems lead to Bessel function forms. The transfer function approach ultimately fails. Difference equations and computational aids are needed to explore nonlinear thermal problems.

BIBLIOGRAPHY

Conduction of Heat in Solids, Carslaw and Jaeger, Oxford University Press, New York, 1947.

Heat Tranfser, M. Jacob, John Wiley & Sons, 1950.

Process Heat Transfer, D. Q. Kern, McGraw-Hill Book Co., New York, 1950.

Introduction to Mechanics and Heat, N. Frank, McGraw-Hill Book Co., New York, 1939.

Introduction to Theoretical Physics, Slater and Frank, McGraw-Hill Company, 1933.

Unit Operations, Brown and Associates, John Wiley & Sons, 1950.

Operation Methods in Applied Mathematics, Carslaw and Jaeger, Oxford University Press, New York, 1941.

Partial Differential Equation in Mathematical Physics, H. Bateman, Dover, 1944.

Fundamental Formulas of Physics, Menzel, Prentice-Hall, New York, 1955.

The Dynamic Behavior and Control of Heat Transfer Processes, L. A. Gould, Sc.D. Thesis, Dept. of Electrical Engineering, Massachusetts Institute of Technology, Cambridge, Mass., 1953.

"Electrical Analogues for Heat Exchangers," R. L. Ford, *Proceedings of the I.E.E.*, Paper No. 1934M, Jan. 1956.

Heat Transmission, W. H. McAdams, McGraw-Hill Book Co., New York, 3rd edition, 1954.

"Predicting Dynamics of Concentric Pipe Heat Exchangers," J. M. Mozley, *Ind. Eng. Chem.*, 1035–1041 (June 1956).

CHAPTER 5

Mass Transfer Dynamics

1. MASS-TRANSFER PROCESSES

Absorption, crystallization, extraction, distillation, stripping, humidification, and drying depend upon the principle of mass transfer to account for the movement of molecules between phases of material present in the processes. Thus, to the processes of materials handling, fluids in movement, and heat transfer, the mass-transfer process must be added in order to explain the dynamic behavior of these new operations.

Two features of mass transfer must be established. First, there is the rate at which mass transfers between phases in solutions, gases, and various mixtures of each. Secondly, there is the identity or composition of the material transferring. The manipulating forces that modulate the rate of mass transfer may be quite different—in fact, they *are* quite different—from those which influence the identity of the molecules of material transferring itself.

The control, regulation, and design of processes in which mass transfer takes place may involve both quantity and quality variables. The rate of mass transfer that can be brought about may be an economic issue because of the process throughput that must be obtained. The quality of process operation may depend upon the distribution in identity and quantity of the material transferred.

Before the manipulation and measurement of mass-transfer processes can be accomplished, the physical variables that represent cause and effect in mass transfer must be identified. First, however, the processes themselves will be briefly described.

Gas Absorption. Gas absorption is a diffusional operation in which molecules from a gas phase transfer to a liquid in which the gas molecules are soluble. The diffusion rate is a function of the state of the gas, the state of the liquid, and the manner of contact between the two. Three situations result in mass transfer by absorption: (1) Chemical action takes place, and the force which would tend to drive the new formed molecules from the liquid back into the gas phase no longer exists, or is small. (2) Chemical action takes place, but the new product generates an internal, or self-regulating, force tending to drive the gas-transfer rate toward zero. (3) No chemical reaction takes place, and the diffusion is dependent solely upon the relative concentrations.

Crystallization. Crystals form in a solution free from all solid particles. They also form around dust particles, crystals of a solute, or other crystals of a different type. In the proper environment, molecules of solute will join and become solid. These solids will continue to grow according to definite geometric patterns as more molecules are added to their surface.

The rate at which material is deposited becomes of interest in assessing the process dynamic response of crystallizers. A combined diffusional and first-order interfacial chemical-reaction process is used to describe the dynamics of crystallization.

Extraction. Extraction involves mass transfer between liquids and between liquids or solids and liquids. No vapor phase is present. Molecules of a material in solution mixed with another liquid tend to migrate, and hence concentrate so that they can be extracted. *Leaching* is a term used when solids are mixed with solvent and the concentration involves the movement of molecules from the solid to the solvent. The diffusion laws determine the rate at which molecules of material transfer from one liquid to another or from the solid to the solvent.

Distillation. Distillation involves mass transfer as molecules of material are carried off from liquid in the form of vapor and later condensed. Provided chemical reaction is not present, the driving force tends to make the "lighter" molecular components in the liquid migrate toward the vapor phase; and another driving force tends to make the "heavier" components in the vapor migrate toward the liquid phase. Thus diffusion takes place in both directions. Equilibrium is a *dynamic* situation in distillation, because the rates of mass transfer in the two directions must be equal. Equilibrium in the migration is disturbed through the medium of composition, vapor pressure, and thermal-energy alteration.

Stripping. Stripping is the reverse of gas absorption. It involves the bringing of a liquid containing dissolved gas into contact with an inert or insoluble gas in order to remove the dissolved gas. The same laws govern the rate of mass transfer in stripping as governed it in absorption, except that the driving forces are reversed.

Humidification and Dehumidification. Humidification and dehumidification—that is, the adding of moisture to solids or gases, or its removal from them—involve mass transfer. The moisture may merely be mechanically locked into the carrying medium, or it may chemically combine through the formation of *water crystals*. The driving force in moisture transfer is the partial-pressure difference between the two mediums between which the moisture moves. The rate of mass transfer, however, is affected by many factors related to the properties of the material being wetted or dried, and the properties of the surrounding medium.

The reader should be aware now of the complexity of the processes which require drying, distillation, crystallization, stripping, and the like. Any one of these problems, if treated in detail, would constitute a chapter, several chapters, or even a complete book.

In the material that follows, drying will be taken up first—after an explanation has been given to mass transfer and the diffusion process. Basic concepts of drying will be applied to a study of a single-roll and multiple-stage drying process.

Then the subject of distillation will be taken up. Many attempts have been made to treat the dynamic behavior of plate and packed types of distillation columns. The work presented is a summary, in brief, of the basic research carried out at the Massachusetts Institute of Technology[*] on distillation dynamics. The mathematical developments, especially the topological studies of distillation columns using signal-flow diagrams to explain the nature of distillation-column transients, were carried through by Mr. Herbert Teager in a doctoral thesis.[†]

2. MOLECULAR DIFFUSION

The movement of materials from one point to another in a stagnant liquid obeys the laws of molecular diffusion. Molecular diffusion is analogous to thermal diffusion or thermal conduction. The basic concepts that explain molecular diffusion are derived from the kinetic gas theory.

The resistance to molecular movement is proportional to: the number of molecules in a gas per unit volume, the mean relative velocity

[*] A project under the direction of the author on the dynamic nature of binary distillation was carried on over the period 1949–1955.

[†] H. M. Teager, *"An Analysis of Transients in Mass Transfer Operations,"* Sc.D. Thesis, M.I.T., 1955.

between two different materials that are mixing, and the length of the path over which the diffusion is taking place.

The potential gradient producing the diffusion is proportional to the resistance.   Thus

$$N_A = KA(f_1 - f_2) \qquad (5.1)$$

where N_A = mols of component A transferred per unit time

K = transfer coefficient mols per unit time, per unit drop in fugacity, and per unit area

A = cross-section area

f_1 = fugacity at point 1

f_2 = fugacity at point 2

Since an ideal gas obeys the relationship that its partial pressure P is equal to fugacity f, the equation which describes mass transfer by diffusion in ideal gas is

$$-\frac{dP_A}{dx} = K_{AB}\left(\frac{\rho_A}{M_A}\right)\left(\frac{\rho_B}{M_B}\right)(u_A - u_B) \qquad (5.2)$$

where the terms are

P_A = partial pressure of the diffusion gas A

K_{AB} = proportionality constant

ρ_A, ρ_B = partial densities of gas A and B, lb/cu ft

M_A, M_B = molecular weights of gas A and B

u_A, u_B = mean velocities of gas A and B, ft/hr

x = length of diffusion path

The differential equations which define the mass-transfer aspect of the operation of the various processes enumerated in section 1 are summarized in the paragraphs that follow.   All of these equations are dependent upon the diffusion equation, eq. 5.1, and ramifications of it.

Gas Absorption.   Diffusion is the basic mechanism, so that

$$-\frac{dC_A}{dx} = K_{AB}C_A C_B(u_A - u_B) \qquad (5.3)$$

where C_A = concentration of soluble gas, lb mols/cu ft

C_B = concentration of other component, lb mols/cu ft

K_{AB} = proportionality constant

u_A = diffusion velocity of component A, ft/hr

u_B = diffusion velocity of component B, ft/hr

Crystallization.   According to the Berthoud-Valeton theory:

$$\frac{dw}{dt} = K'S(C' - C_o) = \frac{KS}{L}(C - C') \tag{5.4}$$

$$= \frac{S(C - C_o)}{1/K' + L/K} \tag{5.5}$$

where w = weight of material deposited
K = diffusion coefficient
K' = rate of reaction of interfacial reaction
S = surface area
L = effective film thickness
C_o = concentration of saturated solution
C = concentration of the bulk solution
C' = concentration of solution in contact with crystal surface

Extraction

$$N_A = KA(C_L - C_i) \tag{5.6}$$

$$= KAC_{\text{ave}}(X_L - X_i) \tag{5.7}$$

where N_A = moles of solute transferred per unit time
K = liquid film coefficient, lb moles/hr sq ft mol/ft^3
A = total interfacial contact area
C_L = concentration of the solute in main body of liquid phase
C_i = concentration of the solute at the interface between two
        liquid films
C_{ave} = average total moles/cu ft over a liquid film
X_L = mole fraction of solute in main body of any liquid phase
X_i = mole fraction of solute at interface, and that in phase E
        in equilibrium with y_i for phase w

Distillation.   The equations for distillation are treated in detail in
section 4.
Stripping.   The basic law is given by eq. (5.3) for gas absorption.

Humidification and Dehumidification

Dehumidification

$$W = KA\,\Delta P_m \tag{5.8}$$

$$Q_s = hA\,\Delta t_m \tag{5.9}$$

$$Q_T = Q_s + Wr \tag{5.10}$$

W = rate of vapor transfer, lb/hr

Q_s = rate of sensible-heat transfer, Btu/hr

Q_T = rate of total heat transfer, Btu/hr

K = mass-transfer coefficient, lb/hr/sq ft/in. Hg difference in partial pressure

h = heat-transfer coefficient, Btu/hr/sq ft/°F difference in temperature

A = surface area, ft^2

ΔP_m = mean difference in partial pressure, in. Hg

Δt_m = mean difference, °F

r = latent heat of vaporization at liquid temperature, Btu/lb

Humidification

$$Q_s = Wr \qquad (5.11)$$

$$hA \,\Delta t_m = KA \,\Delta P_m \, r \qquad (5.12)$$

As in heat transfer, the general equations that govern mass transfer tend to be nonlinear. Mass transfer across interfacial boundaries separating phases also has a distributed nature, thereby requiring partial-derivative equations to express the rate of transfer through space and time. However, good engineering results may be obtained by linearizing the nonlinear equations and using ordinary differential equations or their transformations in process control system designs.

According to the theoretical principles which explain how mass transfer takes place, there is no justification in the macroscopic treatment for assuming that a time lag exists in the generation of a mass-transfer rate. The presence of differential fugacity or differential partial pressure creates instantaneously a rate of mass transfer. The time lags that are noticed in the mass-transfer process generally relate to materials handling and thermal lags. They tend to be not only coincident with mass transfer but inseparable from it.

Therefore it is important to investigate, when working with mass-transfer processes, the relative order of magnitude and importance of the time lags brought about by materials handling and heat transfer as they affect the mass-transfer process dynamics.

3. DRYING

Drying is the process of removing liquid from porous material. It is an industrial operation frequently encountered in the manufacture of paper, cloth, and various granular materials like food, and meal. Even in the manufacture of autos, radios, and electric motors, paint or lacquer may be applied, and drying may be a necessary operation as the object moves through a continuous production line.

Moisture is never fully removed from an object that is dried. A small percentage of moisture always remains. The objective in drying is to begin with wet material and remove sufficient moisture from it so that it can be handled in subsequent operations—such as cutting, printing, packaging, and storing.

The drying rate of an object depends upon the magnitude of the driving force that can be applied to the object by various means. The manipulation of the drying process can be both external and internal to the object. A dry atmosphere will draw moisture from the object. Heating the object will drive moisture from it. Thus, moving a dry gas or vapor rapidly over the surface of an object, or exposing the object to intense radiation which heats it, are procedures for drying.

The purpose of this section is to establish the basic laws of drying and to study some simple problems of dryer regulation and control.

Macroscopic Approach to Drying. The rate of mass transfer in macroscopic types of drying operations depends upon the differential partial pressure that develops between the average moisture contained in the object to be dried and the average moisture contained in the medium surrounding the object. The average partial pressure P_i inside the material to be dried will vary with temperature. Since the temperature of an object cannot be raised instantly, the mass-transfer dynamics is coupled to the thermal dynamics of the body to be dried and the surrounding environment.

A retardation of mass transfer from the surface of the object to be dried can result because of the rise of moisture content in the medium to which the mass transfer takes place.

Ideal Case. First, there is drying in which the rate of moisture transfer is proportional to the differential partial pressure between P_i within the material and the external partial pressure P_o. When the external pressure P_o remains constant,

$$\frac{dM}{dt} = R = K(P_i - P_o) \qquad (5.13)$$

Drying is an integrating process. The transfer function is

$$\frac{M(s)}{P_i(s)} = \frac{K}{s} \qquad (5.14)$$

Degenerative Case. Secondly, when the surrounding vapor changes its moisture concentration, the rate at which the vapor partial pressure P_o increases with respect to time has a retarding effect upon the mass-transfer operation. Where the partial pressure P_o is a function of the moisture removed from the web,

$$\frac{dM}{dt} = R = K(P_i - P_o) \qquad (5.15)$$

and the linear approximation

$$P_o = \phi(M) \simeq K'M \qquad (5.16)$$

can be made, the typical degenerative drying occurs.

$$\frac{dM}{dt} = K_1 P - K_2' M \qquad (5.17)$$

Thus the moisture variation will exhibit a time lag

$$\frac{M(s)}{P_i(s)} = \frac{K_1}{K_2'} \left(\frac{1}{\frac{1}{K_2'} s + 1} \right) \qquad (5.18)$$

Distributed Parameter Approach

A more advanced approach must be taken to the drying problem if the porous solids have sufficient large linear dimensions that they exhibit moisture-content gradients.

The drying of a porous body can be studied using the basic conservation law: accumulation = gain − loss. The accumulation of the moisture in a volume element dV is

$$\iiint \frac{\partial M}{\partial t} \, dx \, dy \, dz \qquad (5.19)$$

The rate at which the region dV gains or loses moisture over its surface S is

$$\iint K \frac{\partial M}{\partial n} \, dS \qquad (5.20)$$

When eq. 5.20 is transformed into a volume integral, it can be equated to the accumulation. The equation for drying becomes

$$\frac{\partial M}{\partial t} = h^2 \nabla^2 M \qquad (5.21)$$

where h^2 is a constant called the transfusivity. The operator ∇^2 is the

Laplacian $\left(\dfrac{\partial^2}{\partial x^2} + \dfrac{\partial^2}{\partial y^2} + \dfrac{\partial^2}{\partial z^2} \right).$

The presence of a source or sink in the volume, or a distributed chemical reaction which uses the moisture can have its influence indicated by means of the form

$$\frac{\partial M}{\partial t} = h^2 \nabla^2 M + P \tag{5.22}$$

where P is the rate of generation or consumption of moisture per unit volume.

The rate at which an object dries may be limited by the rate at which the moisture can move through the object itself to the surface. An object which is highly saturated with liquid will first exhibit a drying rate that is rapid. Later the drying rate will diminish substantially. Some of the driving force is utilized in pushing the liquid through the material structure itself.

Thus, the rate of moisture flow over the surface S into region dV will be influenced by: (a) the moisture gradient $\dfrac{\partial M}{\partial n}$, (b) the hydraulic gradient $\dfrac{\partial h}{\partial n}$, (c) the thermal gradient $\dfrac{\partial T}{\partial n}$ or the partial pressure gradient $\dfrac{\partial P}{\partial n}$, and (d) finally the gravitation force.

$$\iint K \frac{\partial M}{\partial n} \, dS = \iint \left[K_1 \frac{\partial M}{\partial n} + K_2 \frac{\partial h}{\partial n} + K_3 \frac{\partial P}{\partial n} + K_4 \frac{\partial Q}{\partial n} \right] dS \tag{5.23}$$

The general form of the drying equation becomes very complicated especially when provision must be made for studying drying dynamics in three dimensions.

As stated earlier, the manipulation of a porous material to be dried (or wetted) is produced from the outside. The thermal gradient $\partial T/\partial n$ is produced by applying heat to the wet material. The simple operation of mass transfer occurs because moisture is drawn from the material in such a way that a mass gradient $\partial M/\partial n$ exists. The hydraulic gradient is an opposing force to fluid flow. The effect of gravity may retard or aid moisture flow.

Methods of Drying. To dry material, a dry vapor may be moved past the object that is being dried, or the material to be dried can be passed through an environment in which the vapor is hot and dry, and which consequently has a low enough pressure P_o to remove moisture from the material. Also, heat may be transferred to an object so that the vapor pressure P_i of the entrained liquid drives off moisture and brings about drying.

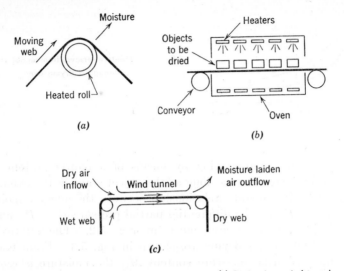

Fig. 5.1. (a) Drying roll; (b) Drying in an oven; (c) Drying in a wind tunnel.

In either type of drying, *the time interval of exposure* is an important factor. The vapor must blow over the object long enough so that the duration of contact of the drying vapor brings about a given degree of moisture removal; or the material must be left in the drying environment long enough for a certain percentage of moisture change per unit volume to be effected.

For example, in Fig. 5.1 a web of wet material passes over a roll. The roll is heated to drive the moisture out of the web. The time during which the web and roll remain in contact will determine the amount of moisture removal. The second figure shows a wet object passing through a drying oven. As the object moves into the oven, it comes in contact with the hot dry gas. The air in contact with the

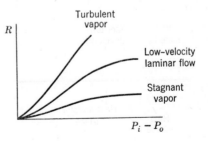

Fig. 5.2. Drying rate as a function of air turbulence.

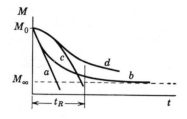

Fig. 5.3. Moisture removal from an object passing
through a drying oven.

web is kept dry and moving by means of a blower system. The
drying process continues as long as the object stays in the oven.

The approximate static relationship between the average moisture-
removal rate R and the differential partial pressure $P_i - P_o$, and the
outside air turbulence are shown in Fig. 5.2. The approximate
dynamic relations for drying are shown in Fig. 5.3. From material
which has an initial moisture content M_o, the moisture is removed
at varying rates throughout the time interval t_R, which is the residence time. Four different modes of the drying transient response
are shown: Curve a signifies the pure integral drying so that $\dfrac{M(s)}{\Delta P(s)}$
$= \dfrac{K}{s}$. Curve b indicates the degenerative case where $\dfrac{M(s)}{\Delta P(s)} = \dfrac{K}{\tau_m s + 1}$
in which the rate of drying depended upon the rate of moisture build-up
in the surrounding vapor.   Curve c shows the integral drying rate $1/s$
influenced by a first order thermal lag τ_t. Thus $\dfrac{M(s)}{\Delta P(s)} = \dfrac{K}{s(\tau_t s + 1)}$.
Curve d shows the combined effect of the thermal lag and the vapor
build-up in the surroundings so that

$$\frac{M(s)}{\Delta P(s)} = \frac{K}{(\tau_m s + 1)(\tau_t s + 1)} \tag{5.24}$$

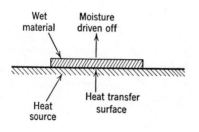

Fig. 5.4. Heat transfer in drying.

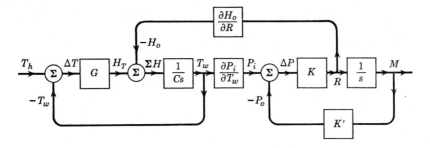

Fig. 5.5. Block diagram for drying process showing both pressure and thermal dynamics (lumped-parameter basis).

However, the influence of thermal dynamics upon drying rate had better be considered as a topic in itself.

Thermal dynamics. Next consider the thermal dynamics associated with the drying problem. Let a thin sheet of material be placed upon a heating element as shown in Fig. 5.4. As heat transfers to the material containing moisture, the temperature T will rise. In turn, the partial pressure P_i in the moisture phase will increase. Increased moisture content in the surrounding vapor will influence the partial pressure P_o. A degenerative effect can be placed upon the drying rate R by the increase in P_o. The moisture also carries away heat, which must be taken into account. The block diagram of Fig. 5.5 shows the approximate relationships.

The temperature T_h of the heated surface transfers heat to the wet material through a conductance G. At the heat-summing point, there is the heat transferred H_T, which is a positive driving force, and the heat which is taken away from the wet object by all means, but principally by the drying rate $-H_o$. The net heat flow to the wet object, integrated and divided by the thermal capacity of the material, produces the wet-object average temperature T_w. A feedback path occurs through the conductance G around the thermal capacity of the material.

Next, the wet-object temperature T_w has an influence upon the integral pressure P_i. If the moisture transferred to the outside has an influence on the outside pressure P_o, then the difference in pressure $P_i - P_o$ produces the incremental pressure ΔP, which when multiplied by the drying-rate constant K produces the drying rate R. The integral of the drying rate gives the moisture removed. The amount of moisture M removed influences the external pressure P_o; so a second degenerative effect occurs.

The rate of drying also has a feedback path into the thermal system because sensible heat is carried away with the moisture. The drying rate also uses a certain amount of heat in order to sustain the evaporation of liquid. Thus the path from the variable R back to the heat-summing point is another negative-feed-back effect. Altogether, in the drying operation there are three degenerative influences, but there are only two integrations shown in the process. Therefore, the over-all relationship between M, the moisture removed, and T_h, the temperature of the heated object that is driving the moisture out of the material, will be a quadratic function. However, the partial differentials $\left(\dfrac{\partial H_o}{\partial R}\right)$ and $\left(\dfrac{\partial P_i}{\partial T_w}\right)$ must be recognized as variables. A linearized approach can be obtained to elementary drying problems by first determining the variation of the partial derivatives and then taking mean values for use in the transfer functions.

To determine the temperature T_h will require that the nature of the specific heater be known. Consider that a steam or hot-water drying roll is used. The drying roll shown in Fig. 5.1a has the equivalent thermal circuit shown in Fig. 5.6. A source of heat H_s, which represents the heat brought into the drum by the hot water or steam, causes heat to flow into the thermal circuit. However, a lag occurs as the flow of steam or hot water adds its heat to the hold-up of hot water already in the roll. After the thermal circuit accounts for the mixing lag, the resistance R_{wm} connects the thermal capacity of the water C_w and the steel C_M. Next the resistance R_{MF} connects the thermal capacity of the metal C_M to that of the web or film C_F. Across C_F is the source or sink (if any) which draws moisture from the film.

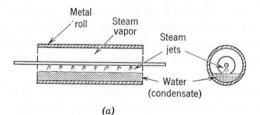

(a)

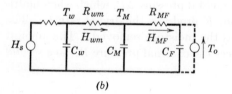

(b)

Fig. 5.6. Equivalent circuit for steam drying roll. (a) Steam heated drying roll. (b) Thermal circuit of drying roll.

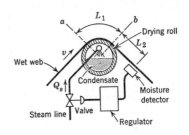

Fig. 5.7.   Regulation of a single-roll drier.

However, the web to be dried generally does not have much thermal capacity compared with that of the water and metal.   Furthermore, as it dries and its moisture content reduces, its thermal capacity C_F tends to diminish significantly.

Single-Roll Drier.   To illustrate the principles of drying control and regulation, consider that a single-roll drier is used to drive moisture from a wet web of material which moves in direct contact with the drying roll.   The arrangement of the equipment is shown in Fig. 5.7.

The web peripheral velocity v is determined by the production rate of the plant.   The drying roll has a hold-up of steam condensate W_c. The steam flow Q_s to the drying roll is adjusted by a control valve. Assume that the steam flow is fully condensing, and that it substantially gives all of its heat to the condensate water contained in the drying roll.   The water, in turn, transfers heat to the metal, and the heated metal in turn heats and drives the moisture from the wet web.

A measurement of the moisture content of the web is made at point c as the web emerges from the drying roll.   The measurement of moisture content sends a signal to the regulator.   The regulator sends a control signal to the valve.   The valve modifies the steam flow.

The block diagram in Fig. 5.8 shows that the error in moisture content ε_m activates the controller.   The controller sends a signal P_c to the valve whose stem position X_v adjusts the steam flow Q_s to the drier.   The steam flow Q_s brings about changes in the temperature T_w of the web.   This, in turn, modifies the partial pressure P_i of the moisture entrained.   When the differential equation,

$$\frac{dM(t)}{dt} = K[P_i(t) - P_o(t)] \tag{5.25}$$

is transformed

$$sM(s) = KP_i(s) - KP_o(s) + M(0^+) \tag{5.26}$$

$$= R_1(s) - R_2(s) + M(0^+) \tag{5.27}$$

the initial moisture content of the web $M(0^+)$ coming into the drying operation becomes the principal disturbing action upon the moisture

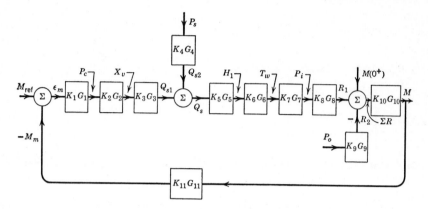

Fig. 5.8.   Block diagram for single-roll steam drier regulator.

content regulator.   The initial moisture content $M(0^+)$ can be added to the summing point where the drying rate $R(s)$ is generated by the difference in the partial pressure P_o and P_i.   The moisture content $M(0^+)$ of the incoming web at the point a in Fig. 5.7 will always be varying; the object of the regulator is to maintain constant moisture content at the point b as the web moves out of the drying operation.

Two other disturbances may be present: The external vapor pressure P_o is a disturbance which affects the drying rate; the steam-supply pressure P_s can fluctuate and interfere with the steam flow Q_s.

A transportation lag $e^{-a_1 s}$ must be included because the web moves through the distance L_1 while drying.   If the moisture detector is located "downstream" by the additional distance L_2, a second transportation lag $e^{-a_2 s}$ must be added to the first.   The dead-times are: $a_1 = L_1/v$ and $a_2 = L_2/v$.   Thus, the total transport lag $a_1 + a_2 = a$ gives the operator e^{-as} which must be apportioned in blocks $K_{10}G_{10}(s)$ and $K_{11}G_{11}(s)$.

Generally, in steam roll drying, the largest time lag will occur because of the amount of condensate water in the drying rolls.   The next largest time lag will be from the metal in the roll.   For most industrial roll driers, the lags in valve positioners and instruments can be ignored in comparison with the two lags of the drying roll.   Therefore, the transfer function $K_5G_5(s)K_6G_6(s)K_7G_7(s)K_8G_8(s)$ can be approximated by

$$\frac{R_1(s)}{Q_s(s)} = \frac{K_{sR}}{(\tau_1 s + 1)(\tau_2 s + 1)} \tag{5.28}$$

which can be derived for the thermal system according to the proce-

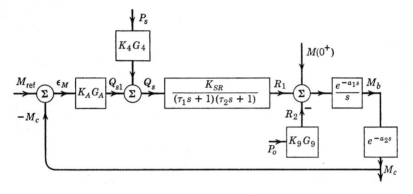

Fig. 5.9. Simplified block diagram for single-roll steam drier regulator.

dures shown in Table 4.1. The simplified signal flow diagram for the moisture content controller is shown in Fig. 5.9.

Multi-stage Drying. Drying operations rarely employ a single drying roll, because a single drying roll cannot remove the moisture from a web quickly enough to permit production processes to have throughput. Therefore, for known production rates and drying rates, drying operations can be spread over a multiple drying-roll arrangement as shown in Fig. 5.10 so that the gross contact time between the web and the drying rolls is adequate.

If the web moves through the multi-stage drier at approximately a constant velocity v, the contact time between the web and each drying roll will be at $\Delta t = d/v$, where d is the distance between the points of initial contact of the web and each consecutive roll.

If the integral law of drying is used so that drying rate is constant and proportional to the manipulation, the manipulation action changes the slope of the moisture versus time curve for each roll as shown in Fig. 5.11. The amount of moisture removed from each during contact with each roll $\Delta M_1, \Delta M_2 \cdots$ then becomes the integral of the drying rate over the contact time.

Fig. 5.10. N-roll drier supplied from a steam manifold.

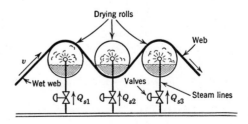

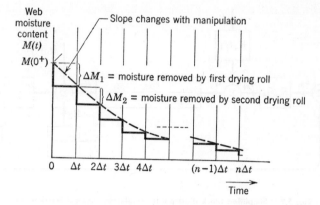

Fig. 5.11.   Moisture removal—N-roll drier.

For an initial moisture content $M(0^+)$ in the web which enters the first roll of the drying operation, an increment of moisture ΔM_1 will be removed in the first stage of drying. The successive removals of moisture will be ΔM_2, $\Delta M_3 \cdots \Delta M_n$. The moisture content of the web will diminish from its initial level $M(0^+)$ at time $t = 0$ to a final level M_n at $n\,\Delta t$.

The equations that relate the drying rate R to the thermal dynamics of each drying stage are identical in form to those of the single roll, although the drying rate constant K_8 may have a different value in each drying roll. Thus

$$R_1(s) = K_{51}G_{51}K_{61}G_{61}K_{71}G_{71}K_{81}G_{81}Q_{s1} \qquad (5.29)$$

$$R_n(s) = K_{5n}G_{5n}K_{6n}G_{6n}K_{7n}G_{7n}K_{8n}G_{8n}Q_{sn}$$

By subtracting the increments of moisture driven off by each drying roll, namely ΔM_1, $\Delta M_2 \cdots \Delta M_n$ from $M(0^+)$, the moisture present in the web emerging from the drier can be obtained.

In the n-roll drying system, the control technique may be primitive or elaborate. The primitive approach would use one steam line to supply all of the valves. The valves might operate in unison from a single regulator. Manifolding arrangements can also be used so that several rolls operate from each manifold, each manifold being operated from a steam line in which there is a control valve. The valves in the lines to the manifolds can be ratio-controlled.

The important aspect of the drying problem is not the manner in which the valves are manipulated, but rather the time lag that is present between the time an initial upsetting moisture content $M(0^+)$ occurs at the entrance to the drier and the time that a measurement of moisture content M_n at the exit of the drier can be made. A large transportation lag through the drier as the web moves slowly over roll after roll, prevents tight control from being obtained with *any* type of regulatory system. A regulator with even moderate gain will become an oscillator because of the large transport lag. Therefore, a low loop gain is predestined for a proportional-type regulator for the drier. In fact, the gain may be much less than unity, which means that substantially no regulation against any sudden upset in the moisture content W_o can be obtained. The addition of integral action to the controller has its benefits. However, derivative and lead types of controller action will be of no practical use.

To improve regulation, two moisture-measuring instruments could be used; one can be located ahead of the drying operation, to determine the initial moisture content $M(0^+)$. Based upon the measured value of moisture, the average steam flow to the drying rolls can be preset. Another moisture measurement further downstream—perhaps midway in the drying system, or even at the end where the web emerges—can then be used to inject a vernier action superposed upon the presetting. The most fundamental way to obtain tight regulation over drying is to build the drier so that the thermal time lags and transport lags are reduced. To reduce the time lags in hot water or steam-roll drying, one must get rid of the condensate water. The amount of condensate water held in most drying rolls has considerable thermal capacity—in fact, it has in some instances more thermal capacity than does the metal of the drying rolls themselves. Heating, drying, and increasing the velocity of movement of air over the material to be dried also improves drying system dynamics.

To bring about rapid drying, the highest possible rate constant in the basic drying equation must be obtained. Agitated, high-velocity air which is hot and dry, moving over a web, may be a better means for drying than is the heat-transfer principle of the drying roll. The possibility of heating by induced methods, in contrast to those by transfer methods, must not be overlooked.

4. DISTILLATION—GENERAL

Distillation separates and concentrates, in a fluid flow, components of different physical identity. The processes of mass transfer, heat transfer, and fluid-materials handling are involved. The operation takes place in a distillation column in which the low-boiling-tempera-

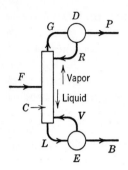

Fig. 5.12.   Distillation column.

ture fluids move toward the top of the column, and the high-boiling-temperature fluids move toward the bottom of the column.   In a distillation column, all the light components cannot be made to go toward the top, nor can all of the heavier components be made to go toward the bottom.   Thus, perfect separation can never be obtained in a physically realizable distillation column.

In a typical column as shown in Fig. 5.12, a fluid feed F enters the column C; a top product P is drawn from the overhead condenser D; and a bottom product B is drawn from the reboiler E.   A liquid flow L down the column enters the reboiler, where it adds to the liquid hold-up.   The product B is a portion of the heavy component concentrated in the reboiler.   As evaporation takes place in the reboiler, a vapor flow V enters the bottom of the column.   All of the top vapor G condenses and adds to the liquid hold-up in the condenser D.   A substantial portion of the total condensate flow into the hold-up is sent back to the column as a reflux flow R.   The remainder of the condensate is taken away as a top product P.

The performance of a distillation column is judged by many factors: the rate at which separation can be made, the energy expended to bring about separation, and the precision with which separation can be made. These factors are not independent.

Materials Handling in Distillation.   In distillation, the materials-handling operations include the movement of liquids and vapors; the mixing of liquids with liquids, vapors with vapors; and the creation of contact between liquids and vapors.

Vapor-flow rate up through a column is determined by the reboiler action at the base of the column.   The reboiler acts like a vapor source. The molal rate of gas evaporation from the reboiler is determined by the rate at which heat is supplied to the reboiler, by the reboiler pressure, and the composition of the liquid in the reboiler.

Liquid flows down the column under the action of gravity. Above the feed point, the liquid flow comes from the reflux flow R and from vapor condensation. Below the feed point, the total liquid flow results from the feed, the reflux, and condensation.

The liquid hold-up in the condenser has an important influence upon the composition variation that may take place in the product outflow P. The outflow composition will differ from the composition of the top gas stream G. Variations in vapor composition will be blended or muffled by the volume of the hold-up in the overhead condenser. The reboiler has the same kind of effect on distillation-column performance. The hold-up of liquid in the reboiler will determine the extent to which the composition of the liquid flow L, into the bottom hold-up experiences mixing or smoothing. The liquid stream coming downward to the reboiler, adding its mass flow of material, may have composition variations which differ considerably from the average composition of the reboiler.

In a distillation column there is also liquid hold-up on the plates and vapor hold-up in the space between plates. Therefore a mixing lag occurs on every plate in the liquid hold-up, and a mixing lag can occur in each gas volume between plates. The mixing lag of the liquid on a plate will be the volume of the liquid held on a plate, divided by the flow of liquid through that plate downward, *modified* by a factor which accounts for the rate of evaporation from the liquid surface.

Generally the vapor velocity in a distillation column is much greater than the corresponding liquid velocities in the column. Therefore the molal hold-up associated with vapor in the column may be considered negligible in comparison with the liquid hold-up. The gas is in a highly turbulent state of movement, and can be regarded as thoroughly mixed across any section perpendicular to the flow. Time lags in vapor composition or any other variable related to vapor flow will be of the *transportation-lag* type rather than the mixing-lag type.

Hydrodynamics. The restriction to liquid flow in a column depends upon the internal construction of the column and the countercurrent vapor flow rate. The hydrodynamic relations between fluid flow and the pressure drop throughout a column are nonlinear. The hydrodynamics, however, proves not to be a basic issue in distillation dynamics, except when extreme conditions of operation are reached— as, for example, when the column floods with liquid or when it loses a liquid feed or a liquid reflux.

The pressure variation throughout a column does not vary widely during normal operations. The pressure in the reboiler is nearly the same as the pressure in the overhead condenser in a column that is operating properly without flooding. Therefore the pressure drop throughout a column can generally be ignored when a study is being made of the incremental dynamic behavior of the column in terms of composition variation.

Heat Transfer. Heat is added to the column by means of sensible heat carried by the feed and reflux streams and heat supplied to the reboiler which produces a vapor flow V. Generally the feed stream passes through a preheater, so that the temperature of the feed will be the same as the temperature of the liquid on the plate at which the feed enters the column. The rising vapor gives up heat to the liquid on the successive plates of the distillation tower. Heat is removed from the rising vapor in the overhead condenser. Heat is also carried away by the top and bottom product streams. Heat is lost through the structure to the outside environment. Thus an over-all heat balance can be made for a column or a section of one.

The condensation of vapor and the generation of vapor in the column at a plate make a more significant heat addition to the liquid, or subtraction from it, than does the sensible heat carried to the plate by the liquid and vapor flows. A change in boil-up rate at the bottom of a column increases the vapor flow to the column. The thermal energy given up in condensing an increment of vapor flow passing through a particular plate or section of the column can evaporate an increment of liquid which is considerably greater than the corresponding evaporation of liquid which would be based upon the sensible heat brought to the plate by the vapor flow. *Thus thermal effects transfer themselves gradually up a column through the mechanism of the heat of condensation and evaporation in the mass-transfer operation*, more so than through the giving up by the vapor flow of its sensible heat to the liquid through which it passes.

Time lags will be associated with the thermal processes in distillation. One thermal lag can occur as a result of convection because of the mixing problems. On each plate, the liquid hold-up has thermal capacity and conductivity; so a thermal lag will occur whenever the temperature is being changed, as in a start-up. The thermal lags associated with the liquid hold-up in the reboiler will determine, to some extent, the rapidity with which the vapor boil-up rate can be changed following a manipulation of the heating means. Thermal lags in the overhead condenser will determine how rapidly the condensation rate can be altered.

However, for plates already evaporating liquid, there is no significant time lag between a change in the rate at which vapor condenses on a plate and the rate of boil-off from a plate, provided that the mixing on a plate is rapid.

Separation of Material. The composition of material that evaporates from a liquid mixture is a function of the liquid composition, the temperature, and the pressure conditions that prevail and that influence the vapor and liquid equilibrium. For all practical purposes, however, the composition of the vapor leaving the surface of the boiling liquid in a distillation operation can be assumed to be a function of the liquid composition only, unless the temperatures and pressures involved vary over wide ranges, or mixtures of unusual chemicals are involved.

To develop the fundamental idea of mass transfer in the distillation column in a macroscopic way, we must determine how the column remains continuously operative. The evaporation of material from the surface of the liquid carries away sensible heat. Therefore, to keep the process of separation going, heat must be added to the liquid. If only heat is added, the lighter components will first boil away, and then the heavier ones will boil away, unless the thermal losses are such that the boiling temperature of the heavier components cannot be reached and maintained; in which case, distillation will cease. To bring about continuous separation, in addition to supplying heat, liquid make-up must be supplied to the volume of liquid from which separation is taking place.

When the rising vapor (which is relatively richer in the lower boiling components than the liquid on the plate or section) condenses on a plate or section of a column, it transfers both heat and mass flow. Further, the liquid flowing onto a plate or packed section from above carries with it the lower boiling components in a higher proportion than the material on the plate or in the section. Then, in a steady-state operation, the composition of material on the plate remains constant. For this reason, distillation can be a continuous rather than a discontinuous or batch type operation.

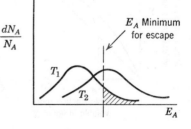

Fig. 5.13. Escape rate of molecules from a mixture.

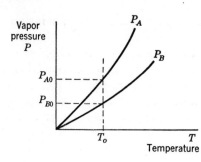

Fig. 5.14. Vapor pressure for a binary mixture.

If the number of molecules dN_A of component A in a binary mixture which has a total number of molecules N_A is plotted as a ratio $dN_A:N_A$ versus energy E_A, as shown in Fig. 5.13 for a temperature T_1, those molecules which have sufficient energy to escape lie in the shaded region of the curve. At a higher temperature $T_2 > T_1$, the curve shifts toward the right; at a lower temperature $T_3 < T_1$, toward the left. In general, for an increase in temperature there is an increase in the number of molecules that can escape from the surface of a liquid. The shaded areas in Fig. 5.13 represent the numbers of molecules or atoms of component A that can escape per unit time. The mass flow per unit time from a liquid surface gives the momentum at the interfacial boundary, from which the pressure creating the flow can be calculated. This pressure is the *vapor pressure* of the component A in the liquid.

Figure 5.14 shows the vapor pressure P versus temperature T for a binary mixture. For a wide range of temperature variation, the ratio between the vapor pressure P_A of component A and P_B of component

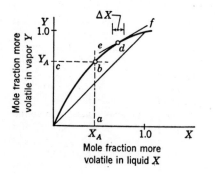

Fig. 5.15. X–Y or liquid–vapor equilibrium diagram for binary mixture.

B remains essentially constant.*   The vapor pressures P_A and P_B are
the driving forces which establish the relative amount of components
A and B in the flow of vapor leaving the liquid.   *Therefore, liquid
temperature is not a primary manipulating variable or a direct-measure-
ment variable in the composition of the boil-off* from the surface of a
liquid in which separation is taking place.   Boiling temperature bears
a fixed relationship to liquid composition only at constant pressure.

Equilibrium Diagram. The liquid-vapor equilibrium diagram
generally referred to as the McCabe–Thiele X–Y diagram is shown in
Fig. 5.15.   According to the diagram, for any composition X_a of the
liquid, the vapor which leaves the liquid will be richer in component a
than the liquid itself.   Thus, if point a in Fig. 5.15 defines the liquid
composition X_a, the line ab intersects the liquid-vapor equilibrium
curve at point b.   Point b, when projected to point c on the vapor concentration axis, gives an ordinate which is greater than the value X_a.

Notwithstanding the fact that the X–Y diagram is called an *equilibrium diagram*, it can be used to determine the time variation in the
composition of vapor leaving the surface of a liquid whose composition
is varying.   Since there appear to be very small time lags associated
with the mass-transfer operation† itself, a static relationship between

* The mathematical form of vapor pressure versus temperature is:

$$P_A = K_1 e^{-\alpha_1/T}$$

Therefore, the ratio of two vapor pressures is given by

$$R = \frac{P_A}{P_B} = \frac{K_1}{K_2} e^{[\alpha_2 - \alpha_1] T}$$

Small variations in the liquid temperature T do not change the vapor-pressure
ratio R.

Since the temperature of the liquid on the plates of a distillation column is not
the controlling variable in determining the composition of vapor which comes from
successive plates or successive volumes of liquid in distillation columns, much of
the regulation and control practice currently used in distillation columns is incor-
rect in fundamental principle.   Liquid composition is the controlling feature, and
temperature is an indirect and secondary variable.   Temperature measurements
do not indicate the instantaneous or dynamic composition conditions in a column
when pressure is also varying.   Many of the problems that arise in automatic
control and regulation over distillation are made difficult to handle because of
temperature controllers operating from thermal detectors submerged in the various
plates in a column, and the measurement does not provide adequate information
to bring about column control through reboiler, overhead-condenser controls, and
reflux ratio manipulation.

† Teager, S. M., "Transients in the Intraphase of a Mass Transfer System,"
M.I.T., S.B. Thesis (Chemical Engineering), 1954.

Y and X can be determined for a sieve plate, bubble plate, or any other type of liquid hold-up structure in distillation columns.

The variation in Y with respect to X, for an equivalent plate, can be expressed by means of a straight-line approximation to the McCabe–Thiele diagram.   In Fig. 5.15, the point d corresponds to the operating composition of the liquid in a given plate in a column.   The line designated by edf has the equation

$$Y = K_o + K_1 X \tag{5.30}$$

For a small range of variation in the liquid composition, eq. 5.30 represents with reasonable accuracy the composition of vapor leaving the plate.   The values for K_o and K_1 can be determined graphically. Provided the operating conditions of the column do not change beyond reasonable ranges, such as would be encountered in start-up or shutdown, eq. 5.30 seems to be a good approximation for linearization of the operation of a single plate.

To predict how the composition of the liquid or the vapor varies as a function of time, at any point in a distillation column, requires that a set of material-balance equations be written for each plate and vapor space in the column.   The form of the equations can be established by a study of one plate.

Three factors, however, must be taken into account when the material-balance equations for a plate are being written: (1) the plate efficiency,* (2) the nature of the mixing† on the plate, and (3) the entrainment,‡ if any, of liquid by the rising vapor.   Then taken in combinations, these three factors give rise to many possible analyses. There can be: (1) inefficient plates which are perfectly mixed, with zero entrainment; (2) perfectly efficient plates perfectly mixed, with zero entrainment; and (3) inefficient and perfectly efficient types with slug flow—also with zero entrainment.   No attempt will be made to develop each possibility independently.

* A perfectly efficient plate fully condenses all of the vapor rising from the plate below.   Inefficient plates permit a fraction of the rising vapor to pass through the plate uncondensed.

† A difficulty arises when a mathematical description of the liquid-with-liquid mixing on plates or in packed sections is needed.   Perfect mixing over an entire plate does not occur.   Slug flow of the liquid from above, across the plate, and down, also does not occur.   Thus, a form of *partial mixing* must occur—but the physical interpretation of partial mixing is difficult; the mathematical methods for its study require careful evaluation.

‡ Entrainment means that the rising vapor carries some liquid droplets from one tray up to the next.

To express composition variation for the entire column, there will be needed—in addition to the sets of equations for the plates—one set of equations to describe the reboiler and one more to describe the overhead condenser. The feed-plate material-balance equation can be modified to account for the liquid feed which comes into the plate from an external source.

By means of a set of equations for a single plate, a block diagram or signal-flow diagram can be drawn for the plate. The graphs for consecutive plates, but with different transmission characteristics in their blocks or directed branches which depend upon the parameters for the particular plate, can be interconnected to describe the vapor and liquid composition at any plate in an n-plate sequence between the reboiler and the condenser. The overhead-condenser graph is added to one end of the diagram, and the reboiler is added to the other end. The feed enters the feed plate at a liquid-composition point or node in the diagram between the first and nth plates.

Composition Variation on a Plate. To determine how the composition x_j of the liquid on the jth plate, or the composition y_j of the vapor leaving the jth plate in a column changes as a function of time, requires that the equations for the material balance on the plate be written. The material-balance equation for a plate must include: the liquid coming down the column, the vapor rising in the column, and the mass transfer taking place between vapor and liquid phases on the plate.

The rate of change of liquid composition on a plate can be written in terms of the hold-up on the plate, the liquid flow rate to and from the plate, and the vapor flow rate to and from the plate. The operating points on the X-Y equilbrium diagram for the particular plate define the parameters in the equations.

For the *perfectly mixed but inefficient plate, with zero entrainment*, the composition variation in the liquid on the plate is given by

$$h_j \frac{dx_j}{dt} = (L_{j+1})x_{j+1} - (L_j)x_j + (A_j)y_{j-1} - B_j\phi(x_j) \quad (5.31)$$

The vapor composition* above the plate (assuming no vapor hold-up) is given by

$$y_j = \frac{(G_{j-1} - A_j)y_{j-1} + B_j\phi(x_j)}{G_j} \quad (5.32)$$

* A material-balance equation for the vapor in the space between plates is not needed, since the amount of vapor hold-up between plates is not large compared with the throughput of vapor. However, if for special reasons it should become necessary to write the equations for the material balance in the vapor space, the procedure is exactly identical with that for studying the liquid material balance.

where j = subscript that identifies the jth plate
$\quad L_j$ = molal liquid flow rate from the jth plate
$\quad L_{j+1}$ = molal liquid flow rate to the jth plate
$\quad A_j$ = molal gas condensation rate on the jth plate
$\quad B_j$ = molal gas evaporation rate from the jth plate
$\quad h_j$ = molal liquid hold-up on the jth plate
$\quad x_j$ = mol ratio (composition) of the liquid on the jth plate
$\quad y_j$ = mol ratio (composition) of the vapor above the jth plate
$\quad G_j$ = molal gas flow rate above the jth plate
$\quad \phi(x_j)$ = composition of the vapor in equilibrium with x_j that evaporates from the liquid on the jth plate

From the equilibrium diagram, Fig. 5.15, the linear relationship between $\phi(x_j)$ and x_j on the jth plate is:

$$y_{\text{equil.}} = \phi(x_j) = K_{oj} + K_{1j}x_j \tag{5.33}$$

Equation 5.33 permits the linearization of the material-balance equations. Thus

$$h_j \frac{dx_j}{dt} = (L_{j+1})x_{j+1} - (L_j)x_j + A_j y_{j-1} - K_{oj}B_j - K_{1j}B_j x_j \tag{5.34}$$

and

$$y_j = \frac{1}{G_j}[(G_{j-1} - A_j)y_{j-1} + B_j K_{oj} + B_j K_{1j}x_j] \tag{5.35}$$

Equation 5.34 establishes for the perfectly mixed plate a transfer function of the form $\dfrac{1}{\tau_j s + 1}$. The operator is similar to the lag operator for perfect mixing; in fact, if the evaporation term $K_{1j}B_j$ were zero, the transfer function that defines the composition variation on an inefficient but perfectly mixed plate would be the same as the transfer function for a perfectly mixed vessel with a hold-up volume equal to the plate hold-up h_j and a throughput equal to the liquid flow L_j. Thus, for the plate with evaporation, the time constant is:

$$\tau_j = \frac{h_j}{L_j + K_{1j}B_j} \tag{5.36}$$

in contrast to $\tau_j = h_j/L_j$ for a tray with zero evaporation.

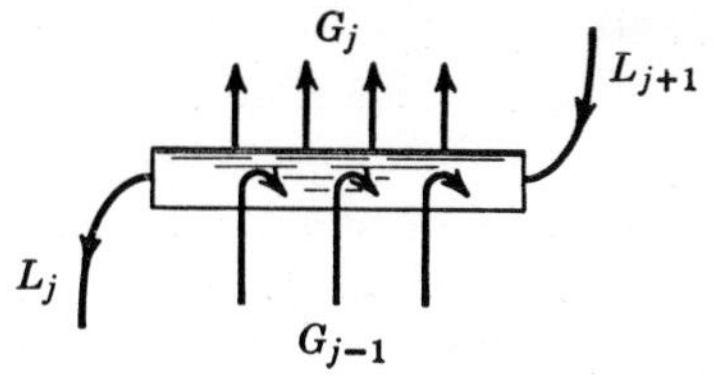

Fig. 5.16. Schematic diagram of a perfectly efficient, perfectly mixed, zero-entrainment plate.

The values of A_j and B_j can be related to each other by expressing them in terms of the molal heat of evaporation of the vapor leaving the plate, and the molal heat of condensation of the vapor condensing on the plate. Thus

$$\frac{A_j}{B_j} = \frac{Q[f(x_j)]}{Q[y_{j-1}]} \tag{5.37}$$

where $Q[y]$ is the molal heat of vaporization of vapor of composition y_{j-1} condensing on the plate.

Perfectly Mixed, Perfectly Efficient Plate. The perfectly mixed and perfectly efficient plate (see Fig. 5.16) has the condition $B_j = G_j$ and $G_{j-1} = A_j$. Therefore eqs. 5.34 and 5.35 combine into a single equation

$$h_j \frac{dx_j}{dt} = (L_{j+1})x_{j+1} - (L_j)x_j + G_{j-1}y_{j-1} - G_j\phi(x_j) \tag{5.38}$$

which has the linear form

$$h_j \frac{dx_j}{dt} = (L_{j+1})x_{j+1} - (L_j)x_j + G_{j-1}y_{j-1} - K_{oj}G_j - K_{1j}G_jx_j \tag{5.39}$$

According to eq. 5.39 the time constant of the perfectly mixed and perfectly efficient plate becomes

$$\tau_j = \frac{h_j}{L_j + K_{1j}G_j} = \frac{h_j/L_j}{1 + K_{1j}(G_j/L_j)} \tag{5.40}$$

From eqs. 5.39 and 5.40 it can be noted that the mixing lag in the liquid on a plate diminishes as the liquid rate (for a fixed hold-up) increases. The ratio between liquid and vapor flows at a given plate is designed in practice to correspond closely to the slope of the equi-

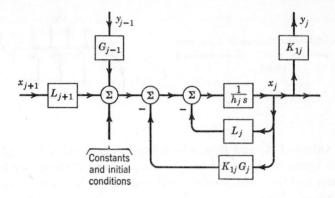

Fig. 5.17. Block diagram for a single perfectly efficient, perfectly mixed, zero-entrainment plate.

librium curve (K_{1j}) due to economic considerations. Thus, in a given column, the group $\dfrac{K_{1j}G_j{}^*}{L_j}$ will not vary greatly from unity.

The extent to which the liquid flow can be increased to minimize the time lag on a plate will indirectly be a function of the maximum vapor rate which can be withstood without causing excessive entrainment. The dynamic characteristics of a column are thus dictated in large measure by economic considerations in the design for steady-state operation, and cannot be considered independently.

Block Diagrams and Signal Flow Diagrams for a Plate. A block diagram which relates the compositions x_j, x_{j+1}, y_j, and y_{j-1} is shown in Fig. 5.17. The simplifications of the primitive diagram are shown in the succeeding figures, Figs. 5.18 and 5.19.

* The group L_j/G_j is referred to as the slope of the "operating line" in chemical engineering terminology. When properly plotted on a "McCabe–Thiele diagram," the operating lines with corresponding feed and output stream compositions can be used to give an approximation to the steady-state compositions on each plate. The upper and lower operating lines intersect at the feed plate, and their slopes must be chosen so that they intersect within the diagram. In the upper section of the column, corresponding to the upper operating line, L/G represents a fraction of the product which is returned to the column as reflux. Obviously, for a given composition of top product, this fraction should be made as small as realizable. This in turn dictates that L/G on the average, for the plates in the upper half will correspond closely to K_1.

Similar considerations hold for the lower section of a column. For a complete derivation of the "McCabe–Thiele diagram" the reader is referred to any of the standard chemical engineering texts on the subject, such as reference 3 in the Bibliography.

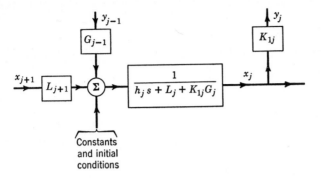

Fig. 5.18. Simplification of Fig. 5.17.

The block diagram in Fig. 5.17 shows why the mixing lag h_j/L_j is modified by the evaporation. The signal path x_j through the transfer function $K_{1j}G_j$ to the mass flow summation point is a degenerative feedback path around the mixing-lag operator $\dfrac{1/L_j}{\dfrac{h_j}{L_j}s+1}$.

A block diagram can be developed for a series of plates. By starting at the jth plate and progressing to plate $j+1$, and up the column to the overhead condenser, and from the $(j-1)$th plate down the column to the reboiler, the block diagram for an entire column can be developed. However, the block diagram becomes rather cumbersome.

The node and directed branch type of signal-flow graph proves to be much easier to manipulate. Thus the signal-flow diagram for a perfectly efficient and perfectly mixed plate with zero entrainment is shown in Fig. 5.20. The x nodes represent liquid compositions; the y nodes represent vapor compositions; the directed branches have the

Fig. 5.19. Further simplification of Fig. 5.17.

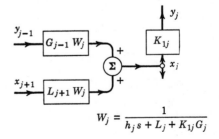

$$W_j = \frac{1}{h_j s + L_j + K_{1j}G_j}$$

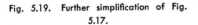

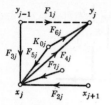

Fig. 5.20. Node and directed branch type of signal-flow diagram for perfectly efficient, perfectly mixed, zero entrainment plate.

transfer characteristics which define the plate dynamics. Thus

$$F_{1j} = 0 \tag{5.41}$$

$$F_{2j} = \frac{L_{j+1}}{h_j s + L_j + K_{1j} G_j} \tag{5.42}$$

$$F_{3j} = \frac{G_{j-1}}{h_j s + L_j + K_{1j} G_j} \tag{5.43}$$

$$F_{4j} = K_{1j} \tag{5.44}$$

$$F_{5j} = \frac{G_j/s}{h_j s + L_j + K_{1j} G_j} \tag{5.45}$$

$$F_{6j} = 1/s \tag{5.46}$$

$$F_{7j} = \frac{h_j}{h_j s + L_j + K_{1j} G_j} \tag{5.47}$$

Feed Plate. For the feed plate, the material-balance equations are:

$$h_j \frac{dx_j}{dt} = L_{j+1} x_{j+1} + L_f x_f - L_j x_j$$
$$+ G_{j-1} y_{j-1} - K_{oj} G_j - K_{1j} G_j x_j \tag{5.48}$$

$$y_j = K_{oj} + K_{1j} x_j \tag{5.49}$$

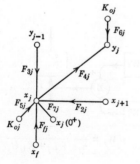

Fig. 5.21. Feed plate signal-flow diagram.

The signal-flow diagram for the feed plate can be developed as shown in Fig. 5.21.   The transfer characteristic F_{fj} is:

$$F_{fj}(s) = \frac{L_f}{h_j s + L_j + K_{1j} G_j} \tag{5.50}$$

Reboiler.   The reboiler material balance is:

$$h_o \frac{dx_o}{dt} = L_1 x_1 - L_o x_o - G_o (K_{oo} + K_{1o} x_o) \tag{5.51}$$

$$y_o = K_{oo} + K_{1o} x_o \tag{5.52}$$

where x_o is the bottoms product that is drawn off.

The signal-flow diagram for the reboiler is given in Fig. 5.22.   The branch transfer functions for the reboiler are:

$$F_{20} = \frac{L_1}{h_o s + L_o + G_o K_{1o}} \tag{5.53}$$

$$F_{40} = K_{1o} \tag{5.54}$$

$$F_{50} = \frac{G_o}{h_o s + L_o + G_o K_{1o}} \tag{5.55}$$

$$F_{70} = \frac{h_o}{h_o s + L_o + K_{1o} G_o} \tag{5.56}$$

The Condenser.   The material balance for the condenser is:

$$h_c \frac{dx_c}{dt} = G_n y_n - L_c x_c \tag{5.57}$$

Since vapor fully condenses, there is only one equation.

Fig. 5.22.   Reboiler signal-flow diagram.

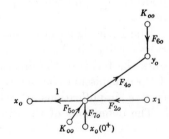

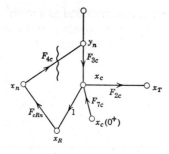

Fig. 5.23.   Overhead-condenser signal-flow graph.

The signal-flow diagram is given in Fig. 5.23.   The definitions of the direct-branch transforms are:

$$F_{2c} = 1 \tag{5.58}$$

$$F_{3c} = \frac{G_n}{h_c s + L_c} \tag{5.59}$$

The branch between the reflux composition node x_r and the nth plate composition node x_n must be defined in terms of the time lags and transportation lags present in the reflux path.   The node x_T represents the top product composition.

Signal-Flow Graph for Column.   The signal-flow diagram for an entire column can be formed by connecting the signal-flow diagrams for a succession of plates in cascade.   The reboiler diagram is placed on one end; the condenser diagram on the other.   The feed node is arbitrarily connected to the jth liquid node.   Figure 5.24 shows the entire signal-flow diagram development.   Figure 5.24a shows the signal-flow diagram for a column in its basic topological form.   The x nodes of this diagram are liquid composition, and the y nodes are vapor composition.   The feed node x_f adds flow of liquid to the jth plate.   Liquid product is taken from the overhead condenser at the node x_T.   Liquid bottom product is removed from the reboiler at the node x_B.

The basic-signal-flow diagram, Fig. 5.24a, can be simplified by the rules outlined in Appendix I so that the successive simplifications produce the forms of the diagram in Figs. 5.24b, 5.24c, 5.24d, and 5.24e. The transmission characteristics for the directed branches in the successive simplifications are related as follows:

The definitions of the directed branch transfer functions $F_{1j}, \cdots$

F_{7j} are given by eqs. 5.41–5.47.   When the signal-flow graph for the plate shown in Fig. 5.20 is transformed into the equivalent circuit, the new transfer functions for the directed branches become:

$$a_j = F_{4j}F_{3(j+1)} \tag{5.60}$$

$$b_j = F_{2j} \tag{5.61}$$

Now the signal-flow diagram has only liquid-composition nodes x_j. For the final simplification in Fig. 5.24e, drawn for an upset in feed composition x_f, the transmissions are:

$$T_{11} = a_o b_o \tag{5.62}$$

$$T_{22} = \frac{a_1 b_1}{1 - a_o b_o} \tag{5.63}$$

$$T_{33} = \cfrac{a_2 b_2}{1 - \cfrac{a_1 b_1}{1 - a_o b_o}} \tag{5.64}$$

$$\cdot$$
$$\cdot$$
$$\cdot$$

$$T_{jj} = \cfrac{a_{j-1}b_{j-1}}{1 - \cfrac{a_{j-2}b_{j-2}}{1 - \cfrac{a_{j-3}b_{j-3}}{1 - }}} + \cfrac{a_j b_j}{1 - \cfrac{a_{j+1}b_{j+1}}{1 - \cfrac{a_{j+2}b_{j+2}}{1 - }}}$$

$$\cfrac{a_1 b_1}{1 - a_o b_o} \qquad\qquad \cfrac{a_{n-1}b_{n-1}}{1 - a_n b_n} \tag{5.65}$$

$$\cdot$$
$$\cdot$$
$$\cdot$$

$$T_{(n-1)(n-1)} = \frac{a_{n-1}b_{n-1}}{1 - a_n b_n} \tag{5.66}$$

$$T_{nn} = a_n b_n \tag{5.67}$$

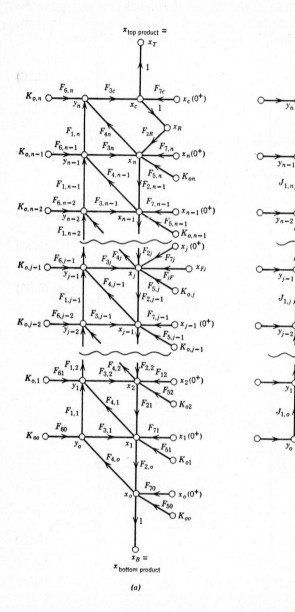

(a)   (b)

Fig. 5.24. Signal-flow diagram for a distillation column with inefficient or efficient, perfectly (inefficient plates); (c) simplification of (a) for $F_{1j} = 0$ (perfectly efficient plates); (d) reduction of

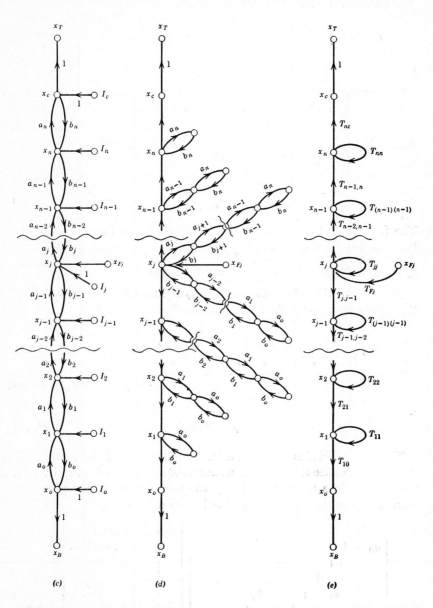

(c) (d) (e)

mixed, zero-entrainment plates. (a) Basic form, general case; (b) simplification of (a) for $F_{1j} \neq 0$ (c) for X_{Fj} input; (e) final reduction of (c).

The branch transfer characteristics become:

$$T_{10} = b_o \qquad (5.68)$$

$$T_{21} = b_1 \qquad (5.69)$$

$$T_{32} = b_2 \qquad (5.70)$$

$$T_{j(j-1)} = b_{j-1} \qquad (5.71)$$

$$T_{j(j+1)} = a_j \qquad (5.72)$$

$$T_{(n-1)n} = a_{n-1} \qquad (5.73)$$

$$T_{nc} = a_n \qquad (5.74)$$

$$T_{Fj} = f \qquad (5.75)$$

The feed point to the column is at the jth liquid node through the transmission characteristics $T_{Fj} = f$.

5. COMPOSITION DYNAMICS IN THE COLUMN

The composition of the top product x_T can be related to the composition of the feed x_F by the continued fraction

$$\frac{x_T}{x_F} = T_{Fj} \frac{1}{1 - T_{jj}} \frac{T_j T_{j+1}}{1 - T_{(j+1)(j+1)}} \frac{T_{(j+1)(j+2)}}{1 - T_{(j+2)(j+2)}}$$

$$\cdots \frac{T_{(n-1)n}}{1 - T_{nn}} T_{nc} \qquad (5.76)$$

where

$$x_T = F_{2c} x_c \qquad (5.77)$$

The characteristics of the overhead condenser and the reflux ratio are inherent in the transmission characteristics F_{3c} and F_{2R} in Fig. 5.24.

However, in a more general way the composition at any plate can be replaced to the feed composition by the matrix

$$
\begin{bmatrix}
-1 & b_0 & & & & & & \\
a_0 - 1 & & b_1 & & & & & \\
& a_1 - 1 & & b_2 & & & & \\
& & a_2 - 1 & & b_3 & & & \\
& & & a_3 - 1 & & b_4 & & \\
& & & & a_j - 1 & & b_{j+1} & \\
& & & & & a_{n-2} - 1 & & b_{n-1} \\
& & & & & & a_{n-1} - 1 & bn \\
& & & & & & & a_n - 1
\end{bmatrix}
\begin{bmatrix}
x_0 \\
x_1 \\
\\
\\
\\
x_j \\
\\
\\
x_c
\end{bmatrix}
=
\begin{bmatrix}
\text{initial} \\
\text{conditions} \\
\\
\\
\\
fx_F \\
\\
\\
\\
\end{bmatrix}
\qquad (5.78)
$$

Once a signal-flow diagram, or the system matrix has been solved for the transmission between a feed composition change and the composition at any plate, the problem of taking inverse transform remains. This can be an extremely trying and time consuming procedure for a column of many plates, as the denominator polynomial is of at least the same order as the number of plates. In addition, what may be desired to determine the columns dynamic characteristics is not a point by point time response for a given shape upset, but rather a means of determining key parameters, and an estimate of the essential response characteristics.

For these purposes, the column impulse response can be treated in the same manner as a probability distribution function in statistics, that is, we can evaluate parameters related to the moment of the impulse response such as RMS deviation and higher moments. These moments can be obtained by simple manipulations upon the system of transfer functions.

$$i.e., \text{ mean time} = \left. \frac{-\dfrac{d}{ds} F(s)}{F(s)} \right|_{s=0}$$

$$\text{RMS time} = \left[\frac{\dfrac{d^2}{ds^2} F(s)}{F(s)} \right]^{\frac{1}{2}} \Bigg|_{s=0}$$

The signal-flow diagram and the transmission matrix for the special case of perfectly efficient plates have been developed in the preceding paragraphs. For the more general cases of inefficient plates, the general form of signal-flow diagram, Fig. 5.24b should be used. No simple reduction of this type of diagram exists, and recourse must be made to a transmission matrix similar to that of eq. 5.78.

To obtain an approximate evaluation for the case of the columns with liquid transportation lags between plates, or mixing of a distributed type, the procedure outlined by Teager can be undertaken.

The matrix of eq. 5.78 can be partitioned, transformed to difference equation form, and expanded into an infinite series. The first few terms in the series can be used to approximate the transient response curve for the composition at any point in the column in terms of the feed stream composition. By means of the approximation, an "average" time constant can be determined for the process response.

The exact approach for calculating the transient response of composition in a column may be warranted when new column designs are being undertaken. Similar topological studies of the heat flow throughout a column can be made. The combined calculations can be carried out on computers by means of difference equations. Before rapid methods can be developed for estimating and making approximate evaluations of automatic control possibilities for distillation columns it will be necessary to study in detail these exact numerical solutions.

6. CONCLUSION

The fact that the equations for fluid handling, thermal energy transfer, and mass transfer become combined in the processes of drying, evaporating, condensing, and distillation made the work of this chapter difficult. The reader must be prepared to go beyond the point where the material ended. He must employ difference equations and machine calculations in order to appraise the dynamic behavior of most mass transfer processes.

Drying, for example, can be studied in a rudimentary way, as was outlined by assuming the lumped process characteristic to be an ideal integration. On the other hand, to give drying of films, webs, and granular material proper study requires that diffusion equations be solved for the particular boundary conditions and time-varying disturbances. This can become a decidedly complicated type of investigation.

The work on distillation treated only binary separation. The perturbations of composition throughout an idealized column were predicted under thermal equilibrium conditions and steady flow. To go further calls for sets of equations to be written which couple the thermal, fluid and vapor flow, and material balances. Even when the use of digital computation is considered, *attention will have to be given* the physics of the problem, the organization of data, and the interpretation of the results.

In distillation a few of the basic problems are: First, to know how changes in the feed flow-rate and feed composition affect the operation of the still. The feed is the primary disturbance point in the system even though it constitutes the inflow point for raw material. Secondly, because the thermal energy is supplied to the system in the reboiler, it is of interest to know the relationship between the vapor flow rate from the bottom of the column and the amount of energy delivered to the liquid hold-up in the reboiler by any means of heating. Thirdly, the influence of reflux flow rate and composition upon the temperature and composition of the vapors which rise through the top part of the column is important. Reflux manipulation at the top often controls many distillation operations.

All of the problems mentioned can be studied by means of a topological study of composition and the additional equations for heat. Generally, different equation sets will be needed for each plate. Clearly, for the study of columns that have more than ten or twenty plates the only recourse is to mechanize the calculations. The reader is to be cautioned upon one point. Such computational problems are costly to perform. Care must be taken to not only set up the equations properly but also the range of variation of the quantities in the equations must be understood. Otherwise, the solution may run beyond the ranges of the machine doing the calculation; alternatively, the computer solution might not fit the practical range of the physical problem.

BIBLIOGRAPHY

A Course of Study in Chemical Principles, A. A. Noyes and M. S. Sherrill, Macmillan Company, New York, 1938.

An Introduction to Probability Theory and Its Applications, W. Feller, John Wiley & Sons, New York, 1950.

Principles of Chemical Engineering, W. H. Walker, W. K. Lewis, W. H. McAdams, and E. R. Gilliland, McGraw-Hill Book Co., New York, 1937.

Unit Operations, G. G. Brown and Associates, John Wiley & Sons, New York, 1950.

Chemical Engineers' Handbook, J. H. Perry (Editor), McGraw-Hill Book Co., 3rd ed., New York, 1950.

Elements of Fractional Distillation, C. S. Robinson, and E. R. Gilliland, McGraw-Hill Book Co., New York, 1950.

"An Analysis of Transients in Mass-Transfer Operations," H. M. Teager, M.I.T. Sc.D. Thesis, 1955.

"The Application of Differential Equations to Chemical Engineering Problems," W. R. Marshall, Jr., and R. L. Pigford, University of Delaware, Newark, Delaware, March 1947.

"Servomechanism Approach to Process Control—Temperature and Ratio Control of Distillation Column Reflux," S.M. Thesis, W. D. Mohr, Massachusetts Institute of Technology, Cambridge, Mass., May 1951.

"Theory of the Performance of Packed Rectifying Columns," J. R. Bowman, and R. C. Briant, *Ind. Eng. Chem.*, **39**, No. 6 (June 1947).

"Mathematical Techniques in Chemical Engineering Research," R. L. Pigford, University of Delaware, Newark, Delaware.

"A Mathematical Theory of the Drying of Wood," F. Tuttle, J. Franklin Inst., Vol. cc, p. 609 (1925).

"A Theory of Porous Flow," E. E. Libman, *Phil. Magazine*, IV, p. 1285 (1927).

Absorption and Extraction, T. K. Sherwood, and R. L. Pigford, McGraw-Hill Book Co., New York, 1952.

Combustion Processes, B. Lewis, R. Pease, and H. S. Taylor, Princeton University Press, 1956.

Mass-Transfer Operations, R. E. Treybal, McGraw-Hill Book Co., New York, 1955.

"Statistical Treatment of Packed Columns," *Ind. Eng. Chem.*, Danckwerts, **43**, p. 1460 (1951).

"Automatic Control in Continuous Distillation," *Ind. Eng. Chem.*, T. J. Williams, R. T. Harnett, and Arthur Rose, **48**, No. 6, 1008–1019 (June 1956).

"An Investigation of the Transient Response of a Distillation Column" reported in *Plant and Process Dynamic Characteristics*, W. L. Wilkinson, and W. D. Armstrong, Academic Press, New York, 1957.

"Response of Concentrations in a Distillation Column to Disturbances in the Feed Composition"; H. Voetter, *Plant and Process Dynamic Characteristics*.

CHAPTER 6

Chemical Process Dynamics

1. CHEMICAL PROCESSES

Chemical processes convert raw materials into bulk chemical products. In production, the aim is to obtain from reactions the maximum molal *yield* of product per mole of raw-material throughput, at the lowest cost. However, side products may also be formed in a chemical reaction, so that the object of chemical-process control may be to maximize the conversion of raw material into product but at the same time to minimize its conversion into side products. When special chemicals such as drugs are made, quality becomes the foremost consideration.

Control of a chemical process consists of the creating and maintaining of conditions that can bring about chemical reactions. It involves keeping these conditions at an *instantaneous* optimum, despite upsets in the environment of reaction, changes in the purity of the raw materials, changes in the throughput or hold-up, and in spite of abrupt or gradual deterioration of catalysts or other controlling agents.

Chemical Reactions. Chemical reactions involve the joining together or the separating of atoms and molecules. The problem is a microscopic one: it involves the interactions between the electrons in the shells of different atoms and molecules; it is also a problem related to probability of collision or near collision between different atoms and molecules. Some reactions yield a specific product; others, specific products and side-products. Finally, there are reactions that yield a complete distribution of products and side-products.

In the reaction $A + B \rightarrow C$, for example, C is the only product formed. In the reaction $A + B \rightarrow C + D$, a definite product C is accompanied by a definite side-product D. When carbon atoms are joined, the chains of carbons may have a definite pattern of formation, but the number of carbon atoms per molecule may vary. Also, differ-

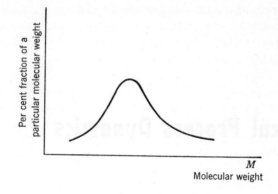

Fig. 6.1. Typical distribution of product yield in an organic reaction.

ent modes of carbon-chain interconnection with the same number of carbon atoms may occur.

Although generalizations are difficult to make, the inorganic reactions tend to yield *definite* products and side-products; whereas the organic reactions, and in particular polymerization types of reactions, yield distributions of molecules of different physical properties during the reaction process.

In the organic chemical reactions, which produce a distribution of molecular weights, the distinction between product and side product may become indefinite. In fact, in a given sample of product the per cent distribution of components versus molecular weight might vary, as shown by the curve in Fig. 6.1.

In the reactions that yield a distributed type of product, in addition to regulating the rate of conversion, the manipulation may be required to concentrate as much as possible of the total conversion into a specific region of the distribution curve. This is easier said than done, for very little quantitative information exists from which direct correlations can be made between the physical properties of a chemical, the structure of the particular molecules, and the manipulating actions that can be brought to bear upon the reactants. The trouble is plain enough to cite, but not easy to eliminate: Macroscopic methods of manipulation cannot produce microscopic regulation of molecular structure.

Types of Reactors. Many different types of reactors are used to bring about chemical reactions. Open vessels, with the materials in them stirred, may be batch reactors; open vessels through which a flow takes place, and in which a fixed amount of material is kept as hold-up, may be used for inorganic reactions, neutralization, the dissolving of metals in acid, and certain types of organic reactions. Pressurized vessels and autoclaves that work upon a batch basis or with a flow through them, may be used for both the inorganic and the organic types of reactions.

Numerous instances occur in industry where short cylindrical tubes or lengths of pipe are used as reactors. A mixture of raw materials, generally fluids or fluidized solids, flows into a pipe or large-diameter tube in which the reaction takes place. The reaction proceeds because of the conditions of concentration, temperature and pressure maintained in the reactor, or because the flow contains an activating agent or passes over a catalyst agent embedded in the reactor. Tubes and

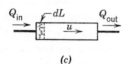

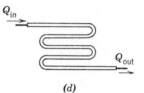

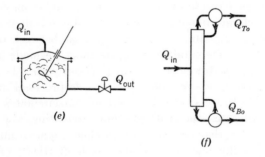

Fig. 6.2. Types of reactors. (a) Stirred reactor: open vessel with flow; (b) Stirred reactor: open vessel, zero flow-batch reactor; (c) Short tubular reactor, flame type; (d) Long tubular reactor, liquid catalyst type; (e) Pressure-stirred reactor; (f) Distillation column reaction on plates in liquid phase.

short pipes are also used as flame reactors.   As gas mixtures burn, the products of the partial or total combustion are gathered.

Chemical reactions take place in combination with other basic processes: for example, a reaction may be brought about in a distillation column.   The column may serve to strip gas free from a reaction. The bottom plates of the column may bring about polymerization. The product can then be drawn from the reboiler.   In some reactions the top product is sought.   Figure 6.2 shows several different types of reactors.

Process Configurations.   A raw material can enter a reactor, and the product is made upon a *single pass*—that is, the flow takes place through the reactor only once.   In the single-pass reactors, shown in Fig. 6.3, the conversion per pass becomes an important issue.   The hold-up to throughput ratio for the stirred reactor is the same as the "mean residence time" for a particle.   Therefore $W/Q = \tau$ will be an important design parameter.   In a tubular reactor, the amount of product made as the raw material passes through a unit length of reactor will depend upon the reactor conversion rate and the contact time of the material flowing through the tube.   The transportation lag is also W/Q.

In the single-pass reactor the product is recovered at the reactor exit or farther downstream.   However, certain kinds of reactions have a low yield per unit time, even under the most favorable environmental conditions.   Therefore *cascades of reactors* must be used to improve process yield.   The first stage of reaction brings about partial conversion of raw material into product; a second reactor placed in series with the first, and a third, and so on, brings about addition conversion. In the limit, a long *continuous type of pipe reactor* results.   The multiple-reactor cascade or the continuous reactor may have several points at which additional raw material and catalysts can be added.

When the contact time in the reaction zone between the raw materials and the various catalyzing agents must be made great, but an unusually long reactor or a very large vessel with a low throughput proves impractical, *re-circulation* or *re-cycle* processes may be used. In the re-cycle process, the flow of material circulates continuously through a moderate-sized reactor.   The circulating flow may be substantially greater than the flow of product taken from the process. The circulating flow contains raw-materials, partially converted raw-material product, side-products, and inert materials.   A *make-up* flow brings in new raw material, and a *purge* properly located in the closed material flow loop can remove inert materials.   Products and side-products are removed in product separators.   Although the yield per pass through the reactor may be low, the re-cycle process nevertheless has a high conversion of material into product. The waste is low, because the unused raw material circulates.

Product Recovery. When chemical products are made in reactors, the product is recovered in a downstream *product-recovery vessel*. Material that is reacted and formed into product is separated from the unused raw materials. Whatever side products are made, the remaining inert materials and leftovers, such as catalysts and impurities, must also be removed.

Three arrangements for product recovery are shown in Fig. 6.4. The first, in Fig. 6.4a, shows a vessel which receives the total flow from

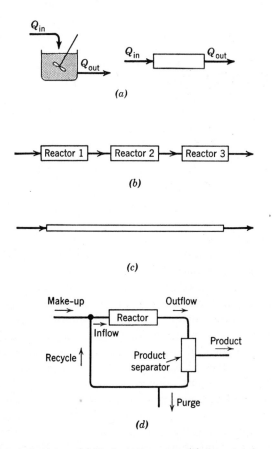

Fig. 6.3. Reactor configurations; (a) Single-pass reactors; (b) Cascade of reactors; (c) Long pipe or tube reactor; (d) Recycle system.

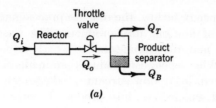

(a)

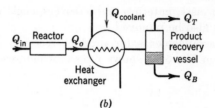

(b)

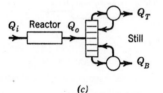

(c)

Fig. 6.4.   Product recovery.   (a) Pressure-drop product separation; (b) Heat-exchange product
separation; (c) Distillation column as a separator.

the reactor.   The pressure in the vessel is maintained at a considerably
lower level than the pressure in the reactor, by means of the throttling
valve located in the pipe line between the reactor and the product
extractor.   The drop in pressure allows vapors to come off overhead
in the product separator.   The liquid product comes from the bottom.
The liquid held in the bottom may contain liquid-phase product with
entrained impurities, inerts, and side-products.   Multi-stage product
separators may be needed to bring about precise product separation.
The product separators will have mixing lags that can be calculated by
means of the hold-up over throughput procedure outlined in Chapter 1.

A second type of product-recovery device uses a heat exchanger to
separate product.   The temperature of the material that flows from
the reactor is lowered sufficiently to condense out a fraction of the
material.   The fraction condensed may contain the product, or the
product may be present in the vapor component which does not con-

dense.   The heat-exchange product separator shown in Fig. 6.4*b* represents a single-stage condensation device for releasing the product. Multi-stage heat exchangers may be needed.   Whether the product is in the form of vapor or in the form of liquid, there will also be time-lag effects in composition based upon the volume and throughput of the particular component of product.

Distillation type of separation is another possibility.   The outflow from a chemical reactor can be sent to a distillation column as a feed stream.   The feed may be a vapor or a liquid.   The distillation column separates, by means of mass transfer, the light and the heavy components in the manner described in Chapter 5.   The purity or precision of separation of product from nonproduct depends upon both the static and the dynamic perfection of operation of the distillation column.

Many other types of product-separation techniques employ mechanical filtering, centrifuging, and other principles.

2. REACTION KINETICS

A chemical reaction is of necessity a microscopic process.   However, the interatomic or intermolecular forces that cause individual atoms and molecules to join or disjoin cannot be given consideration at this point in the chemical-process control theory.   The formation of material or the breaking-down of material must be considered upon a gross or macroscopic basis.   Average rates of reaction are expressed by differential equations which originate in the theory of reaction kinetics. These equations account for the amount of raw material used up per unit time, or the amount of product formed per unit time.

Rate Equation.   The basic form of the reaction equation*

$$-\frac{dN_1}{dt} = K(T)N_1C_1{}^{\alpha-1}C_2{}^{\beta}C_3{}^{\gamma} \cdot \cdot \cdot \tag{6.1}$$

expresses the rate at which the moles of material N_1 are used with respect to time.   The terms in the equation are:

N_1 = number of moles of species 1 present in unit reacting mass

C_1 = concentration of species 1 present, mole fraction of unit mass

C_2 = concentration of species 2 present, mole fraction of unit mass

---

* Section 4, "Chemical Reaction Kinetics," p. 321, *Chemical Engineers Handbook*, McGraw-Hill Book Co., New York, John H. Perry, Editor, 3rd edition, 1950.

C_3 = concentration of species 3 present, mole fraction of unit mass

$K(T)$ = reaction rate constant which is a function of temperature T

T = temperature

The exponents α, β, γ $\cdot$ $\cdot$ $\cdot$ are the numerical coefficients in the reaction equation.

A more convenient form of eq. 6.1 can be written for reaction at constant volume. Since $N_1 = VC_1$,

$$-\frac{dC_1}{dt} = KC_1{}^{\alpha}C_2{}^{\beta}C_3{}^{\gamma} \cdot \cdot \cdot \tag{6.2}$$

For different orders of complexity of chemical reaction, eq. 6.1 reduces to simple forms, some of which are linear, or at least not beyond solution by means of integration. The integrated forms of the rate equation are given in Table 6.1. The graphs in the last column of the table are indicative of the dynamic behavior of a single substance, isothermal reaction. The solid curves show the growth of the product. The dotted curves show the consumption of raw material.

Even though no sufficiently simple industrial chemical reaction of any importance falls into the linear category of the rate equation, the rate equation can be linearized around an operating point, when a quantitative treatment of the chemical-reaction control problem is necessary. Difference equations and numerical-calculation procedures also permit exploration of the dynamic behavior of chemical reactions.

Yield Curves. Experimental data referred to as *yield* or *conversion* curves procured from the study of pilot-scale processes provide the empirical information that also defines reaction rate as a function of concentrations, temperature, pressure, pH, and other physical variables. Operating points can be chosen in the yield curves, and the variation of the conversion rate for small departures of the reaction from equilibrium can be studied upon a linearized basis. Curve-fitting permits simple relationships to define reaction rates in an otherwise highly nonlinear and complex situation.

Yield curves, or conversion curves, are generally plotted in the form shown in Fig. 6.5. The mole conversion of product per mole of raw material N_p/N_{rm} is plotted against a variable such as N_A/N_B, the concentration in moles of A as compared with component B in the raw-material stream. Frequently a second ratio N_B/N_C, the moles of

TABLE 6.1. SUMMARY OF DATA FOR VARIOUS ORDER, SINGLE-SUBSTANCE, ISOTHERMAL REACTIONS

Order	Differential Equation	Step Function Transient	Half-Lives	Raw Material–Product Graphs
Zero	$-\dfrac{dC}{dt} = K_o$	$\dfrac{C}{C_o} = 1 - \dfrac{K_o}{C_o}t$	$\tau_{1/2} = \dfrac{C_o}{2K_o}$	$P = 1 - \dfrac{C}{C_o}$, $t_f = \dfrac{C_o}{K_o}$
One-half	$-\dfrac{dC}{dt} = K_{1/2}C^{1/2}$	$\dfrac{C}{C_o} = \left(1 - \dfrac{K_{1/2}}{2C_o^{1/2}}t\right)^2$	$\tau_{1/2} = (2 - 2^{1/2})\dfrac{C_o^{1/2}}{K_{1/2}}$	$\alpha = \dfrac{K_{1/2}}{2C_o^{1/2}}$, $t_f = \dfrac{2\sqrt{C_o}}{K_{1/2}} = \dfrac{1}{\alpha}$
First	$-\dfrac{dC}{dt} = K_1 C$	$\dfrac{C}{C_o} = e^{-K_1 t}$	$\tau_{1/2} = \dfrac{\ln 2}{K_1}$	Slope $= K_1$, $t = \dfrac{1}{K_1}$
Three halves	$-\dfrac{dC}{dt} = K_{3/2}C^{3/2}$	$\dfrac{C}{C_o} = \dfrac{1}{\left(1 + \dfrac{C_o^{1/2}K_{3/2}t}{2}\right)^2}$	$\tau_{1/2} = \dfrac{(8^{1/2} - 2)}{C_o^{1/2}K_{3/2}}$	$\alpha = 1 = \dfrac{C_o^{1/2}K_{3/2}}{2}$
Second	$-\dfrac{dC}{dt} = K_2 C^2$ (when two reacting substances are at same concentration)	$\dfrac{C}{C_o} = \dfrac{1}{1 + C_o K_2 t}$	$\tau_{1/2} = \dfrac{1}{C_o K_2}$	$\alpha = C_o K_2$

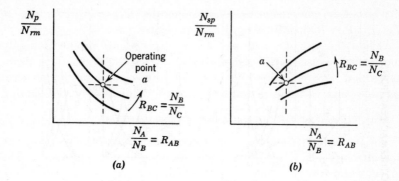

Fig. 6.5. (a) Product yield versus ratios R_{AB} and R_{BC}; (b) Side-product yield versus ratios R_{AB} and R_{BC}.

B with respect to the mols of C, may be influential as a parametric change in the yield-curve graph.

The amount of side-product formation can be determined by a similar set of yield curves that define the side-reaction kinetics. Around an operating point a shown in the two yield curves, the variations in N_p/N_{rm} and N_{sp}/N_{rm} can be expressed by means of a linear equation in terms of the ratios N_A/N_B and N_B/N_C. Thus the incremental change in product conversion rate is

$$d\left(\frac{N_p}{N_{rm}}\right) = K_1 d\left(\frac{N_A}{N_B}\right) + K_2 d\left(\frac{N_B}{N_C}\right) \tag{6.3}$$

and the incremental change in side-product formation rate is

$$d\left(\frac{N_{sp}}{N_{rm}}\right) = K_3 d\left(\frac{N_A}{N_B}\right) + K_4 d\left(\frac{N_B}{N_C}\right) \tag{6.4}$$

expressed in terms of the incremental changes in the mole ratios R_{AB} and R_{BC}.

Additional curves can be drawn to show the influence of temperature, pressure, and the other physical variables. The partial-differential procedure can be used to determine the linear variation in conversion around an operating point for all the variables. Thus:

$$dC = \frac{\partial C}{\partial R_{AB}} dR_{AB} + \frac{\partial C}{\partial R_{BC}} dR_{BC} + \frac{\partial C}{\partial T} dT + \frac{\partial C}{\partial P} dP \cdots \tag{6.5}$$

in which C = conversion or conversion rate, $R_{AB} = N_A/N_B$, $R_{BC} = N_B/N_C$, T = temperature, and P = pressure.

At best the rate of conversion of raw material into product is highly uncertain because of the complexity of the chemical reactions themselves and because of the complicated interrelation of the physical variables such as temperature and pressure with the reaction kinetics.

3. MANIPULATION OF CHEMICAL-REACTION SYSTEMS

The fundamental macroscopic ways to manipulate the reaction rate in a chemical reaction can be noted from the kinetic equations. The concentration of raw materials, the temperature, the pressure, and, in some reactions, the rate of free radical formation serve as manipulation variables. Among the fundamental ways in which the reaction rate in a chemical process can be manipulated, some are more advantageous than others.

The *concentration* of raw materials with respect to one another and to catalyzing or activating agents can be changed by ratioing and mixing procedures applied to the inflowing streams to the volume where the reaction is going to take place. Even in the presence of the proper mixture, the *temperature* of the material in the reaction region influences reaction rate. The temperature may be controlled by limiting the rate of reaction and hence the thermal-energy take-up or release. Also, temperature control can be brought about by various heat-exchanging procedures. *Pressure* sometimes becomes a variable which can influence the rate at which a reaction takes place. If the pressure in a reacting vessel must be maintained constant, this is generally a matter of hydrodynamics. Certain kinds of chemical materials can be affected by *radiation*. Visible light, x-rays, and other types of radiation can bring about free radical formation and reactions. To some extent the presence of strong *electrostatic* or *electromagnetic* fields in materials creates a kind of work potential that helps release free radicals in the material.

The concentration of a material in a vessel cannot be changed instantly, because there is a mixing lag which depends upon the reactor volume and flow situation. Large mixing lags tend to limit the possibilities of precise and rapid control over reactors by means of concentration manipulation.

Three procedures for temperature control are possible: first, to control the average temperature of the mixture in a reactor by the addition of the correct amounts of *sensible heat* in the flow streams. Secondly, to control by bringing about a *heat exchange* between the reacting material and a control medium which can take up or give off heat.

Thirdly, by altering the rate at which heat is taken up or given off by the reaction itself, to regulate temperature by controlling the ratio of ingredients in the reacting zone.

In the first method of temperature control, there will be the same time lag in bringing about a change in the temperature of the mixture by means of sensible heat as there will be by bringing about a change in the concentration of a material in the mixture. The mixing lags involved in materials handling are also involved in convection by the mixing of hot and cold materials.

In the second procedure, the thermal lags of the fluids that are being reacted, and also the thermal lags of the metal containers—namely, the reactors—prevent instantaneous heat transfer and temperature changes. The thermal capacities of materials and the thermally conducting films between different materials give the data that can define the thermal time constants.

In the third method, a catalyst concentration may be varied to control reaction rate, which in turn determines the rate at which heat is released or taken up in the reactor. Mixing lags dominate this type of control.

The net flow of material to reactor vessels, and the pressure and flow in the pipelines and vessels that are associated with the reactor, give equations like those which were developed in Chapter 2 to predict the hydrodynamics. One additional effect should be noted in connection with chemical reactions, especially gas reactions. The pressure is also a function of temperature, and the temperature in turn is a function of the reaction rate. Therefore there is coupling of temperature, pressure, and reaction rate in the gas-reaction type of chemical reactor because of the gas laws.

In Fig. 6.6, several methods for controlling the important variables in a chemical reaction are indicated. The first two diagrams in the table show how the concentration of ingredients in the reacting volume can be controlled upon a ratioed basis. Figure 6.6a shows how several positive-displacement pumps deliver flows Q_1, Q_2, and Q_3 to the reactor. The pump speeds Ω_1, Ω_2, and Ω_3 are adjusted to vary the pump flows, which makes possible the regulation of the concentration of component C_1, C_2, or C_3 in the reactor. Figure 6.6b shows a throttle valve procedure which can accomplish the same type of control over concentration.

Two methods for temperature control are shown in Figs. 6.6c and d of the table. A hot and a cold stream, Q_a and Q_b, can be mixed at the inlet to a reactor so that the temperature T within the reactor is controlled by controlling the inflow of sensible heat. The outflow of heat takes place because flow Q leaves the reactor. The reaction generates or absorbs heat; consequently the inflowing heat must provide for the dynamic heat balance. The mixing lag may determine the possibility of temperature control based upon manipulating the sensible heat inflow.

Figure 6.6d shows a jacket heat exchanger. Here the flow of material Q into the reactor releases heat when the reaction takes place. The heat is extracted by the jacket heat exchanger, through which a flow of coolant Q_c passes. The heat removed from the fluid in the reactor passes through the metal of the reactor. In this instance the

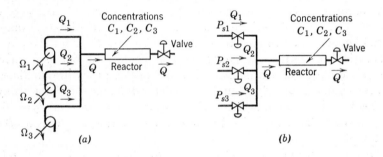

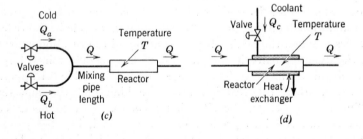

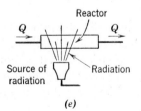

Fig. 6.6. Chemical reactor manipulation. (a) Variable-speed pump control over concentration; (b) Throttle-valve control over concentration; (c) Mixing hot and cold streams for temperature manipulation; (d) Jacket heat exchanger for temperature manipulation; (e) Radiation as a manipulator.

dynamics of the temperature manipulation will be governed largely by the thermal lags in the fluids and metal wall separating the two fluids.

The last item in Fig. 6.6 shows a source of radiation used to influence reaction. The intensity of the radiation falling upon a cube of reactor volume can be adjusted by shield movement, moving of the source and the reactor, or reduction of the source intensity.

4. ELEMENTS OF REACTOR DYNAMICS

The dynamic behavior of chemical reactors depends upon the chemical kinetics of the particular reaction, upon the manner in which the environment variables change with time, and upon the geometry of the reactor. To relate these factors quantitatively requires that differential equations be formed to express the interrelations for the physical variables. Often the equations can be formed but not solved except by means of arithmetical methods because they are nonlinear. However, an exact study of chemical-reactor dynamics need not always be made. Transfer functions which approximate reactor dynamics to a degreee that can be used to obtain engineering results can often be found.

Reaction rates may range from very slow to very rapid. The relative speed of the reaction with respect to the mean residence time of a molecule in a reactor determines whether the chemical reaction process or the materials-handling process has the dominant role in the reactor dynamics. When the mixing lags are small and the reaction rates are slow, the dynamic behavior of the reactor may be determined largely by the chemical kinetics. The equations given in Table 6.1 apply.

However, when the reaction rates are high and the materials-handling lags are large, the situation reverses. Instantaneous conversion of material into product can be assumed, but the product emerging from the reactor may experience materials-handling lags or dead times.

If the principal issue is materials handling, the conversion of raw material into product can be determined for an *ideal* reactor by means of static material balance equations. These equations can then be modified by the appropriate transfer functions for mixing and transportation of material which describe the macroscopic dynamics of the materials handling.

In the batch type of reactor, whether the batch has been put into the reactor before the reaction starts, or whether the reaction goes on as the reactor is filling, may become important. When the reactors have no flow the process tends to exhibit an *integrating* type of action.

For the stirred reactors with time-varying throughput, the same situation arises; the reactor dynamic behavior will be different depending upon whether the head is changing or the head or the hold-up in the reaction vessel remains constant. The exponential mixing lag $\dfrac{1}{\dfrac{V}{Q}s + 1}$ describes approximately the concentration variation in stirred reaction vessels with constant average flow.

In the tubular types of reactors, slug-flow of material through the reactor may be assumed. The products may form instantly at the entrance to the reactor, but a transportation time passes before the products of reaction emerge from the exit end of the reactor. Alternatively, the reaction may not be instantaneous at the entrance: As the slug of material moves along with the flow, the reaction may continue. Diffusion can take place between adjacent slugs as they flow along the axis of the reactor. The residence time of the chemicals in the reactor may have important influence over the composition of the mixture and the yield of product which emerges from the reactor.

Two basically different catalyst-bed types of reactors are used. Gas may flow through a catalyzing gauze placed perpendicular to the direction of flow. The reaction takes place at the surface of the catalyst or at least is confined to a small region near the surface. The second kind of catalyst reactor contains a porous catalyst bed through which either liquids or gases flow and in contact with the surface of the catalyzing material.

In the catalyst-type reactors in which the gas flows through the mesh or gauze located perpendicular to the plane of the flow, the products formed are obtained instantaneously as the flow passes through the reaction region. However, for catalyst-bed reactors in which the reacting gases contact the packed bed or flow through the granular structure of the bed the reaction is distributed throughout the bed. Partial differential equations are required to express the extent of the conversion as a function of distance along the bed.

Fluidized catalyst types of reactors find much use. The principal issue is mixing: finely divided solid or liquid catalyst is kept in intimate contact with one or more reactants. Counter-current flow of the reactants and the catalysts or the action of gravity upon the heavier particles may be used to keep the reaction located in a specific zone of the equipment. The concentration may be regulated by ratio.

Reactor temperature is an important variable in chemical-reactor dynamics. The temperature of a reactor rises if it cannot dissipate the heat generated by a reaction quickly enough through sensible heat flow or by means of conduction and radiation. Some reactors—notably the gas or combustion types—can radiate enough heat so that they become thermally self-regulatory. On the other hand, polymerization reactions which are exothermic may release so much heat that the mixture of raw materials, finished product, and partly finished product suffer product decomposition. The reaction rates are a rising function of temperature so that the reaction ultimately runs away.

The structural design of a reactor itself may prevent proper heat exchange and consequently prevent good regulation of reactor temperature. The runaway reactions also result from improper mixing in the reactor—"hot spots" form in the reactors and the reaction rate in these regions can make a reaction proceed at almost an explosive condition.

Batch Reactors

When hold-up vessels are used as batch reactors, reaction may take place while the vessel is filling or the reaction may initiate after the vessel has been filled. Both products and side-products may be formed. The residence time of the raw material in the reactor determines the fraction of the raw material which is converted into product. The variation of the amount of the raw material in the reaction region must be expressed. The moles of raw material N_1 in the reactor vary from the initial amount N_{10} because the material is used by the reaction at the rate R or because the vessel is being filled or emptied by the flow Q. The material balance equation for the raw material N_1 is

$$N_1 = N_{10} - \int_0^t R \, dt \pm \int_0^t Q \, dt \tag{6.6}$$

The reaction rate R can be expressed in terms of the reaction kinetics.

$$R = K(t)N_1 C_1^{\alpha-1} C_2^{\beta} \cdots \tag{6.7}$$

The flow Q may vary according to any time pattern if the vessel is filling. However, outflow may be related to the head in the vessel.

Equations 6.6 and 6.7 can be combined to predict the batch reactor dynamics provided the reaction rate is defined and the hold-up and flow relationships are given. If the reaction rate is a function of concentration to an exponent greater than unity or a function of temperature, the equations are nonlinear and difficult to solve.

However, when the hold-up N = constant, the reaction rate R is a constant K_o, and isothermal conditions prevail, the equations

$$N_1 = N_{10} - \int_0^t R \, dt \tag{6.8}$$

$$R = K_o \tag{6.9}$$

show that the batch reactor is an *integrating process*. The moles of product N_p formed increase linearly with time. If the reaction happened to be a photo or radiation activated type, the reaction rate has the form $R = KI$ where I is the radiation intensity. Thus the accumulation of product becomes $P(s) = \dfrac{K}{s} I(s)$. The radiation intensity $I(s)$ is the manipulating variable.

When the reaction vessel is filling, the reaction rate $R = $ constant and isothermal conditions prevail, the equations which describe the reactor dynamics are

$$N_1 = N_{10} - \int_0^t K \, dt + \int_0^t Q_1 \, dt \qquad (6.10)$$

where Q_1 is the mole fraction of the total molal flow which contains raw material. By adjusting the flow Q_1 properly the rate of product formation can be regulated. However, when the reaction rate is not constant, the material balance becomes

$$\frac{dN_1}{dt} = -R(T)N_1 C_1^{\alpha-1} \cdots + Q_{1i} \qquad (6.11)$$

$$C_1 = \frac{N_1}{N} \qquad (6.12)$$

$$Q_{1i} = \frac{N_{1i}}{N_i} Q_i \qquad (6.13)$$

Equations 6.10–6.13 can be combined and numerical integration carried out to determine the time varying relationship between $N_1(t)$ and $Q_{1i}(t)$. If reaction rate R is great compared to the filling rate, the entire contents of the reactor tend to always be product. Alternatively, if $R \ll Q$, mixing lags in the reactor dominate the dynamics.

Stirred-Flow-Type Reactors

Next consider the stirred vessel with a steady throughput as a reactor. One or more flows Q_1, $Q_2 \cdots$ fill a stirred hold-up vessel. Generally a single flow Q_o empties the vessel. The contents of the reactor are perfectly mixed. Two cases must be considered again: the hold-up may remain constant; the reaction may take place while the head or the hold-up varies.

Constant Hold-Up

When the reaction take place in a perfectly mixed vessel with constant hold-up and constant throughput, the instantaneous concentrations of the reacting materials, as well as the product, will be time-varying for inflow concentration changes and reaction-rate changes. The rate at which material is converted into product must be taken into account along with the inflow and the outflow of material, when the instantaneous materials-balance equation is written. Thus

$$W \frac{dC_A}{dt} = N_i C_{iA} - N_o C_{oA} - N_i R \qquad (6.14)$$

$$= N(C_{iA} - C_{oA}) - NR \qquad (6.15)$$

provided $$N \simeq N_i \simeq N_o \qquad (6.16)$$

The terms in eqs. 6.14 and 6.16 are defined as:

W = moles of hold-up in the mixing vessel
N_i = molal flow rate of the vessel
N_o = molal flow rate from the vessel
N = average molal throughput
C_{iA} = concentration of component A in the inflow
C_{oA} = concentration of component A in the outflow
C_A = concentration of component A in the vessel
R = molal conversion rate per mole of feed N_i due to chemical reaction

Therefore the transfer function which relates concentration C_A in the vessel, the inflow-stream concentration C_{iA}, and the reaction rate R, is:

$$C_A(s) = \left[\frac{1}{\dfrac{W}{N} s + 1} \right] [C_{iA}(s) - R(s)] \qquad (6.17)$$

When the reaction rate $R(s)$ is a function of the concentration C_A and, in particular, for the first-order reaction where $R = K_R C_A(s)$, the transform modifies to the form

$$C_A(s) = \left[\frac{\dfrac{1}{1 + K_R}}{\left(\dfrac{W}{N(1 + K_R)} \right) s + 1} \right] C_{iA}(s) \qquad (6.18)$$

According to eq. 6.18, a result occurs similar to that which was developed in Chapter 5 in connection with evaporation. The time constant diminishes as the reaction rate increases in the perfectly mixed reaction vessel.

Variable-Holdup

The material balance for the throughput type of reactor becomes

$$\frac{d}{dt}[W(t)C_A(t)] = N_i C_{iA} - N_o C_{oA} - N_i R \tag{6.19}$$

where

$$W(t) = W_{1o} + \int_0^t [Q_1(t) - Q_o(t)] \, dt. \tag{6.20}$$

Once again a nonlinear equation results. To go beyond this point we must use graphical integration methods or carry on a numerical solution.

Ideal Gas Reactors

A multi-component, homogeneous mixture of gases flows into a tubular type of reactor at a flow rate N_i moles per second. The flow N_i is made up of components N_{i1}, N_{i2}, N_{i3}, $\cdots N_{in}$. The reaction kinetics equation gives the rate of formation of moles of product N_p as a function of the concentrations C_1, C_2, $C_3 \cdots$ or the concentration ratios $C_{12} = \dfrac{N_1}{N_2}$, $C_{23} = \dfrac{N_2}{N_3} \cdots$ which govern the reaction. Alternatively by choosing an operating point in the yield curves, Fig. 6.5, and assuming small departures of the reaction from the operating point, the yield of product N_p expressed in terms of the moles of product formed per unit time per mole of raw material N flowing into the reaction zone per unit time, can be written as the linear equation

$$N_p = (K_1 C_{12} + K_2 C_{23})N \tag{6.21}$$

in terms of the concentration ratios C_{12} and C_{23}. The yield of side products can be expressed similarly:

$$N_{sp} = (K_3 C_{12} + K_2 C_{23})N \tag{6.22}$$

In eqs. 6.21 and 6.22 the constants K_1, K_2, K_3 and K_4 are determined by curve-fitting procedures.

When the reaction is very fast and mixing is not a problem in the reaction zone, eqs. 6.21 and 6.22 can be expressed in terms of the molal flow rates or mole ratios in the feed stream. Thus,

$$N_p = (K_1' C_{i12} + K_2' C_{i23})N_i \tag{6.23}$$

and

$$N_{sp} = (K_3' C_{i12} + K_4' C_{i23})N_i \tag{6.24}$$

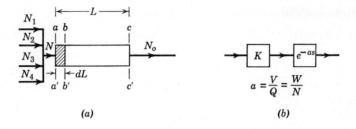

Fig. 6.7. Dynamics of gas reactor. (a) Ideal gas reactor; (b) Signal-flow diagram.

in which the subscript i designates that the ratio C_i is for the feed stream N_i.

On the assumption that the gas molecules pass axially through the reactor, the product and the side-products formed in a volume defined by the length dL at the entrance end of the reactor can be determined from the static rate or yield equations. In the remaining length $L - dL$ of the reactor, the products, side products, unused raw materials, and inert gases undergo the ordinary materials-handling operations of slug flow.

Thus the flow $N_{aa'}$ across line aa' of the reactor shown in Fig. 6.7 contains N_1, N_2, N_3, and N_n. The flow $N_{bb'}$ across line bb' contains N_p, N_{sp}, N_1, N_2, $N_3 \cdots N_n$, where N_p is the molal rate of product flow and N_{sp} is the molal rate of side-product flow. Unless one of the inflow components is completely used up in the reaction, the outflow from the reactor N_o across cc' contains the same components N_p, N_{sp}, N_1, N_2, N_3, $\cdots N_n$.

The instantaneous molal concentrations C_p, C_{sp}, $\cdots$ in the exit flow N_o, can be related to the concentrations C_{12}, $C_{23} \cdots$ in the reaction zone by multiplying eq. 6.21 by the transportation-lag operator. Thus

$$C_{po}(s) = e^{-as}[K_1 C_{12}(s) + K_2 C_{23}(s)] \tag{6.25}$$

The transportation lag

$$a = \frac{W}{Q} = \frac{PA \cdot L}{P \cdot A \cdot V} = \frac{L}{V} \tag{6.26}$$

If the molal flow $N_{bb'}$ from the reaction mixes with the moles of hold-up in a product recovery vessel in which a condition of perfect mixing can be assumed, the product concentration in the outflow from the product separator will be related to the concentration of product $C_{pbb'}$ leaving the reaction zone by the combination of the transportation lag operator and the mixing-lag operator

$$\frac{C_{po}(s)}{C_{pbb'}(s)} = \frac{e^{-as}}{\tau_{ps}s + 1} \qquad (6.27)$$

and the static material balance can be taken into account in the over-all operation

$$C_{po}(s) = \left[\frac{e^{-as}}{\tau_{ps}s + 1}\right][K_1 C_{12}(s) + K_2 C_{23}(s)] \qquad (6.28)$$

The concentration of any other component can also be expressed in the same manner.

Chemical Reaction on the Trays of a Distillation Column

A somewhat more complicated situation occurs when a chemical reaction takes place in the liquid hold-up on the trays in a distillation column. The feed stream to the column generally provides the chemicals which react. A catalyst may be injected into the tower along with the feed stream. The product sought in the chemical reaction may be taken off overhead or at the bottom of the distillation column.

Provided liquid mixture on the trays can be considered a binary mixture, the developments in Chapter 5 can be used to predict the composition of the top product or the bottom product. The yield will depend upon the throughput of the column.

According to equation 5.33, the composition of the vapor y_j coming from an inefficient but perfectly mixed plate with zero entrainment in the distillation column was expressed as a function of the liquid composition x_j on the trays.

$$y_j = \frac{(G_{j-1} - A_j)y_{j-1} + B_j\phi(x_j)}{G_j} \qquad (6.29)$$

$$h_j \frac{dx_j}{dt} = L_{j+1}x_{j+1} - L_j x_j + A_j y_{j-1} - B\phi(x_j) \qquad (6.30)$$

The equation for the material balance on the tray must now incorporate a term which describes the influence of the chemical reaction upon the composition x_j.

If the equation which expresses the rate of conversion of raw material to product on the tray is

$$R_j = K_j(T_j)x_j^a \cdots \qquad (6.31)$$

the material-balance equation which predicts the composition of the rising vapor becomes

$$h_j \frac{dx_j}{dt} = L_{j+1}x_{j+1} - L_jx_j + A_jy_{j-1} - B\phi(x_j) - R_j \quad (6.32)$$

The chemical reaction taking place will be influenced by the tray composition and vice versa. The temperature and pressure variables in the column may also have significant effects upon the reaction.

Provided the temperature of the fluid on the trays does not vary widely and the distillation column performs its mass transfer operations without a large pressure gradient, the chemical reaction will affect only the material-handling time constant for the plate. The greater the rate at which the product is formed or the raw material is converted, the smaller will be the mixing lag on the plate. Generally, the presence of a fast gas-generating reaction upon the trays of a distillation column increases the speed of response of the process.

In the event that the chemical reaction is exothermic, equations for the heat balance may be needed in addition to those for materials handling. The heat balance from the jth tray can be written. The materials-handling and the heat-balance equation can each be developed into separate signal-flow diagrams. The two signal-flow diagrams can be interconnected.

5. COMPOSITION REGULATION

In the preceding sections we have learned that the reaction rate of most chemical processes can be manipulated by varying the concentration of raw materials and activating agents in the zone of reaction. Thus, composition regulation forms one of the most readily used schemes for chemical reaction control.

Composition regulation requires that the relative molal fractions of materials in the reaction volume or in the flow streams to the reactor be maintained constant. Sometimes composition control requires that they be adjusted according to a time-varying pattern. Ratio control over flow rates is the most direct procedure for manipulating the composition in a reactor.

Ratio Control. Ratio control requires that a controller set one or more flow rates of liquid or gas so that they have the proper mass-flow ratio. If a main flow has a control stream added to it, the addition stream is usually placed under manipulation. Ratio controls may adjust only one flow, but often more than one component must be ratioed in a total flow.

Ratio control is accomplished *indirectly* by permitting the measurement of the main stream flow to bring about the manipulation of the control flow. As shown in Fig. 6.8a, flow measurement on stream Q_A is used to establish open-loop control over flow Q_B. The actual ratio $Q_A : Q_B$, or the mole fraction of N_A in comparison with N_B in the total flow N—that is, the concentration ratio $C_A : C_B$—is never measured, nor does it enter into the regulator action.

A feedback procedure for ratioing the flow Q_B relative to Q_A is shown in Fig. 6.8b. The flow Q_B, as well as Q_A, is measured. The control sets the valve according to the measured ratio $\dfrac{Q_{BM}}{Q_{AM}}$. Despite the feedback principle, this is still indirect control over the ratio $Q_B : Q_A$ because the amount of Q_B present in the total flow Q, after the addition of Q_B, is *never* measured.

Direct ratio control can also be accomplished, as shown in Fig. 6.8c. An actual measurement can be made of the composition of the flow Q. The composition analyzer CA measures the concentration of

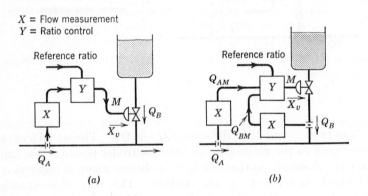

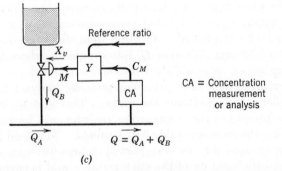

Fig. 6.8. Ratio Control. (a) Indirect measurement, open-loop control; (b) Indirect measurement, closed-loop control; (c) Direct measurement and closed-loop control.

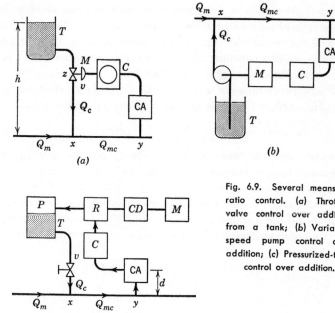

Fig. 6.9. Several means of ratio control. (a) Throttle-valve control over addition from a tank; (b) Variable-speed pump control over addition; (c) Pressurized-tank control over addition.

A or B, or both A and B, in the stream $Q_A + Q_B$. The signal from the analyzer goes to the controller, and the controller positions the valve in the control stream so that the flow Q_B brings about a regulation of the composition C_A or C_B in the outflow. This type of composition regulation is direct; it employs feedback; and it is superior in principle.

In Fig. 6.9 are shown several arrangements which can ratio the flow of liquids or gases so that composition control in the total flow Q_{mc} can be accomplished. The first item shows an overhead tank with a head h forcing fluid flow Q_c into a pipeline whose flow is Q_m. Throttling action is established by the control valve v. The composition measurement made by the composition analyzer CA energizes a controller which positions the valve. This system, except for the time lags present in the composition analyzer, will have the same dynamics as did the incompressible flow systems. The dead times in the closed-loop system due to transport distances between the addition point x and the location of the analyzer at y, and between the valve located at point z and the addition point, will determine the gain that can be obtained for the closed-loop regulating system.

The second arrangement, Fig. 6.9b, shows a pump metering a material from a supply tank into the main flow stream. The composition analyzer and the control equipment, in this instance, may either adjust the displacement of the pump, if it is a variable-displacement type, or adjust the speed of the drive motor, which in turn adjusts the flow Q_c of the pump. Whatever lags occur in the pump and motor must be taken into account, as well as the transportation lag between the addition point x and the analyzer point y.

Of course, if the analyzer itself is located at a distance d from the main pipeline, another transportation distance will have to be taken into account. Large-diameter, long "sample lines" to analyzers can often have very large transportation lags. Furthermore, time lags of the mixing-lag type which occur in the composition analyzer itself cannot be overlooked. The lags in the analyzer may often be greater than the transportation lag associated with the transport of the fluid between points x and y in the process.

Sometimes back pressure P in a vessel, as shown in Fig. 6.9c, is used to meter liquid flow Q_c into a stream Q_m in order to bring about ratio control. A compressor may provide air pressure P, which can be established in the tank above a liquid level. The controlled flow of liquid will pass into the main pipe through a restriction, such as a valve with a permanent setting. The composition analyzer and the controller act upon a pressure regulator so that the pressure in the vessel P is regulated and in turn brings about a controlled flow of liquid Q_c in the ratio-control system.

Many other arrangements can bring about the addition of materials to pipelines, but the few cited should be enough to give the reader the idea that the ratio-control problem becomes a transportation-lag and a mixing-lag problem. The analyzer and the associated control equipment may often have greater time lags than does the process.

Composition Regulation in a Stirred Reactor. Upsets in the composition of the inflow stream to a hold-up vessel type of reactor cause variation in the average composition of the mixture in the vessel. Figure 6.10 shows a typical reaction process in which changes in composition in the inflow stream Q_a alter the composition in the reactor, thereby altering the conversion rate of chemical into product.

A composition detector may be located either in the tank or in the outflow line from the tank. It provides a measurement of the concentration C. The measured value of concentration, designated as C_M, is compared with a reference signal designating desired composition C_{ref}. The difference, $\epsilon_c = C_{ref} - C_M$, then energizes a controller which in turn positions the valve stem X_v. The valve-stem setting X_v manip-

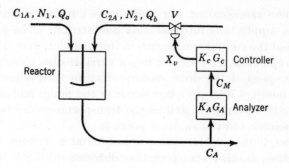

Fig. 6.10. Composition regulation in a stirred reactor.

ulates the flow Q_b through the valve. The relative amount of Q_a and Q_b determines the inflow composition C_i, which in turn manipulates C_A in the reactor.

Assume that the composition detector makes perfect static and dynamic measurement of composition. Thus, the comparison between actual composition and the reference composition is instantaneously obtained. Furthermore, assume that the valve can adjust the flow of the correcting flow Q_b instantaneously and in proportion to the magnitude of composition error. A proportional type of continuous composition regulation results.

The differential equation which governs the behavior of the process is the material balance:

$$W \frac{dC_A}{dt} = N_i C_{iA} - N_o C_A - N_i R \qquad (6.33)$$

If $N_i = N_o = N$ and a first-order reaction $R = K_R C_A$ is assumed, the transfer function which relates the concentration C_A in the vessel to the disturbance and control streams is

$$C_A(s) = \left[\frac{K}{\tau s + 1} \right] \left[\frac{N_1}{N_i} C_{1A} + \frac{N_2}{N_i} C_{2A} \right] \qquad (6.34)$$

in which

$$N_i C_{iA} = N_1 C_{1A} + N_2 C_{2A} \qquad (6.35)$$

$$N_0 = N_1 + N_2 \qquad (6.36)$$

and

$$K = \frac{1}{N + K_R} \qquad (6.37)$$

$$\tau = \frac{W}{(N + K_R)} \qquad (6.38)$$

The signal flow diagram for the composition regulator is shown in Fig. 6.11. The stream N_1 is the disturbance. The stream N_2 is the manipulation.

Since the process is characterized by a single time constant τ, there should be no limit on the loop gain of the regulator. Practically speaking, however, the composition analyzer and the valve-positioning device which controls the manipulating flow will both have time lags. The reader will recall from the work done in Chapter 1 that definite performance limits are imposed upon closed-loop systems which have time lags and transportation lags. Therefore, even for perfect and instantaneous measurement by the composition analyzer and for perfect and instantaneous valve operation, the precision of composition regulation will be limited by the time lag of the reactor and by the physical location of the analyzer. In particular, if the analyzer is located some distance from the main stream so that a transportation lag must be considered in the closed-loop operation, the performance of the regulating system will be limited regardless of the speed of response of the reactor.

An interesting development can take place in this type of chemical reactor control. The reaction rate influences the size of the time constant τ. As the reaction rate increases the time constant becomes smaller. Provided the time lags in the valve positioner and other accessories are smaller than the time lag τ of the reactor, as the reactor temperature rises gradually the reaction rate will increase, the time lag of the reactor will decrease and the regulator will tend toward instability.

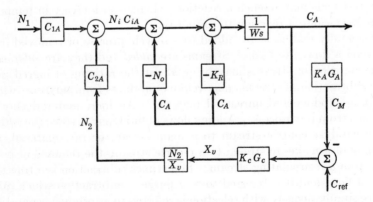

Fig. 6.11. Signal-flow diagram for composition regulation in a stirred reactor—first-order reaction.

6. RECYCLE PROCESSES

In many chemical processes the rate of reaction is low, or the contact time is short, so that raw material passes through the reactor without being totally converted into product. The outflow stream from the reactor has a concentration of product, waste, and recoverable raw material. If the flow is put through a product-recovery process which extracts the product, the remaining material can be sent back through the reactor. The unused raw material can be converted upon successive passages through the reactor into product.

The recycle process has a small inflow of new material called the "make-up," a small outflow stream of "product," and a fairly substantial circulating flow of material through the reactor, through a product-recovery operation, and through various other processing operations, some of which may involve heat exchange, washing, condensing, and compressing. Generally a pump or compressor must be put in the feedback path to insure the return of the recycle flow under the proper conditions of pressure to re-enter the fluid flow system. However, instances occur where solids are recirculated using conveyors where only kinematics treatment is needed.

Basically, there are two problems. First, it is necessary to be able to write the static equations for molal flow and concentration at any point in the recycle process. Secondly, it is necessary to supplement these static equations with the appropriate materials handling dynamics as obtained in Chapter 1. An interesting feedback situation occurs: recycle processes are regenerative by their very nature because the mass flow in the recycle stream cannot be negative. The build-up of inert material in the system can be an integral action. Poisoning of catalyst beds may quench a reaction, whereas an increase in temperature may cause a reaction to run away.

Generally materials are added to a recycle process or removed from it upon a flow-rate basis. Streams are *added* and they are *subtracted*. The addition of streams may bring about the ratioing of ingredients; the subtraction of streams may remove products from mixtures which contain product and unreacted material. An inert material may be purged from the process. Adding flows of fluid may involve the adding of a catalyst control stream to a main stream or raw material, the adding of a make-up stream to a recycle stream, the removal of product from a recirculating stream. Sometimes subtraction is a fractioning of flow, and it is referred to as a purge. Subtraction which takes place simultaneously with selection is referred to as product separation.

In the recycle processes, the composition must be traced around a closed path. Static composition studies can be made for adding and

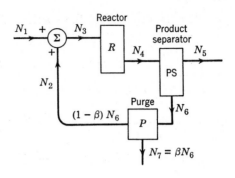

Fig. 6.12. Recycle process.

subtracting flows by writing sets of static flow-rate equations. The compositions of mixtures before and after the various points of addition and subtraction in the processes can be determined by forming the appropriate molal flow ratios.

In the re-cycle process shown in Fig. 6.12, the make-up molal flow N_1 adds to the re-cycle flow N_2. The combined flow N_3 enters a reactor or a processing vessel where conversion of raw material into product can take place. The product, or at least a substantial portion of it, is removed in the product separator as the flow N_5. A purge N_7 fractions the flow N_6 so that it removes inert materials which may tend to build up in the re-circulation stream. The remainder of the flow N_6 after the purge N_7 is the re-cycle flow N_2.

The make-up flow N_1 must supply a molal inflow which equals the sum of the product outflow and the purge flow; otherwise, the system will empty or build up hydraulic pressure or material inventory.

Consider that the make-up stream contains two raw-material components A and B and an inert component X. Thus

$$N_1 = N_{A1} + N_{B1} + N_{X1} \tag{6.39}$$

where N_{A1} and N_{B1} are the molal flow rates of raw materials and N_{X1} is the molal flow rate of inert material. The re-cycle flow is

$$N_2 = (1 - \beta)N_6 \tag{6.40}$$

The inflow to the reactor is

$$N_3 = N_1 + N_2 \tag{6.41}$$

$$= [N_{A1} + (1 - \beta)N_{A6}] + [N_{B1} + (1 - \beta)N_{B6}] \\ + [N_{X1} + (1 - \beta)N_{X6}] \tag{6.42}$$

$$= N_{A3} + N_{B3} + N_{X3} \tag{6.43}$$

Let the reactor convert the portion γN_{A3} and δN_{B3} into product N_{P4}. Assume that no side products are formed.   Thus

$$N_4 = (1 - \gamma)N_{A3} + (1 - \delta)N_{B3} + N_{P4} + N_{X3} \qquad (6.44)$$

After product separation, in which

$$N_5 = \alpha N_{P4} \qquad (6.45)$$

is removed,

$$N_6 = (1 - \delta)N_{A3} + (1 - \delta)N_{B3} + (1 - \alpha)N_{P4} + N_{X3} \quad (6.46)$$

The purge flow βN_6 is a fraction of the total molal flow N_6 but is nonselective.   Thus

$$N_7 = \beta N_6 \qquad (6.47)$$

$$= \beta(1 - \gamma)N_{A3} + \beta(1 - \delta)N_{B3} + \beta(1 - \alpha)N_{P4} + \beta N_{X3} \quad (6.48)$$

Situations occur in which the concentration of raw materials or catalysts in stream N_3 may determine the reaction rate, or where the concentration of inert material in stream N_3, N_4, or N_2 may determine the economy of production.   Thus the concentration equations have to be written.

In the make-up stream the concentration of the component N_{A1} in the total molal *flow rate* N_1 is

$$C_{A1} = \frac{N_{A1}}{N_1} = \frac{N_{A1}}{N_{A1} + N_{B1} + N_{X1}} \qquad (6.49)$$

or

$$C_{A1} = \frac{\dfrac{Q_{A1}}{M_A}}{\dfrac{Q_{A1}}{M_A} + \dfrac{Q_{B1}}{M_B} + \dfrac{Q_{X1}}{M_X}} \qquad (6.50)$$

where Q = mass flow and M is molecular weight.   For gas flow, the volumetric flow must be multiplied by the density.

After the recycle and the make up streams add, the concentration becomes

$$C_{A3} = \frac{N_{A3}}{N_1 + N_2} \qquad (6.51)$$

$$= \frac{N_{A1} + N_{A2}}{N_1 + N_2} \qquad (6.52)$$

The reaction rate R will depend upon the concentrations C_{A3} and C_{B3}. The moles of product N_p in the flow N_S will depend upon the residence time of the reactants in the reactor.

A purely *hydrodynamic purge* of gas or liquid from a fluid flow system will not be selective in composition of the material being purged. A *separation* process will be needed ahead of the purge in order that a specified component shall appear in the purge flow.

For example, if a gas flow passes through a processing operation, such as a vapor condensation, so that the condensed fraction of the flow of gas does not have an opportunity to leave by means of a gas purge from the flow which leaves the condenser, the combination process is "selective." Alternatively, if a liquid is heated, it may vaporize a fraction of material which cannot be purged when a liquid flow is drawn from the vaporizer. However, these processes should be recognized as combination processes rather than a simple purge operation.

In Fig. 6.12, the flow N_4 is made up of product N_p and inert material N_1, so that

$$N_4 = N_{p4} + N_1' \tag{6.53}$$

and product separation removes all or a large portion of N_{p4}. The remaining flow after product removal is

$$N_6 = (1 - \alpha)N_{p4} + N_1' \tag{6.54}$$

where $\alpha \leq 1$. The purge flow is a fraction of the total remaining flow N' so that

$$N_7 = \beta N_6 = \beta[(1 - \alpha)N_{p4} + N_1'] \tag{6.55}$$

Equation 6.55 shows that the purge is a nonselective fraction of N_6.

Figure 6.13 shows several arrangements for purging a liquid or vapor system. Items a and b indicate that fixed resistance or a valve in a side-stream can be adjusted so that a specific molal flow βN of purged material occurs.

Item c shows a flow N into a low-pressure vessel where product removal occurs in the liquid phase and a purge takes place from the vapor phase. Item d shows how gas compression can be used to liquefy a fraction of material which is then purged in total from the gas product stream. The first two arrangements are nonselective purge, whereas the latter two schemes represent combined operations of product removal and selective purge.

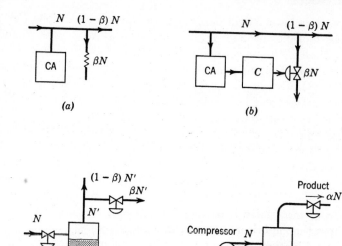

(a) (b) (c)

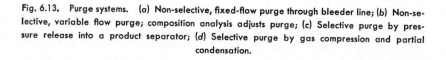

(d)

Fig. 6.13. Purge systems. (a) Non-selective, fixed-flow purge through bleeder line; (b) Non-selective, variable flow purge; composition analysis adjusts purge; (c) Selective purge by pressure release into a product separator; (d) Selective purge by gas compression and partial condensation.

The inert material build-up in the recycle process can be determined by writing the inert concentration in the reactor inlet stream.

$$C_{X3} = \frac{N_{X3}}{N_3} \tag{6.56}$$

$$= \frac{1}{N_3}\left[\frac{1}{1 - (1 - \beta)}\right] N_{X1} \tag{6.57}$$

For a constant molal in flow rate N_{X1}, the concentration of inert C_X at the inflow of the reactor will build up provided $\beta < 1$. For $\beta = 0$, the concentration of inert material becomes infinite.

If a mixing lag τ occurs in either the reactor or the product recovery vessel

$$N_{X3} = N_{X1} + (1 - \beta) \left(\frac{1}{\tau s + 1}\right) N_{X3} \tag{6.58}$$

Thus

$$C_{X3} = \frac{1}{N_3} \frac{(\tau s + 1)}{(\tau s + \beta)} N_{X1} \tag{6.59}$$

For a step-function change of the inert molal concentration N_{X1}, the transient rise in the concentration C_{X3} will be

$$C_{X3}(t) = \frac{1}{N_3} \frac{1}{\beta} [1 - (1 - \beta)e^{-\frac{\beta}{\tau}t}] \tag{6.60}$$

Thus the purge limits the rate of inert build-up.

Several control problems arise in connection with the recycle process. It may be important to keep the concentration of a particular component in the make-up stream entering the process constant, despite the fact that the conversion of raw material into product in the reactor may vary. The removal of product in the product separator may not be continuous. The recirculation or recycle of unused raw material may contain an inert material whose concentration disturbs the make-up stream. Situations may occur when the conversion rate in the reactor changes. The product separator may foul and not remove product as it should. The purge may be an intermittent operation, not operating until there is a specific level of inert material built up in the recirculation stream, and then the purge may operate for a short period until the concentration of inert material in the recirculation stream has dropped below a required minimum.

In summary, unless unusual situations arise in the reactor or product separator, the dynamic behavior of most recycle processes can be predicted by superimposing the transfer functions for storage variation, transport lag and mixing

$$\frac{1}{s}, \qquad e^{-as}, \qquad \text{and} \qquad \frac{1}{\tau s + 1} \tag{6.61}$$

upon the static concentration of equations.

The "drift" in operation of many recycle processes is quite likely to be not drift at all, but low-frequency oscillation because of *inherent instability*. The frequency of oscillation is low because of the great time lags in production-scale recycle processes due to hold-up and transportation lags. The nonlinearity of the system, especially saturation, is often the only thing that saves the process from runaway to destruction—the complete failure to operate. The manual control actions made continually during the drifts in an effort to bring the process back to equilibrium are often worthless or even aggravating adjustments.

BIBLIOGRAPHY

Kinetics of Chemical Change in Solution, Edward S. Amis, The MacMillan Company, New York, 1949.

The Kinetics of Reaction in Solution, E. A. Moelwyn-Hughes, Clarendon Press, Oxford, 1933.

Chemical Kinetics, K. L. Laidler, McGraw-Hill Book Co., New York, 1950.

Equilibrium and Kinetics of Gas Reactions, an Introduction to the Quantum-Statistical Treatment of the Chemical Process, R. N. Pease, Princeton University Press, 1942.

Technology of High Polymer Synthetic High Polymers (in its Chemical and Physical Aspects), R. Houwink, Elsevier Publishing Co., New York, 1947.

"Molecular Structure of Polyethylene," *J. Am. Chem. Soc.,* **75**, (1953).

Technical Reports Nos. 1, 2, and 3, Arthur D. Little Company
  (a) *Dependence of Physical Properties of High Polymers on Molecular Structure: Statistical Investigations with Aid of Punched-Card Methods.*
  (b) *New Methods in Statistical Mechanics of High Polymers.*
  (c) *New Methods in the Statistical Mechanics of High Polymers.*

Chemical Process Principles, Part III, *Kinetics and Catalysis,* O. A. Hougen and K. M. Watson, John Wiley & Sons, New York, 1947.

Chemical Engineering Kinetics, J. M. Smith, McGraw-Hill Book Co., New York, 1956.

"An Analysis of Chemical Reactor Stability and Control," R. Aris, and N. R. Amundson, to be published in *Chem. Eng. Sci.*

"Control of Continuous Flow Chemical Reactors," O. Bilous, H. D. Block, and E. L. Piret, *A.I.Ch.E. J.* **3**, 248–261 (1957).

The Dynamics and Control of Chemical Processes, J. R. Ehrenfeld, Sc.D. Thesis, Massachusetts Institute of Technology, Cambridge, Mass., 1957.

Problems

CHAPTER 1

1. Assume an oil refinery supplies fuel oil to storage depots in two cities which are located at distances d_1 and d_2 from the refinery. The oil is carried from the refinery to the storage depots in tankers of capacity W_T tons at velocity V_T. The inventory of oil at the cities is W_1 and W_2 and the demand upon each is Q_{10} and Q_{20}. The number of tanker arrivals per unit time at each city is N_1 and N_2.

A severe cold period causes the demand Q_{20} for oil in the city at distance d_2 to exceed in the average inflow from the tanker deliveries to such an extent that the inventory of oil W_2 will be depleted in one week.

Determine an inventory regulation strategy based upon the following factors:

(*a*) That the two cities are on the same route so that $d_2 > d_1$ and that deliveries normally intended for the first city can be diverted to the one at d_2 but that the total number of tankers cannot be increased nor can their velocity be changed. The inventory at d_1 must not fall below 0.5 of its average level.

(*b*) That the cities are a distance d_2 apart and d_1, d_2, d_3 form a triangle. Deliveries to d_1 can be diverted. Oil at d_1 can be shipped by tankers which arrive at d_1 and dispatch their load. Assume $d_3 < d_1/2$. The inventory at d_1 must not fall below 0.5, the average level prior to the storm.

2. Calculate the energy, power, and momentum associated with the flow Q of material through a self regulated storage process like the one shown in Fig. 1.5.

3. Assume the quality-control system shown in Fig. 1.21 is a proportional sampler-clamper which has a gain K_c and a sampling time T.

(1) Express the open-loop transfer function for the complete system as a transfer function $KG(z)$, where $z = e^{Ts}$ and where $T =$ the sampling time.

(2) Determine the loop gain that will arise in the system with a sustained oscillation.

(3) Take the loop gain to be 50 per cent of the value found in (2) and show the transient up-set in the product quality p_8 for a step function disturbance $D(t)$ applied exactly at the instant of a sample.

TABLE OF NUMERICAL VALUES

$\tau_g = $ 2 minutes

$\tau_R = $ 30 minutes

$a = $ 5 minutes

$b = $ 5 minutes

$K_D = 50$

$K_m = 25$

$K_A = 1$

$K_B = $ to be determined

$T = 0.5$ minute

4. Three mixing vessels operate in noninteracting cascade. The inflow to the first vessel is the inflow of material to be blended. The outflow from the third vessel is divided so that the fraction α is sent back to the first vessel. The fraction $1 - \alpha$ is taken out of the mixing system.

If the mean residence time for a particle in each vessel is τ, determine the conditions under which composition oscillation may occur in the mixing process as a result of the positive feedback.

Provided stable operation can be achieved, is there any advantage in having the fraction α of the outflow fed back and mixed with the contents of the first or second mixing vessel?

5. Given a production process with three parallel lines with unit capacities of 1.0, 0.8, and 0.5 per hour. The cost of operating each line is given as x_1, x_2, and x_3. The cost versus production level for each line is given by a typical U curve. The average production rate is 0.8 per hour per line. The average inventory level is 100 units. Data are also available which show the U curve for "cost of inventory."

For a steady running condition of the plant, develop the pulse-duration procedure for regulating the production schedule so that the inventory costs and the production costs remain a minimum. Assume a particular production line can only be given two values of operation, zero or maximum. Assume also the minimum time interval of a shut down is one half-day.

CHAPTER 2

1. Determine the impedance of a compressor as seen from the pipeline. Show that a positive-displacement type of compressor acts as a flow source with a shunt impedance, whereas a centrifugal type or a vane type of pump or compressor acts as a pressure source with a series impedance. Under what condition will the source not reflect a traveling wave which approaches the compressor from the pipe line? Specifically, what requirements will be necessary in the compressor design?

2. A pressure pulse of unit area is applied to an instrument line whose parameters per foot are:

$$R_L = 301 \; \frac{\text{lb-sec}}{\text{ft}^6}$$

$$C_L = 5.19 \times 10^{-3} \; \text{ft}^4/\text{lb}$$

$$M_L = 21.0 \; \frac{\text{lb-sec}^2}{\text{ft}^6}$$

The line is terminated in a bellows of volume V_B whose elastic deformation is K.

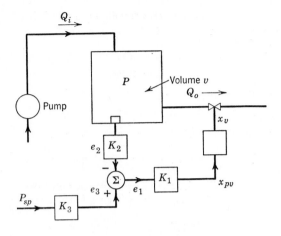

Problem 2.4(1).   Pressure control system.

Predict the movement of the bellows $x(t)$ as a result of the pulse when the line is 200 ft in length.

3. Assume you can place three poles of the transfer function for a passive low pass acoustic filter anywhere in the left-hand plane of s. What is the attenuation characteristic (asymptotes) for the best possible filter?

4. A pressure-control system is shown above. A pump delivers an inflow Q_i to a tank whose volume is v. The outflow Q_o from the tank is adjusted by a valve positioner whose stem is attached to a hydraulic piston. The stem movement x_v follows a pilot valve movement x_{pv} in the hydraulic feedback system shown below. The movement of the pilot valve is set by an ideal solenoid type of motor which displaces the valve K_1 units for a unit voltage e_1. There are no lags in the solenoid mechanism. The pressure in the chamber is measured by a strain cell that gives a voltage e_2 proportional to the pressure in the tank P. The set-point pressure flow that is to be

Problem 2.4(2).   Hydraulic feedback.

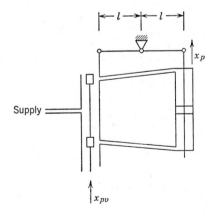

maintained in the tank P_{sp} generates a voltage e_3 which is compared to the measured voltage e_2 at a summing point and the error voltage e_1 applies to the solenoid positioner.

Assume that the outflow from the tank is given by the equation

$$Q_o = k_p P x_v$$

where k_p is the process sensitivity.

Determine the following:

(1) The signal-flow diagram for the system so that the inflow to the tank Q_i appears as a disturbance and the set point P_{sp} appears as a reference or command.

(2) The transfer function for the valve positioner between e_1 and the valve movement x_v.

(3) The transfer function for the process around an operating point that is determined by a through-flow of Q_{io} cu ft/sec when the pressure is maintained at a level of P_o lb/sq in.

CHAPTER 3

1. Assume speed control at 100 hp nominal rating is desired over range $0.1 < \Omega < \Omega_{max} = 1.0$. Make a cost study of the various schemes available on a commercial basis.

To what extent can these systems be "stiffened" by under compensated integral without substantial cost increase?

2. A weighted roll of mass M and radius of gyration r_o is hung upon an elastic web between two guide rolls which are positively engaged with the web. For a step function of acceleration of one of the guide rolls, what will be the tension in the web between the weighted roll and the forward and back guide rolls? Regard the web as an elastic material having zero mass. The deformation obeys Hooke's law.

3. A dancer roll arrangement as shown in the accompanying figure is used to measure the tension in an elastic web of material. The web makes a right-angle turn over the guide rolls as it passes around the dancer roll. The dancer roll is free-running on its pivot and the pivot is restrained by a spring and a dashpot to a fixed base. The mass of the dancer roll is M_d, the moment of inertia about its own axis is J_d, and it has a radius of gyra-

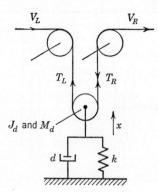

Problem 3.3.

tion R. The tension to the left of the dancer roll is T_L, the tension to the right is T_R. The velocity of the incoming web is V_L; the velocity of the outgoing web is V_R.

Develop the relationship between the position x of the dancer roll and the tension on the left and right side of the dancer roll.

To what extent does the moment of inertia of the roll impair in any serious way the qualitative performance numerically obtained for this kind of measuring instrument?

CHAPTER 4

1. A thermal equivalent of a heating system, somewhat simplified, is shown below. The system comprises an on-off controlled furnace whose heat rate is 75,000 Btu/hr when it is on. The reference temperature is 67.5°. By using the attached sheets and the describing function method find the frequency of oscillation, the period of oscillation in hours, the on-time in hours, the off-time in hours, the average error and the magnitude of the fluctuating part of the error.

Optional. If you are interested in pursuing the investigation further, consider ambient temperatures of 30°, 45°. All other adjustments are unchanged. Assess the result of changes in Δ_h by repeating with $\Delta_h = 1°$ and $\frac{1}{2}°$. Suppose Q_M is doubled, all other adjustments as in original problem? If Q_M is doubled and $\Delta_h = 4°$? Suppose all thermal capacities are doubled? Suppose R_3 is doubled—what is the effect?

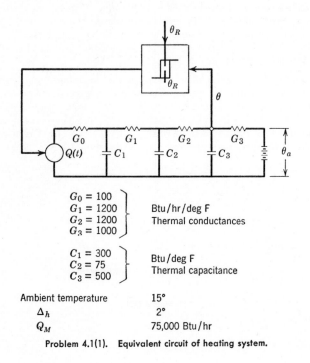

$$G_0 = 100$$
$$G_1 = 1200$$
$$G_2 = 1200$$
$$G_3 = 1000$$
Btu/hr/deg F
Thermal conductances

$$C_1 = 300$$
$$C_2 = 75$$
$$C_3 = 500$$
Btu/deg F
Thermal capacitance

Ambient temperature	15°
Δ_h	2°
Q_M	75,000 Btu/hr

Problem 4.1(1).   Equivalent circuit of heating system.

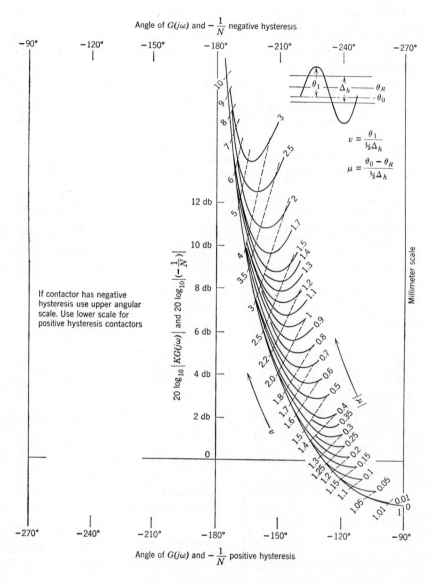

Angle of $G(j\omega)$ and $-\frac{1}{N}$ negative hysteresis

$-90°$ $-120°$ $-150°$ $-180°$ $-210°$ $-240°$ $-270°$

$$v = \frac{\theta_1}{\frac{1}{2}\Delta_h}$$

$$\mu = \frac{\theta_0 - \theta_R}{\frac{1}{2}\Delta_h}$$

Millimeter scale

If contactor has negative hysteresis use upper angular scale. Use lower scale for positive hysteresis contactors

$20 \log_{10} |KG(j\omega)|$ and $20 \log_{10} |(-\frac{1}{N})|$

12 db

10 db

8 db

6 db

4 db

2 db

0

$-270°$ $-240°$ $-210°$ $-180°$ $-150°$ $-120°$ $-90°$

Angle of $G(j\omega)$ and $-\frac{1}{N}$ positive hysteresis

Problem 4.1(2).

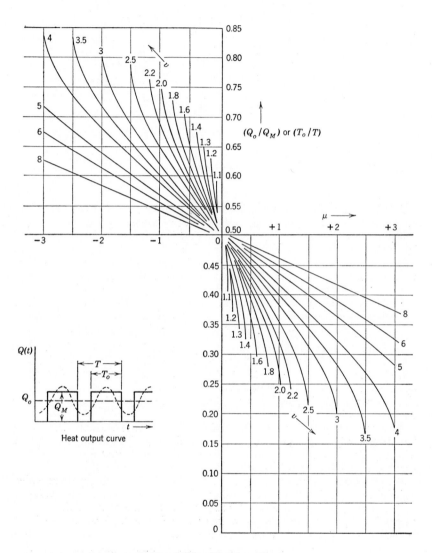

Problem 4.1(3).   Direct heat function.

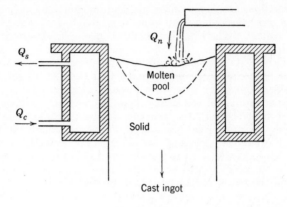

Problem 4.2.

2. Molten material of specific heat C_{p1}, density ρ_1, and temperature T_1 pours into the heat-exchange mold shown in the accompanying figure.

The coolant flow Q_c is constant. The flow is high enough to assume there is a completely mixed and turbulent condition in the exchanger outer chamber. The volume of the exchanger outer space is V_1. The surface area through which heat transfers is A_1. The heat transfer coefficient for the molten metal to die is h_1. The heat-transfer coefficient for the coolant to die is h_2.

Determine the general relationship among the heat-removal rate, the geometry of the die exchanger, and the rate at which metal can be continuously cast. Assume the metal must be solidified before it emerges from the die.

3. The refractory bricks of a furnace wall are of two different kinds. The layer exposed to the hot gases is an expensive, high-purity material which permits the furnace to operate at high temperature without fusion. The outer layer of brick is less expensive. It supports the inner lining and also absorbs a reasonable portion of the temperature drop between the interior and the outside.

Assume the heat falling upon the surface of the furnace is evenly distributed but sinusoidally varying in time. The outside wall of the furnace is kept at a temperature T_o. Assume the constants for each layer of the refractory are: C_1, G_1, C_2, G_2 per unit length.

Perfect contact between the refractory layers and the wall may be regarded as infinite in extent (hence only one-dimensional heat flow must be considered).

Determine the temperature attenuation through the wall. Calculate the thermal energy absorbed by each layer of refractory. Assume the inner layer is L_1-ft thick, the outer layer L_2-ft thick.

4. A thermal bulb filled with vapor is used to detect temperature changes in a liquid bath. The bulb is connected by means of a capillary tube to a small bellows of volume V whose linear expansion indicates the temperature.

Determine: (a) The equivalent thermal, acoustic circuit; (b) the response $\dfrac{x(s)}{H(s)}$ for the detector.

5. The equations for energy, mass, momentum, and state have been derived for a fluid flowing through a tube which is surrounded by a variable temperature environment. The equations have been simplified so that there is no axial conduction in either the fluid or the walls. The only temperature gradient which exists is in the axial direction, since the radial temperature gradient has been eliminated by assuming that the fluid in the tube has an average temperature which is uniform throughout a section.

Set up the equations for the energy, mass, momentum, and state when two fluids flow concurrently in the concentric tube pair shown in the figure. Assume there are no thermal losses to the outside through the tube wall b. Include in the analysis provision for the thermal capacity of the tube a. Assume that the velocities of the two streams are not equal.

Set up the same equations for counter-flow. Assume for this particular situation that the two velocities are equal.

Problem 4.5.

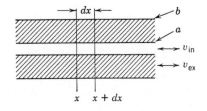

Discuss the possibilities of using difference equations for the solution of the transient response of this type of heat exchanger. Enumerate the steps that would be necessary to convert the equations in their partial form into differential equations suitable for use on a digital computer.

CHAPTER 5

1. Consider a 5-plate section of a distillation column such that h_j, L_j, G_j, and K_{1j} are all constant for $j = 1$ through $j = 5$. Under the assumption that the plates are perfectly mixed and efficient, draw the signal-flow diagram between y_o and y_5—i.e., the input vapor composition to the bottom plate and the output vapor composition from the top plate. Reduce the signal flow diagram to a single transmission between y_o and y_5.

2. Draw the signal-flow diagram for the column of Problem 1 for the inefficient plate case where $\dfrac{A_j}{G_j} = R_1$, and $\dfrac{B_j}{G_j} = R_2$. Reduce to a single transmission between y_o and y_5.

3. In general, the transient response of a distillation column is due to a set of poles lying on the negative real axis of the s-plane. No one of these poles is dominant. To evaluate the transient response without carrying out the inverse transformation, one may resort to the "moments" of the impulse response. Using the mean response time as a measure of the transient response, find the mean time for the column section of Problem 1 for $h/L = 1$

and $K_1G/L = 0.8$, 1, and 1.2. Compare this to the mean time if $\dfrac{y_5}{y_o} = a_5$, i.e., if no feedback paths, b, were present.

4. Using the values given in Problem 3 and $R_1 = 0.5$ and 0.7, determine the mean response time for the column section of Problem 2.

CHAPTER 6

1. Consider that the gas flow through a catalyst bed reactor is divided among ten tubes. The ten tubes enter a manifold with a hold-up volume V which collects their total flow Q_o. Assume that each tube brings reacted material through the catalyst and that the material arriving at the manifold mixes in a blending operation. If one tube bringing material suddenly develops an upset condition of reaction, so that the average molecular weight emerging from it is 20 per cent higher than normal, describe the manner in which the composition in the manifold will change as a function of time.

Block Diagrams
and Signal-Flow Diagrams

Block diagrams and signal-flow diagrams are cause-and-effect diagrams which establish a procedure for quantitatively evaluating the dynamic behavior of a process. Pertinent physical variables for measurement and manipulation in a process or control system become clear from the diagram. The static and dynamic relationships for cause and effect can be quantitatively evaluated with the aid of the diagrams. The general nature of system stability can be discerned. Perhaps most important of all, the diagrams provide a topology of the process.

Two forms of diagrams are currently in use: the block diagram and the node and directed-branch graph. The primitive block diagram is set up from the differential equations that describe the dynamic response of a process. The independent variables in the equations which express process behavior become the commands, disturbances, and manipulation signals, which are represented by arrows in the diagrams. The dependent variables become the response signals, and are similarly represented. Operators identify the action taken upon "signals" as they pass through "blocks" in the diagram.

The block diagram is developed by means of the symbols in Table A.1. For example: When a mass M moves under the action of a force F, but experiences damping and elastance forces of restraint, the block diagram is as shown in Fig. A.1. The applied force F, minus the opposing forces F_D and F_K, produces the net force ΣF, which acts upon the mass M and produces acceleration A. The acceleration, when integrated, becomes velocity V, which—when integrated—becomes

TABLE A.1. SYMBOLS FOR BLOCK-DIAGRAM DEVELOPMENT

Signal flow	
Addition or subtraction	
Split of signal	
Multiplication of signals	
Division of signals	
Magnification of a signal by K	
"Operation" upon a signal	

displacement x. By means of the rules for block-diagram simplification in Table A.2, Fig. A.1a simplifies in the single block of Fig. A.1b.

Initial conditions are often needed in the study of dynamics problems. They can be added directly to the linear form of the block diagram: for example, for the mass M under the action of force F, in Fig. A.1a, the differential equations which relate displacement x

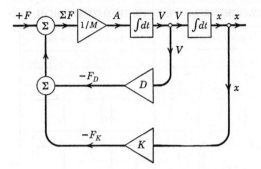

Fig. A.1(a). Example of primitive block diagram.

Fig. A.1(b). Reduction of primitive block diagram (Fig. A.1(a)) to single block.

to force F in the time domain are:

$$M\frac{d^2x}{dt} = F - F_D - F_K$$

$$F_D = D\frac{dx}{dt}$$

$$F_K = Kx$$

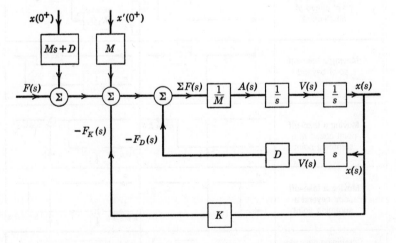

Fig. A.2. Signal-flow diagram of Fig. A.1(a) with initial conditions added.

TABLE A.2. THEOREMS FOR THE TRANSFORMATION AND

Theorem	Original Network	Equivalent Network
1. Interchange of elements		
2. Interchange of summing points		
3. Rearrangement of summing points		
4. Interchange of take-off points		
5. Moving a summing point ahead of an element		
6. Moving a summing point beyond an element		
7. Moving a take-off point ahead of an element		
8. Moving a take-off point beyond an element		
9. Moving a take-off point ahead of a summing point		
10. Moving a take-off point beyond a summing point		
11. Combining cascade elements		

* "Transformation of Block Diagram Networks"

REDUCTION OF BLOCK DIAGRAM NETWORKS*

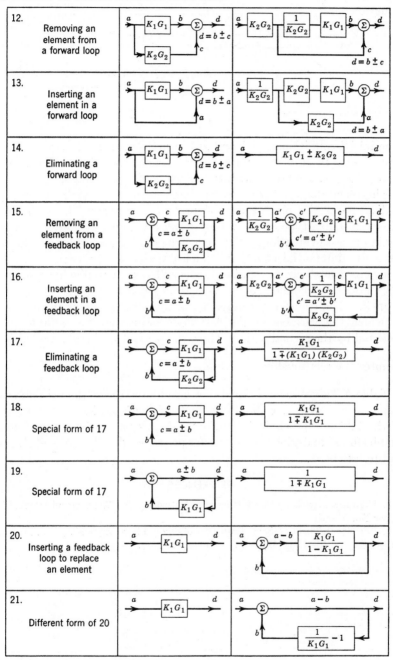

by T. D. Graybeal, AIEE Paper No. 51-298.

The Laplace transformations (see Appendix II) of these differential equations are:

$$Ms^2x(s) - \underbrace{Msx(0^+) - M\dot{x}(0^+)}_{\text{Initial conditions}} = F(s) - F_D(s) - F_K(s)$$

$$F_D(s) = Dsx(s) - \underbrace{Dx(0^+)}_{\substack{\text{Initial} \\ \text{conditions}}}$$

$$F_K(s) = Kx(s)$$

The initial conditions $x(0^+)$ and $\dot{x}(0^+)$, multiplied by the proper constants, can be applied to the force summation point. Figure A.2 shows the block diagram with the initial conditions added.

The block diagram becomes cumbersome to work with as the size and scope of the process control problem increase. The node and directed-branch type of signal-flow graph makes possible greater facility in process evaluation. The node type of diagram is also developed from the differential equations which describe the process. A node, drawn as a small circle, represents every physical variable in a process. Two nodes are connected by an arrow which represents a directed branch. The transfer characteristic of the branch defines the manner in which the variable at the first node influences the variable represented by the second node. Thus, the symbol g_{jK} beside the branch denotes the relationship $\dfrac{x_K}{x_j} = g_{jK}$.

Table A.3 gives several signal-flow graphs and shows their simplifications. Particular note should be made of the items in the latter part of the table. The chain type of cascade is typical of the signal-flow graphs found in drying, mass-transfer processes, distillation, and chemical processes.

REFERENCES

1. "Transformation of Block Diagrams Network," by T. D. Graybeal, AIEE Paper No. 51-298.
2. "Feedback Theory—Some Properties of Signal Flow Graphs," by S. J. Mason, Proceedings of the IRE, **41,** No. 9 (September 1953).

TABLE A.3. SIGNAL-FLOW GRAPHS

Cascade

1.

$$x_3 = bx_2 = bax_1$$

Parallel

2.

$$x_2 = (a + b) x_1$$

3.

$$x_2 = x_1 + gx_2$$

$$x_2 = x_1 \left(\frac{1}{1 - g} \right)$$

4.

$$x_1 = x_0 + bx_2$$
$$x_2 = ax_1 = ax_0 + abx_2$$

$$\frac{x_3}{x_0} = \frac{a}{1 - ab}$$

TABLE A.3.　SIGNAL-FLOW GRAPHS (Continued)

$$g_{11} = a_1 b_1 + a_0 b_0$$

5.

$$\frac{x_B}{x_3} = \frac{b_1 b_0}{1 - g_{11}} = \frac{b_1 b_0}{1 - a_1 b_1 - a_0 b_0}$$

6.

$$\frac{x_3}{x_1} = G = \frac{g_1 g_2}{1 - g_{a1} g_{b1}}$$

$$G = \frac{x_3}{x_1} = \cfrac{g_1 g_2}{1 - \cfrac{g_{a1} g_{b1}}{1 - g_{a2} g_{b2}}}$$

7.

$$G = \frac{x_3}{x_1} = \cfrac{g_1 g_2}{1 - \cfrac{g_{a1} g_{b1}}{1 - \cfrac{g_{a2} g_{b2}}{1 - \cfrac{g_{a3} g_{b3}}{1 - g_{a4} g_{b4}}}}}$$

TABLE A.3. SIGNAL-FLOW GRAPHS (Continued)

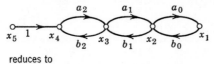

reduces to

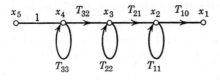

8.

which reduces to

then $\dfrac{x_1}{x_5} = a_0 \left[\dfrac{1}{1-a_0 b_0}\right] a_1 \left[\dfrac{1}{1-\dfrac{a_1 b_1}{1-a_0 b_0}}\right] a_2 \left[\dfrac{1}{1-\dfrac{a_2 b_2}{1-\dfrac{a_1 b_1}{1-a_0 b_0}}}\right]$

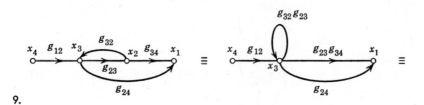

9.

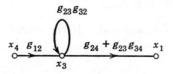

Fourier and
Laplace Transformations

The use of Fourier and Laplace transformations proves expedient in the treatment-process control problems. A summary of the theory which justifies transformation, and some of the practical aspects of transformation theory, are enumerated in this appendix.

Fourier Transformation

A periodic function of the time $f(t)$ with T as the period, can be represented by the Fourier series:

$$f(t) = b_o + \sum_{n=1}^{\infty} b_n \cos n\omega t + \sum_{n=1}^{\infty} a_n \sin n\omega t \qquad \text{(A.1)}$$

where

$$a_n = \frac{2}{T} \int_{\theta}^{\theta+T} dt\, f(t)\, \sin n\omega t \qquad \text{(A.2)}$$

$$b_n = \frac{2}{T} \int_{\theta}^{\theta+T} dt\, f(t)\, \cos n\omega t \qquad \text{(A.3)}$$

$$b_o = \frac{1}{T} \int_{\theta}^{\theta+T} dt\, f(t) \qquad \text{(A.4)}$$

The coefficients a_n and b_n are real. If the complex representation is used, the function becomes

$$f(t) = \sum_{n=-\infty}^{\infty} c_n e^{jn\omega t} \qquad \text{(A.5)}$$

where c_n is a complex coefficient defined by the integral:

$$c_n = \frac{1}{T} \int_\theta^{\theta+T} dt\, f(t) e^{-jn\omega t} \tag{A.6}$$

Therefore, any periodic function can be represented as a sum of sinusoidal functions the frequency spectrum of which is not continuous. The coefficient c_n characterizes the amplitude and phase of the nth component. Both positive and negative frequencies are involved in the complex representation.

A nonperiodic function $f(t)$ can be thought of as a periodic function with an infinite period so that the previous series analysis procedure may be extended. The coefficient c_n becomes a continuous function $G(\omega)$ of frequency ω. The corresponding formulas are:

$$f(t) = \int_{-\infty}^{\infty} G(\omega) e^{j\omega t}\, d\omega \tag{A.7}$$

$$G(\omega) = \frac{1}{2\pi} \int_{-\infty}^{\infty} dt\, f(t) e^{-j\omega t} \tag{A.8}$$

The Fourier transform of the time function $f(t)$ is simply 2π times $G(\omega)$. The eqs. A.1 and A.2 become

$$F(\omega) = \int_{-\infty}^{\infty} dt\, e^{-j\omega t} f(t) \tag{A.9}$$

$$f(t) = \frac{1}{2\pi} \int_{-\infty}^{\infty} d\omega\, e^{j\omega t} F(\omega) \tag{A.10}$$

In eq. A.9 and A.10 $F(\omega)$ can be considered as a complex function of the *real variable* ω. However, it may also be considered a function of the *imaginary variable* $j\omega$. In the s-plane a function which is well defined along the entire imaginary axis is known in the entire s-plane. Thus F is a function of the *complex variable* s. By replacing $j\omega$ by s, the new formulas become:

$$F(s) = \int_{-\infty}^{\infty} dt\, e^{-st} f(t) \tag{A.11}$$

$$f(t) = \frac{1}{2\pi j} \int_{-j\infty}^{j\infty} ds\, e^{st} F(s) \tag{A.12}$$

the two relations can be put together to obtain:

$$f(t) = \frac{1}{2\pi j} \int_{-j\infty}^{j\infty} d(j\omega) e^{j\omega x} \int_{-\infty}^{\infty} dt\, e^{-j\omega t} f(t) \tag{A.13}$$

The expression in eq. A.13 is called the development of $f(t)$ in the Fourier integral. It exists only if certain conditions are fulfilled:

(a) $f(t)$ has a finite number of discontinuities in the t-range: $-\infty$ to ∞.

(b) $f(t)$ does not reach infinite values more than a finite number of times in the t-range: $-\infty$ to $+\infty$.

(c) The integral $\int_{-\infty}^{\infty} |f(t)|, dt$ is finite.

(d) $f(t)$ has a finite number of maxima and minima.

However mathematicians extend the possibility of finding Fourier transforms for functions which do not satisfy the condition c. The discussion and the handling of such cases are delicate. Therefore, from an engineering point of view, it is best to say that a function must satisfy the four conditions in order to have a Fourier transform.

PLAUSIBLE ARGUMENT FOR INTRODUCING LAPLACE TRANSFORMATION

Consider a function $f(t)$ *which is zero for* $t < 0$ and does not fulfill the condition: $\int_{0}^{\infty} |f(t)| \, dt$. But we can find c such that: $\int_{0}^{\infty} dt \, f(t) e^{-ct} < \infty$.

According to the previous statements:

(a) $f(t)$ has no Fourier transform.

(b) $f(t)e^{-ct}$ has a Fourier transform.

A new transformation can be defined where $f(t)$ has a transform. First, we can write the development of $f(t)e^{-ct}$ in Fourier integral form:

$$e^{-cx}f(x) = \frac{1}{2\pi j} \int_{-j\infty}^{j\infty} d(j\omega)e^{j\omega x} \underbrace{\int_{0}^{\infty} dt \, e^{-j\omega t}e^{-ct}f(t)}_{\text{Fourier transform of } f(t)e^{-ct}} \qquad (A.14)$$

Then multiplying both sides by e^{cx} and introducing this factor in the

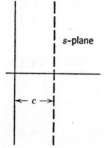

Fig. A.3.

TABLE A.4. LAPLACE TRANSFORMS
Operation—Transform Pairs
General Laplace Transform Theorems

No.	$f(t) \quad t \geq 0$	$F(s)$	Remarks
1	$f(t)$	$\int_0^\infty f(t)e^{-st}dt$	The Laplace transform
2	$\dfrac{1}{2\pi_j}\displaystyle\int_{c-j\infty}^{c+j\infty} F(s)e^{st}ds$ where $c >$ abscissa of absolute convergence	$F(s)$	The inverse Laplace transform
3	$\dfrac{d}{dt}f(t)$	$sF(s) - f(0+)$	Real differentiation
4	$\int f(t)dt$	$\dfrac{F(s)}{s} + \dfrac{f^{-1}(0+)}{s}$	Real integration
5	$f\left(\dfrac{t}{a}\right)$	$aF(as)$	Scale change
6	$f(t-a)$ if $f(t-a) = 0$, $\quad 0 < t < a$ $f(t+a)$ if $f(t+a) = 0$, $\quad -a < t < 0$ a is a nonnegative real number	$e^{-as}F(s)$ $e^{as}F(s)$	Real translation
7	$e^{-at}f(t)$ $e^{at}f(t)$ a has a nonnegative real part	$F(s+a)$ $F(s-a)$	Complex translation
8	$tf(t)$	$-\dfrac{d}{ds}F(s)$	Complex differentiation
9	$\dfrac{1}{t}f(t)$	$\displaystyle\int_s^\infty F(s)ds$	Complex integration
10	$\displaystyle\int_0^t f_1(t-\sigma)f_2(\sigma)d\sigma$ $= f_1(t) * f_2(t)$	$F_1(s)F_2(s)$	Complex multiplication (convolution)

TABLE A.4.   LAPLACE TRANSFORMS (*Continued*)

No.	$f(t)$ $t \geq 0$	$F(s)$	Remarks
11	$f_1(t)f_2(t)$	$\displaystyle\sum_{k=1}^{q} \frac{A_1(s_k)}{B_1(s_k)} F_2(s - s_k)$ if $F_1(s) \triangleq \dfrac{A_1(s)}{B_1(s)}$ has only first-order poles	Real multiplication
12	$\displaystyle\lim_{t \to 0} f(t)$	$\displaystyle\lim_{s \to \infty} sF(s)$	Initial value
13	$\displaystyle\lim_{t \to \infty} f(t)$	$\displaystyle\lim_{s \to 0} sF(s)$	Final value

integral of the right hand member, because x is not the variable of integration, we obtain:

$$f(x) = \frac{1}{2\pi j} \int_{-j\infty}^{j\infty} d(j\omega)e^{x(c+j\omega)} \underbrace{\int_0^\infty dt\, e^{-j\omega t}e^{-ct}f(t)}_{L(c,j\omega)} \qquad (A.15)$$

If c is a real constant, $L(c, j\omega)$ is a complex function, which in the s-plane is defined along the axis $(c, j\omega)$. In accord with the theorem of continuity, the function L is defined in the entire complex plane and we do not need any more to consider c as a constant. Let us replace $c + j\omega$ by the variable s.

$$f(x) = \frac{1}{2\pi j} \int_{c-j\infty}^{c+j\infty} ds\, e^{sx} \int_0^\infty dt\, e^{-st}f(t) \qquad (A.16)$$

The function $L(s)$ is called the Laplace transform of $f(t)$ and the second integral constitute the inverse Laplace transformation. The two formulas which govern those two operations are:

$$L(s) = \int_0^\infty dt\, f(t)e^{-st} \qquad (A.17)$$

$$f(t) = \frac{1}{2\pi j} \int_{c-j\infty}^{c+j\infty} ds\, e^{st}L(s) \qquad (A.18)$$

From the preceding argument it follows:

(a) A function which is such that $\int_0^\infty f(t)\, dt < \infty$ and $f(t) = 0$ for $t < 0$ has both a Fourier and a Laplace transform.

(b) A function which does not fulfill the condition $\int_0^\infty |f(t)|\, dt < \infty$ and is zero for $t < 0$ but for which we can find c such that $\int_0^\infty dt\, |f(t)| e^{-ct}$ has a Laplace transform but no Fourier transform.

(c) A function which is nonzero for $t < 0$ and fulfills the condition $\int_{-\infty}^\infty dt\, |f(t)| < \infty$ has a Fourier transform but no Laplace transform.

(d) A function which is nonzero for $t < 0$ and does not fulfill the condition $\int_{-\infty}^\infty dt\, |f(t)| < \infty$ has neither Laplace nor Fourier transform.

(e) In the Laplace transformation we use a convergence factor, but we forget about it after. Nevertheless it has to be remembered when one wants to take the inverse transform, as we shall see later on.

These foregoing remarks are made on a rather elementary basis because mathematicians have extended the possibilities of the Fourier transformation. The procedure is based upon limit considerations and use of a convergence factor. From an advanced point of view, no great difference exists between the two transformations; and the Fourier transformation appears to be more general than the Laplace. However, from an engineer's point of view, we deal mostly with Laplace transformations.

PROPERTIES OF LAPLACE AND FOURIER TRANSFORMATIONS

Some basic properties of the two transformations can be stated. They are the same for both, except in some details. Since we are mainly interested in the Laplace transformation, the Laplace transformation rules will be given. The differences which apply for Fourier transformation will be mentioned when necessary.

The symbol L indicates the Laplace transform of the function $f(t)$. The symbol F stands for the Fourier transform.

Linearity Theorems

If $L_1(s)$ and $L_2(s)$ are the transforms of $f_1(t)$ and $f_2(t)$ the transform of

$$f(t) = f_1(t) + f_2(t)$$

is

$$L(s) = L_1(s) + L_2(s)$$

and the transform of:

$$f(t) = af_1(t)$$

is

$$L(s) = aL_1(s)$$

TABLE A.5. LAPLACE TRANSFORMS
Some Common Transform-Function Pairs

No.	$F(s)$	$f(t) \quad t \geq 0$	Remarks
1	1	$\mathcal{u}'(t)$	Unit impulse at $t = 0$
2	$\dfrac{1}{s}$	1 or $\mathcal{u}(t)$	Unit step function
3	$\dfrac{1}{s^2}$	t	Unit ramp
4	$\dfrac{1}{\tau s + 1}$	$\dfrac{1}{\tau} e^{-\frac{t}{\tau}}$	Exponential lag
5	$\dfrac{\omega}{s^2 + \omega^2}$	$\sin \omega t$	
6	$\dfrac{s}{s^2 + \omega^2}$	$\cos \omega t$	
7	$\dfrac{1}{s^2 + 2\zeta\omega_n s + \omega_n^2}$	$\zeta < 1: \dfrac{1}{\omega_n \sqrt{1 - \zeta^2}} e^{-\zeta\omega_n t} \sin \omega_n t \sqrt{1 - \zeta^2}$ $\zeta = 1: t e^{-\omega_n t}$ $\zeta > 1: \dfrac{1}{\omega_n \sqrt{\zeta^2 - 1}} e^{-\zeta\omega_n t} \sinh \omega_n t \sqrt{\zeta^2 - 1}$	Underdamped quadratic Critically damped quadratic Overdamped quadratic
8	$\dfrac{\beta}{(s + \alpha)^2 + \beta^2}$	$e^{-\alpha t} \sin \beta t$	Damped oscillations

9	$\dfrac{s+\alpha}{(s+\alpha)^2+\beta^2}$	$e^{-\alpha t}\cos\beta t$	Damped oscillations
10	$\dfrac{1}{s^n}$	$\dfrac{1}{(n-1)!}t^{n-1}$	
11	$\dfrac{1}{(\tau s+1)^n}$	$\dfrac{1}{(n-1)!}\dfrac{t^{n-1}}{\tau^n}e^{-\frac{t}{\tau}}$	nth order exponential lag
12	$\dfrac{1}{s}e^{-as}$	$\mathrm{u}(t-a)$	Delayed unit step function
13	$\dfrac{1}{s}(1-e^{-bs})$	$\mathrm{u}(t)-\mathrm{u}(t-b);\,b>0$	Pulse of duration b beginning at time $t=0$
14	$\dfrac{e^{-as}}{s}(1-e^{-bs})$	$\mathrm{u}(t-a)-\mathrm{u}(t-a-b);\,a>0,\,b>0$	Pulse of duration b beginning at time $t=a$
15	$\dfrac{1}{s(1+e^{-s})}$	$\displaystyle\sum_{k=0}^{\infty}(-1)^k\mathrm{u}(t-k)$	
16	$\dfrac{1}{s}\tanh\left(\dfrac{as}{2}\right)$	$1+2\displaystyle\sum_{k=1}^{\infty}(-1)^k\mathrm{u}(t-ak)$	

309

TABLE A.6. PARTIAL FRACTION EXPANSION OF TRANSFORMS OF THE FORM

$F(s) = \dfrac{A(s)}{B(s)}$ WHERE $B(s)$ IS A HIGHER ORDER POLYNOMIAL THAN $A(s)$

$$\mathcal{L}^{-1}\left[\frac{A(s)}{B(s)}\right] = \mathcal{L}^{-1}\left[\sum_{k=1}^{n}\sum_{j=1}^{m_k}\frac{K_{kj}}{(s-s_k)^{m_k-j+1}}\right]$$

$$K_{kj} \triangleq \frac{1}{(j-1)!}\left[\frac{d^{j-1}}{ds^{j-1}}\frac{(s-s_k)^{m_k}A(s)}{B(s)}\right]_{s=s_k}$$

$$m_k = \text{order of pole at } s = s_k.$$

NOTE: For single order poles of $F(s) = \dfrac{A(s)}{B(s)}$

$$\mathcal{L}^{-1}\left[\frac{A(s)}{B(s)}\right] = \mathcal{L}^{-1}\left[\sum_{k=1}^{n}\frac{K_k}{s-s_k}\right]$$

$$K_k \triangleq \left[\frac{(s-s_k)A(s)}{B(s)}\right]_{s=s_k} = \left[\frac{A(s)}{B'(s)}\right]_{s=s_k}$$

NOTE: If $B(s)$ is not a higher order polynomial than $A(s)$, then $F(s)$ can be reduced to a polynomial in s plus $F_1(s) = \dfrac{A_1(s)}{B(s)}$ where $B(s)$ is a higher order polynomial than $A_1(s)$.

Change of Scale

If a change of scale is made in the time domain:

$$\text{the transform of } f\left(\frac{t}{a}\right) \text{ is } aL(as)$$

For the Laplace transform a is necessarily positive. But even for the Fourier transformation a has to be positive otherwise the statement is not true.

Translation of the Real Variable

If a is a positive real number:

$$\text{the transform of } f(t+a) \text{ is } e^{as}L(s)$$
$$\text{the transform of } f(t-a) \text{ is } e^{-as}L(s)$$

This statement is true for both transformations, but for the Laplace transformation it should be remembered that $f(t)$ is such that:

$$f(t-a) \text{ is zero for } t < 0$$

and it should be added that for the first property we must have:

$$f(t+a) \text{ is zero for } -a < t < 0.$$

TABLE A.7. SPECIAL TRANSFORM FUNCTION PAIRS USEFUL IN THE SOLUTION OF SOME PARTIAL DIFFERENTIAL EQUATIONS

No	$F(s)$	$f(t) \quad t \geq 0$	Remarks
1	$\dfrac{1}{\sqrt{s}}$	$\dfrac{1}{\sqrt{\pi t}}$	
2	$s^{-3/2}$	$2\sqrt{\dfrac{t}{\pi}}$	
3	$\dfrac{s}{(s-a)^{3/2}}$	$\dfrac{1}{\sqrt{\pi t}}\, e^{at}(1+2at)$	
4	$\sqrt{s-a} - \sqrt{s-b}$	$\dfrac{1}{2\sqrt{\pi t^3}}\,(e^{bt}-e^{at})$	
5	$\dfrac{1}{\sqrt{s}+a}$	$\dfrac{1}{\sqrt{\pi t}} -$ $ae^{a^2 t}cerf(a\sqrt{t})$	$cerfy \triangleq 1-erfy$ $\triangleq 1 - \dfrac{2}{\sqrt{\pi}}\displaystyle\int_0^y e^{-x^2}\,dx$
6	$\dfrac{1}{\sqrt{s}\,(s-a^2)}$	$\dfrac{1}{a}\,e^{a^2 t}erf(a\sqrt{t})$	
7	$\dfrac{1}{\sqrt{s}\,(\sqrt{s}+a)}$	$e^{a^2 t}cerf(a\sqrt{t})$	
8	$\dfrac{1}{(s+a)\sqrt{s+b}}$	$\dfrac{1}{\sqrt{b-a}}\,e^{-at}erf(\sqrt{b-a}\,\sqrt{t})$	
9	$\dfrac{1}{s}\,e^{-\frac{a}{s}}$	$J_0(2\sqrt{at})$	
10	$\dfrac{1}{\sqrt{s}}\,e^{-\frac{a}{s}}$	$\dfrac{1}{\sqrt{\pi t}}\cos 2\sqrt{at}$	
11	$\dfrac{1}{s^{3/2}}\,e^{-\frac{a}{s}}$	$\dfrac{1}{\sqrt{\pi k}}\sin 2\sqrt{at}$	
12	$\dfrac{1}{\sqrt{s}}\,e^{a/s}$	$\dfrac{1}{\sqrt{\pi t}}\cosh 2\sqrt{at}$	
13	$\dfrac{1}{s^{3/2}}\,e^{a/s}$	$\dfrac{1}{\sqrt{\pi k}}\sinh 2\sqrt{at}$	

TABLE A.7. SPECIAL TRANSFORM FUNCTION PAIRS USEFUL IN THE SOLUTION OF SOME PARTIAL DIFFERENTIAL EQUATIONS (Continued)

No	$F(s)$	$f(t) \quad t \geq 0$	Remarks
14	$e^{-a\sqrt{s}}$	$\dfrac{a}{2}\dfrac{e^{-a^2/4t}}{\sqrt{\pi t^3}}$	$a > 0$
15	$\dfrac{1}{\sqrt{s}}e^{-a\sqrt{s}}$	$\dfrac{e^{-a^2/4t}}{\sqrt{\pi t}}$	$a \geq 0$
16	$\dfrac{1}{s}e^{-a\sqrt{s}}$	$cerf\left(\dfrac{a}{2\sqrt{t}}\right)$	$a \geq 0$
17	$\dfrac{1}{\sqrt{s^2 + a^2}}$	$J_0(at)$	
18	$\dfrac{1}{\sqrt{s^2 + a^2}\,(\sqrt{s^2 + a^2} + s)}$	$\dfrac{1}{a}J_1(at)$	
19	$\dfrac{1}{\sqrt{s^2 + a^2} + s}$	$\dfrac{1}{a}\dfrac{J_1(at)}{t}$	
20	$\dfrac{1}{\sqrt{s^2 + a^2}\,(\sqrt{s^2 + a^2} + s)^n}$	$\dfrac{1}{a^n}J_n(at)$	n is a non-negative integer
21	$\dfrac{1}{(\sqrt{s^2 + a^2} + s)^n}$	$\dfrac{n}{a^n}\dfrac{J_n(at)}{t}$	n is a positive integer
22	$\dfrac{1}{\sqrt{s^2 - a^2}}$	$I_0(at) = J_0(iat)$	
23	$e^{a^2 s^2}cerf(as)$	$\dfrac{1}{a\sqrt{\pi}}e^{-t^2/4a^2}$	$a > 0$
24	$\dfrac{1}{s}e^{a^2 s^2}cerf(as)$	$erf\left(\dfrac{t}{2a}\right)$	$a > 0$
25	$\dfrac{1}{\sqrt{s}}cerf(\sqrt{as})$	0 for $0 < t < a$ $\dfrac{1}{\sqrt{\pi t}}$ for $t > a$	
26	$e^{as}cerf(\sqrt{as})$	$\dfrac{\sqrt{a}}{\pi\sqrt{t\,(t + a)}}$	$a > 0$

TABLE A.7. SPECIAL TRANSFORM FUNCTION PAIRS USEFUL IN THE SOLUTION
OF SOME PARTIAL DIFFERENTIAL EQUATIONS (Continued)

No	$F(s)$	$f(t) \quad t \geq 0$	Remarks
27	$\dfrac{1}{\sqrt{s}} e^{as} cerf(\sqrt{as})$	$\dfrac{1}{\sqrt{\pi(t+a)}}$	$a > 0$
28	$erf\left(\dfrac{a}{\sqrt{s}}\right)$	$\dfrac{1}{\pi t} \sin 2a \sqrt{t}$	
29	$\dfrac{1}{\sqrt{s}} e^{a^2/s} cerf\left(\dfrac{a}{\sqrt{s}}\right)$	$\dfrac{1}{\sqrt{\pi t}} e^{-2a\sqrt{t}}$	

NOTE: An extensive set of transform function pairs is available in *Fourier Integrals* by Campbell and Foster Only those entries containing the condition $0 < g$ or $k < g$ where $g \equiv t$ and $p \equiv s$ are Laplace transforms.

Index